C0-AMX-879

# INTRODUCTION TO

# LIGHTING

# INTRODUCTION TO

# LIGHTING

By

## HOWARD M. SHARP

Consulting Engineer
Assistant Professor of Engineering
University of Buffalo
Past President, Illuminating Engineering Society

New York

PRENTICE-HALL, INC.

1951

COPYRIGHT, 1951, BY
PRENTICE-HALL, INC.
70 FIFTH AVENUE, NEW YORK

*All rights reserved. No part of this book
may be reproduced in any form, by mimeo-
graph or any other means, without permission in writing from the publishers.*

PRINTED IN THE UNITED STATES OF AMERICA

621.32
S53

# PREFACE

THIS BOOK is the outgrowth of many years of experience in training men and women in the science of light and the art of lighting. The approach is from the viewpoint of the practicing engineer. The underlying concepts are clearly developed and coordinated, using both simple mathematics and geometric solids to convey a physical impression of these concepts and, where applicable, the calculus as well, to prepare the student for more advanced study. Well aware of the difficulty encountered by students in relating the basic mathematical concepts to actual application practice, the author has endeavored first to make the fundamentals clear, and then to emphasize constantly those fundamentals as they appear in application techniques.

Each portion of the work is complete in itself. A student continuing to more advanced studies does not have to retrace his steps, yet if he goes no further in his lighting practice he will have a workable appreciation and understanding of the majority of common lighting problems.

The production, control, and measurement of light as a scientific tool is first explained, and then across the bridge of vision the application of light is developed into lighting. The student moves from cause to effect and, if he will, acquires confidence in his ability to apply fundamentals to the workable solution of everyday lighting problems.

The material is suitable for a formal college course, or portions of it may be utilized for industry training programs. Problems based upon actual situations are provided liberally, along with extensive luminaire photometric data. Thus the student is oriented with the

33822

developing world of illuminating engineering, and pursues his study with a sense of reality.

The author has drawn his information from the myriads of sources within the profession. The references can only express those which are the most immediately pertinent.

Grateful appreciation is due Mr. Karl Staley for reading the manuscript and contributing immensely to form, style, and contents of the work. Professor Rudolph Biesele, who reviewed the work for the publishers, made many valuable suggestions as to emphasis and arrangement of material. Mr. Michael Thachik, who prepared all the drawings, did so with a background of lighting knowledge that made for excellent coordination with the spirit of the text. Sincere thanks, publicly expressed, is the least that can be given to my wife for deciphering my atrocious handwriting, for typing and proofreading the work, and for her invaluable suggestions on style and usage.

HOWARD M. SHARP

*Buffalo, N.Y.*

# CONTENTS

1 NOMENCLATURE . . . . . . . . . . 1

1.1. The language of lighting. 1.2. The lighting industry.

2 BASIC CONCEPTS . . . . . . . . . . 9

2.1. Lumen. 2.2. Footlambert. 2.3. Candlepower. 2.4. Lambert's law of emission. 2.5. Light from a single surface. 2.6. Light from a double surface. 2.7. Light from a cylinder. 2.8. Light from an infinite plane. 2.9. Spherical reduction factor.

3 ELECTRIC LAMPS. . . . . . . . . . 24

3.1. Filament. 3.2. Bases. 3.3. Bulb. 3.4. Characteristics. 3.5. Neon. 3.6. Sodium. 3.7. Mercury. 3.8. Fluorescent lamps.

4 BALLASTS, TRANSFORMERS, AND STARTERS 47

4.1. Neon. 4.2. Iron-cathode fluorescent. 4.3. Type-H mercury lamps. 4.4. Sodium-vapor lamps. 4.5. Slimline fluorescent lamps. 4.6. Preheat cathode fluorescent lamps. 4.7. Direct-current operation. 4.8. Flicker or stroboscopic effect. 4.9. Transformer hum. 4.10 Radio interference. 4.11. Starters.

5 CONTROL OF LIGHT . . . . . . . . . 58

5.1. Absorption. 5.2. Reflection. 5.3. Transmission. 5.4. Effect of angle of incidence. 5.5 Effect of color of light. 5.6. Characteristics of materials. 5.7. Interpretation of photometric data. 5.8. Basic reflector contours. 5.9. Effect of light source upon performance. 5.10. Refraction. 5.11. Polarization.

# 6 LUMINAIRES . . . . . . . . . . . . 80

6.1. Component parts. 6.2. Types of luminaires. 6.3. Efficiency. 6.4. Selecting the luminaire. 6.5. Luminare brightness and glare. 6.6. Light flux control.

# 7 MEASUREMENTS OF LIGHT AND LIGHTING 96

7.1. Comparison instruments. 7.2. Direct-reading instruments. 7.3. Measurement of reflectance and transmission. 7.4. Measurement of brightness. 7.5. Field measurements of footcandles.

# 8 CANDLEPOWER DISTRIBUTION CURVES . 123

8.1. Desirable form for presentation of data. 8.2. Points of brightness measurement. 8.3. Test conditions for filament and fluorescent lamps. 8.4 Calculating light flux. 8.5. Simple flux calculations. 8.6. Effect of lamp size on candlepower.

# 9 COEFFICIENTS OF UTILIZATION . . . . 141

9.1. Room shape. 9.2. Effect of light distribution from luminaires. 9.3. Analyzing the distribution curve. 9.4. Determining reflection factors. 9.5. Simplified coefficients.

# 10 PRINCIPLES OF LIGHTING DESIGN . . . . 165

10.1. The point-by-point method. 10.2. Linear and non-point sources. 10.3. Rectangular luminous areas. 10.4. Circular luminous areas. 10.5. Flux-of-light method.

# 11 VISION . . . . . . . . . . . . . . 189

11.1. Definitions. 11.2. Structure of the eye. 11.3. Visibility curves. 11.4. Field of vision. 11.5. Fundamental external vision factors. 11.6. Lighting to facilitate vision.

# 12 OFFICES AND SCHOOLS . . . . . . . 207

12.1. Quantity of light. 12.2. Lighting design. 12.3. Brightness limits for luminaires. 12.4. Brightness ratios in the visual field.

**13 FACTORIES** . . . . . . . . . . . . **230**

13.1. General lighting.   13.2. Supplementary lighting.

**14 STORES** . . . . . . . . . . . . . . **257**

14.1. Footcandles.   14.2. Brightness.   14.3. General lighting.
14.4. Supplementary lighting.   14.5. Show windows.

**15 LIGHTING DESIGN—SPECIALIZED
TECHNIQUES** . . . . . . . . . . . . . **282**

15.1. Floodlighting.   15.2. Cove lighting.   15.3. Downlighting.

**16 LIGHTING COST ANALYSIS** . . . . . . **317**

**INDEX** . . . . . . . . . . . . . . **331**

# INTRODUCTION TO

# LIGHTING

# 1

# NOMENCLATURE

## 1.1. The Language of Lighting

Each science and profession has its own terms—nomenclature—that provide world wide communication. This nomenclature is a product of evolution, just as is any language. Some of it is logical and consistent, some is quite the opposite. For practical purposes, however, the important thing for us is to be able to understand each other, and to use the terms correctly. Since 1910, the American Illuminating Engineering Society has worked continuously to classify and standardize the nomenclature in this field. The definitions included here have been adopted by the American Standards Association. They are based upon the English system, that is, with the foot as a unit of length. For the student who wishes to convert from the English system to the metric system (meter or centimeter as a unit of length), Table 1-1 is provided. The standard definitions that follow are given in quotation marks. Explanatory material is added where it seems desirable.

Light: "For the purposes of illuminating engineering, light is visually evaluated radiant energy."

Of all the great band of radiant energy from cosmic rays through radio waves only a minute portion, roughly between 4,000 and 7,600 angstroms (400 to 760 millimicrons), is capable of producing the sensation of light in the human eye. Energy outside of this band is not capable of producing this sensation. It is incorrect to speak of "black" light, or "ultra-violet" light.

Luminous flux (F): "This is the time rate of flow of light."

Inasmuch as light flows at a constant rate, matters are usually simplified by dropping the factor of time. Radiant flux is the time rate of flow of radiant energy in any part of the spectrum. Radiant flux within the limits of 4,000 to 7,600 angstroms is simply luminous flux.

**Lumen (lm):** The unit of luminous flux. "It is equal to the luminous flux through a unit solid angle (steradian) from a uniform

### TABLE 1-1

#### Equivalents and Conversion Factors

*Equivalents*

| Quantity | English system | Metric system |
|---|---|---|
| Illumination (E) | Footcandle (ft-c):<br>1 lm per sq ft | Phot:<br>1 lm incident per sq cm<br>Lux:<br>1 lm incident per sq m |
| Brightness (B) | Footlambert (ft-L):<br>1 lm emitted per sq ft | Lambert:<br>1 lm emitted per sq cm |
| | Candles per sq in. | Stilb:<br>1 candle per sq cm |

*Conversion Factors*

| Quantity | English system | Metric system |
|---|---|---|
| Illumination (E) | 1 footcandle | 929 Phot<br>.0929 Lux |
| Brightness (B) | 1 footlambert | 929. lamberts<br>.929 millilambert<br>.00221 candle per sq in.<br>2,919. stilb |
| | 1 candle per sq in. | 6.45 stilb<br>452. footlamberts |

point source of 1 candle, or to the luminous flux on a unit surface all points of which are unit distance from a uniform point source of 1 candle."

In the English system, the unit surface is 1 square foot (sq ft), and the unit distance is 1 foot (ft). In the metric system, when the unit surface is 1 square meter (sq m), the unit distance is 1 meter (m). When the area is 1 square centimeter (sq cm), the unit distance is 1 centimeter (cm).

Because the element of time is ordinarily omitted, the lumen may be considered as the *unit quantity of light.*

**Illumination (E):** "The density of the luminous flux on a surface;" hence it is flux divided by the area over which the flux is distributed.

**Footcandle (ft-c):** "The unit of illumination when the foot is taken as the unit of length." It is, therefore, the illumination produced *on or at a surface* all points of which are at a distance of 1 foot from a uniform point source of 1 candle. It is also the illumination produced by spreading 1 lumen uniformly over an area 1 foot square.

The footcandle is the term used in the English system and is standard in the literature of the English-speaking peoples. Note that it is lumens per square foot *at* or *on* a surface; in other words, incident luminous flux.

**Brightness (B):** "The luminous intensity of any surface in a given direction per unit of projected area of the surface as viewed from that direction."

Note carefully that brightness is the property of a surface.

**Footlambert (ft-L):** "The unit of brightness of a perfectly diffusing surface emitting or reflecting light at the rate of 1 lumen per square foot." It is also the average brightness of any surface emitting or reflecting light at that rate.

The footlambert and the footcandle are two of the most widely used terms in the English system of illumination units. Never forget that both are an expression for similar quantities, namely, *lumens per square foot.* When the lumens per square foot are measured *at or incident to* the surface, the term *footcandle* is used. When the lumens per square foot are coming *from* the surface, the term *footlambert* is used. Thus, it is evident that the product of footcandles multiplied by *reflection factor,* or footcandles by *transmission factor,* yields footlamberts. It is easy to see that a footlambert is the same as an *apparent footcandle.*

**Reflection factor, or reflectance ($\rho$):** "The ratio of the light reflected by a body to the incident light."

**Transmission factor ($\tau$):** "The ratio of the light transmitted by a body to the incident light."

**Luminous intensity (I):** "The solid angular flux density in a given direction."

**Candlepower (cp):** "The luminous intensity expressed in candles." Candlepower always has a directional connotation, and it is a property of the source. Thus we speak of horizontal candlepower, or candlepower at 60°, or spherical candlepower. If a source or a luminous area is said to have a candlepower of 100, in a specified direction, this candlepower is the same whether measured at 10 ft or 1,000 ft, provided there is no atmospheric absorption.

**Mean horizontal candlepower (hcp):** "The average candlepower in the horizontal plane passing through the luminous center of the light source."

**Mean spherical candlepower (scp):** "The average candlepower of a light source in all directions in space."

**Lamp:** A generic term for a man-made source of light.

**Reflector:** A device for redirecting the light of a lamp by reflection in a desired direction.

**Globe:** An enclosing device of clear or diffusing material whose chief uses are to protect the lamp, diffuse or redirect its light, or modify its color.

**Luminaire:** A complete lighting unit consisting of a light source, together with its direct appurtenances, such as globe, reflector, refractor, housing, and so forth.

A luminaire is often but incorrectly referred to as a fixture.

**Efficiency:** "The luminous efficiency of radiant energy is the ratio of luminous flux to radiant flux."

The efficiency of a light source is the ratio of the total luminous flux to the total power input. In the case of an electric lamp, it is expressed in *lumens per watt*. Strictly speaking this ratio is not efficiency since it consists of a fraction made up of diverse terms. It is actually "efficacy," but because it expresses so well the engineering concept, "output over input," the word "efficiency" is commonly accepted.

**Angstrom:** Wavelengths within the range of radiant energy are generally measured in millimicrons so as to work with whole numbers of moderate size. A smaller unit, one-tenth of a millimicron, is often used in lighting practice, and this is termed an *angstrom*. Thus the visual region of radiant energy extends from about 400 to 760 millimicrons, or 4,000 to 7,600 angstroms.

The foregoing definitions are only a portion of those used in the field of lighting. Others will be introduced as the subject is developed; for the purpose of enabling a student to make a start with a minimum of confusion, the above are sufficient.

One mark of a trained practitioner in any art or science, is precision in the use of its specialized language. Avoid such errors as "footcandle power," "ultra-violet light," "footcandle intensity." When using the term candlepower, specify a direction, such as horizontal candlepower or spherical candlepower.

Do not speak of an electric lamp as a bulb or tube or globe. An almost universal misuse of words occurs in the term "fixture." It will be difficult to avoid calling a luminaire a fixture because the correct word is so lightly honored.

### 1.2. The Lighting Industry

The industry serving the field in which the engineer is active furnishes a great deal of the information which he requires for technical development. A knowledge of the industry is important, for it enables one to evaluate the worth of that information. The very structure of the industry furnishes names, initials, and terms that are as much a part of the nomenclature as the technical terms; hence this seems a logical place to introduce the subject. The hours devoted to class and laboratory work offer the opportunity for only the merest opening of the doors of knowledge. Continuous reading, studying of installations and the technical literature, and personal association with fellow engineers is necessary for the attainment and maintenance of professional competence. The brief discussion given here will enable the student to understand better the functions of the various component parts of the lighting industry and the literature which it produces.

**Lamp manufacturers.** The manufacture of electric lamps is largely in the hands of three companies, with a few small companies limiting their output to a restricted range. Commercial and technical competition is keen. Inasmuch as there is no monopoly on brains, considerable time and talent are devoted to research. Consequently, improvements in the products are almost continuous.

Technical data on electric lamps, supplied by the manufacturers, is extensive and competent. The source is clearly stated and may be relied upon. Every engineer engaged in lighting should possess the latest published data because textbook or handbook figures are quickly obsolete.

**Luminaire manufacturers.** The manufacture of luminaires is spread out among a large number of relatively small companies. Commercial competition is keen, but extensive engineering or research is not common enough.

Literature descriptive of the product is largely directed to sales, and technical data upon which application can be based is presented with considerable simplification.

Precise performance data must generally be sought after specifically. Luminaire designs, like those of many other products, lag behind scientific knowledge.

**Trade associations.** Trade associations provide the means for interchange of ideas between "competing" members. The American philosophy of business is to work for the improvement of the "market," with individual members prospering according to their skill in manufacturing, marketing, selling, and product quality.

The National Electric Manufacturers Association (NEMA) includes many luminaire manufacturers. Appropriate committees prepare standards of performance, organize standardization of parts, and the like, and cooperate with other groups in the preparation of application data. This leads to improved performance and consumer satisfaction.

The Edison Electric Institute (EEI) is an association of electric power utilities. It serves its members by the collection of statistical and technical data, and by cooperative design action with manufacturers of equipment. This association sponsors various programs in the field of marketing designed to increase the use of electric energy. All such programs are participated in by manufacturers of equipment in appropriate fields.

Peculiar to the lighting industry is the existence of specifications covering the manufacture, testing, and labeling of luminaires. Any manufacturer is free to utilize this data and these facilities provided that he agrees to conform to the standards as set forth and pay his share of any of the costs so incurred. Obviously the basic specifications and the means for insuring compliance are of great importance in arriving at the basic value of the activity. The plans are a matter of record, and the engineer should familiarize himself with them before specifying equipment bearing their label.

The oldest of such plans was prepared jointly by luminaire manufacturers and (formerly) lamp manufacturers and is sponsored by the RLM Standards Institute. The RLM label is a familiar mark on luminaires used for industrial lighting. The specifications cover the use of both incandescent and fluorescent lamps.

The Fleur-O-Lier Association sponsors a specification-certification program for fluorescent lamp luminaires designed for the lighting of stores, offices, schools, and the like.

Because the electrical characteristics of ballasts directly affect the performance of fluorescent lamps, it is highly desirable that they be standardized. The consumer can thereby interchange lamps and ballasts without fear of poor performance. Ballast manufacturers working with lamp manufacturers have prepared standards under which ballasts are certified and labeled.

In the field of residential lighting, two programs are in effect. One covers the manufacture of portable luminaires, commonly known as floor and table lamps. The activity is entitled Certified Lamp Manufacture (CLM). The other program covers fixed luminaires for ceiling and wall mounting and is named the American Home Lighting Institute.

It is common practice to speak of these activities as "Certification Programs." They have in common (1) specifications covering electrical, mechanical, and illumination characteristics; (2) test procedures; (3) an independent testing agency that certifies whether specific luminaires are in compliance with the specifications and, if so, authorizes attachment of the label.

It should be emphasized that a manufacturer may have any number of his luminaire designs certified; a label on one design does not signify that all products comply. Nor does notice that the manufacturer belongs or subscribes to any group indicate that all of his products are certified.

Likewise, it cannot be assumed that a manufacturer not subscribing to a certification program is producing sub-standard equipment. The skill and integrity of the individual manufacturer is still the best guarantee of performance. Conversely there are wide variations possible under a certification program. In short, there is no substitute for the professional skill of the engineer responsible for the design of the lighting system. It is his duty to know the products he specifies. The best of equipment can render poor service if improperly applied.

**Testing laboratories.** Independently owned and operated testing laboratories are a vital force in the electrical industry. The competence of the staff and the nature of the testing equipment determines the degree of efficiency. In the field of lighting, independent tests are necessary for the proper functioning of any certification program. But it must be borne in mind that while a laboratory brooks no interference with its testing methods, it can only test what is presented to it. Unless proper selection procedures are prescribed, one sample may not truly represent the run-of-mine commercial product. Therefore, the engineer must interpret data with due regard to all the factors.

Standard test procedures for lamps and luminaires have been prepared by various associations, and the Illuminating Engineering Society. When the test conforms to these standards there is no uncertainty as to procedure. Generally speaking, a test by an independent laboratory should be available before any considerable specification of lighting equipment is undertaken.

**Technical societies.** On the North American continent, there is only one technical society devoted solely to illumination. This is the Illuminating Engineering Society (IES). It provides a common meeting ground for people engaged in the practice of illuminating engineering and allied arts and sciences. Through voluntary committees, formed of its members and others interested and competent, it prepares and publishes standards of application, testing procedures, and nomenclature. Basic research is encouraged and conducted through the IES Research Fund. A monthly journal, *Illuminating Engineering,* publishes technical papers, application articles, and discussion. Through local chapters and sections, members have the opportunity to meet and discuss matters of technical and professional interest. Similar societies exist in Great Britain and Australia; the British one in particular is highly active in basic scientific determinations.

At best, the work of a technical society represents the average professional opinion of its members. The individual engineer is aided greatly by the published data, but he should always exercise his own judgment and apply the basic scientific material to the problem as he sees it.

# 2

# BASIC CONCEPTS

---

Throughout the literature of lighting, reference is constantly made to a "point" source of light. While a point may exist mathematically, it cannot exist as a light source. If light sources were points, it would be possible theoretically to obtain infinite illumination, but this is, of course, impossible. Considered as a sphere or cylinder, a light source produces a finite illumination because the maximum illumination must occur at the boundary of the source. This boundary is a finite distance (radius) from the center. From the practical point of view a source may be considered as a point, if the distance of viewing is great with respect to the projected area of the source.

It is well to keep in mind that any light source appears to an observer as a surface. Thus, regardless of its shape, it presents to the observer a projected area which can be treated as a surface source. This surface will have "apparent" candlepower per unit of projected area, or brightness.

The mathematical treatment of light sources with respect to flux output, candlepower, and brightness is accomplished by considering them as:

1. Spheres.
2. Cylinders.
3. Plane surfaces.

## 2.1. Lumen

By definition, a lumen is equal to the light flux incident on a unit surface, all points of which are at unit distance from a uniform point source of 1 candle. In the English system the unit is 1 ft. Consider a source emitting 1 candlepower in all directions, in short

exhibiting one spherical candlepower.   Place this source in a sphere
of 1 ft radius.   (Fig. 2-1.)   The unit surface of our definition is the
1 sq ft shown as $ABCD$.

The surface of a sphere is $4\pi R^2$ in area.   Then, in our unit sphere,
we have 12.57 sq ft of surface.   Obviously the flux on the whole
surface is 12.57 lm, and we arrive at the relationship

$$\text{lumens} = 4\pi I_{\text{scp}} \qquad (2\text{-}1)$$

In solid angular measure a sphere is composed of $4\pi$ steradians.
Since the surface of our unit sphere is composed of $4\pi$ units of area,
1 unit of area subtends 1 steradian.   The flux of 1 lm is therefore
contained in unit solid angle, thus satisfying the definition.

Consider the sphere enlarged to 2 ft in radius.   One steradian,
still containing 1 lm, now subtends an area of 4 sq ft, $A'B'C'D'$.
This lumen is now spread over the 4 sq ft of $A'B'C'D'$, thus producing $\frac{1}{4}$ ft-c.

If the sphere were enlarged to 3 ft radius, its area would be $4\pi 9$.
The number of steradians is still $4\pi$, so the area subtended by 1
steradian, still containing 1 lm, is 9 sq ft.   The illumination on this
area is $\frac{1}{9}$ ft-c.

We thus arrive at the basic inverse square law which states that
for light sources of "point" character the illumination varies
inversely as the square of the distance from the source or

$$\frac{E_1}{E_2} = \frac{D_2{}^2}{D_1{}^2} \qquad (2\text{-}2)$$

Another fundamental relationship is disclosed by a study of the
sphere in Fig. 2-1.   The light source has a rating of 1 mean spherical
candlepower, that is, the candlepower is 1 in every direction.   The
illumination on area $ABCD$ is 1 ft-c.   Therefore we can say that

$$E = \frac{I}{D^2}$$

or $\qquad\qquad 1 \text{ ft-c} = \dfrac{1 \text{ cp}}{1} \qquad (2\text{-}3)$

On area $A'B'C'D'$ the illumination is $\frac{1}{4}$ ft-c or

$$E = \frac{I}{D^2} \qquad \text{or} \qquad \tfrac{1}{4} \text{ ft-c} = \frac{1 \text{ cp}}{4}$$

This relationship is the basis of the point-by-point method of calculating illumination, to be discussed in Chapter 10.

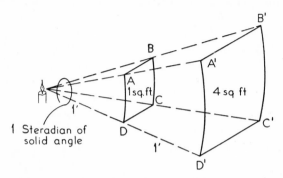

Fig. 2-1.    Explanation of lumen and inverse-square
law.

When working in the metric system the analysis is the same, but the unit sphere is taken either as 1 cm in radius with the unit area 1 sq cm, or 1 m in radius with the unit area 1 sq m.

## 2.2. Footlambert

By definition, a footlambert is the uniform brightness of a perfectly diffusing surface emitting or reflecting light at the rate of 1 lumen per sq ft.    Therefore

$$B = \frac{F}{A}$$

Suppose you are located at the center of the sphere in Fig. 2-1. If the area $ABCD$ diffusely reflected 100% of the lumens incident upon it, it would emit flux toward you at the rate of 1 lm per sq ft. It would then have a brightness of 1 ft-l.    In other words, incident lumens per square foot multiplied by the diffuse reflection factor of the surface yields footlamberts.

Consider the area $ABCD$ to be covered by a perfectly diffusing translucent surface which absorbs no light.    It will then emit light at the rate of 1 lm per sq ft.    It will have a brightness of 1 ft-L.

Evidently for a diffusely transmitting material the brightness is equal to incident lumens per square foot multiplied by the transmission factor of the material.  Thus for a reflecting surface

footlamberts = footcandles (lumens per sq ft) × reflection factor

or (ft-c × ρ), and for a transmitting medium,

footlamberts = footcandles × transmission factor

or (ft-c × τ).  Confusion is avoided by keeping in mind that footcandles and footlamberts are both measured in lumens per square
foot but that footcandles are lumens per square foot *incident* on a
surface, and footlamberts are lumens per square foot emitted or
reflected by a surface.

EXAMPLES:

**1.** A surface 10 sq ft in area has 100 lm incident upon it.  What is
the illumination in footcandles?

$$\text{ft-c} = \frac{100 \text{ lm}}{10 \text{ sq ft}} = 10$$

This same surface has a diffuse reflection factor of 80%.  What is its
brightness in footlamberts?

$$\text{ft-L} = \text{ft-c} \times \text{R.F.} = 10 \times 80\% = 8 \text{ ft-L}$$

**2.** A diffusing glass panel is illuminated on one side to a level of 20 ft-c.
It has a transmission factor of 60%.  What is the brightness of the other
side, in footlamberts?

$$\text{ft-L} = \text{ft-c} \times \text{transmission factor} = 20 \times 60\% = 12 \text{ ft-L}$$

Brightness may also be expressed in terms of candlepower per
unit area of surface.  This follows quite logically from a study of
the definitions of brightness, luminous intensity, and candlepower
as given in Chapter 1.  In the English system, brightness can be
stated in candles per square inch, in the metric system in candles
per square centimeter.  Hence $b = I/a$.  A surface has a brightness of 1 candle per sq in. if an area of 1 sq in. has a candlepower of
unity in a direction normal to it.

This unit of brightness is used in photometric reports, but has
no meaning in the calculation of illumination by the lumen concept.
Any value of brightness in candles per square inch may, however,

be converted to footlamberts by the multiplier $144\pi$ or 452, as will be proved later.

## 2.3. Candlepower

The standard definition of candlepower is "solid angular flux density." It is easy to imagine a cone filled with light flux. This would be a solid angle possessing some value of flux density. The light flux would strike the base of the cone and produce there some value of flux per unit area, or illumination.

Thus we see that candlepower is simply an index of the ability of a light source to produce illumination. Candlepower is the property of a source and represents a quantity that is fixed for any source under specified conditions. Candlepower represents the cause, and illumination the effect. If we measure the effect (illumination), we can calculate the cause (candlepower). There is no mystery about this essential quantity. It is an index of the ability of a light source to produce illumination.

Matters are simplified for measurement, if the point in space is selected so that $I = ED^2$. Since $I$ is a constant for any source operated under constant specified conditions, the quantities $E$ and $D^2$, while varying, must end up with a constant value as their product. Experiment has shown that $ED^2$ approaches a constant value when $D$ is greater than five times the maximum dimension of the light source. Under these circumstances the source is considered to be a "point" and the inverse square law applies. However, any source has candlepower whether or not the conditions of measurement have been adjusted so that it acts like a point.

A very simple experiment will demonstrate a number of these fundamental relationships. Arrange a setup, as shown in Fig. 2-2, on a bench or a bar photometer. A primary light source of 1,000 hcp is placed at $A$. At $G$ place a piece of good diffusing glass which is 6 in. square. Place over this piece of glass a mask of black opaque paper with a 1-in. square hole cut in it. At $C$ take a measurement of the illumination. Substitute this value and that of $D$ in the equation $I = ED^2$ and note the value of the candlepower $I$.

We can reason that if a piece of this surface 1 in. square has a certain candlepower, the entire piece of 36 square in. should have 36 times as much candlepower. We can easily determine the truth of this. Remove the mask, and move the light meter to point $Y$. Measure the illumination, substitute the values of $E$ and $D$ in the formula $I = ED^2$ and it will be found that the value of $I$ is approximately 36 times that calculated for the 1-in.-square area.

Instrument error and the difficulty of excluding all but the light from the secondary source will cause unavoidable experimental error. The work should be done in a dark room with black surfaces. Points $G$, $C$, and $Y$ should be in a black tunnel.

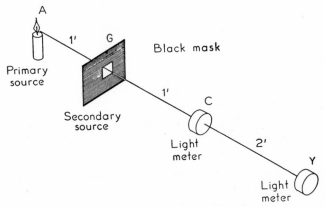

Fig. 2-2. Experimental setup for demonstrating candlepower, illumination, and brightness relationships.

Let us utilize this same setup to analyze brightness in terms of candles per square inch. It is quite obvious that when we know the candlepower of a source 1 sq in. in area we can state it as "candles per square inch." If the source is perfectly uniform in brightness, only 1 sq in. need be measured. If it is not uniform, an average value can be found by measuring every square inch of the surface.

The light source $A$ is assumed as having 1,000 hcp. The diffusing glass $G$ can be measured for its transmission value; let it be assumed to be 50%. The illumination on the surface of the glass facing the source is

$$E = \frac{I}{D^2} \qquad E = \frac{1,000}{1} = 1,000 \text{ ft-c}$$

In other words the glass is receiving light flux at the rate of 1,000 lm per sq ft. The other side of the glass is emitting lumens at a lower rate due to losses in the glass. The emission is just one-half the amount received, or at the rate of 500 lm per sq ft.   Its brightness in footlamberts is then 500 [(ft-L = ft-c × τ).]

Place the black mask on the glass and with a suitable instrument measure the brightness of the 1-sq-in. opening.   It will be found to be approximately 500 ft-L.   The brightness in candles per square inch is then

$$\tfrac{500}{452} = 1.1 \text{ candles per sq in.}$$

(The common factor of 452 is explained later in this chapter.)

The candlepower of this one square inch is likewise 1.1.   Check back on your values from the preceding demonstration and this will be verified.   Likewise the candlepower of the entire diffusing glass will be 36 × 1.1 = 40 cp, and this too will be verified from the preceding demonstration.

### 2.4. Lambert's Law of Emission

This law states that a surface is perfectly diffusing when the candlepower in any direction varies from the candlepower normal to the surface by the cosine of the angle between the normal and the desired direction.   In Fig. 2-3, the candlepower $I_\theta$ is directly proportional to the product of candlepower $I_N$ and the cosine of the angle $\theta$.   Thus

$$I_\theta = I_N \cos \theta \qquad (2\text{-}4)$$

This is an important relationship in illuminating engineering.   Very few surfaces in practice follow this law throughout the entire 90°, but many do so over a considerable portion of the quadrant.

If very few of the practical materials encountered in lighting practice are perfectly diffuse, can the theories based upon this assumption be applied?

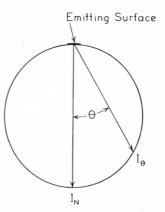

Fig. 2-3.   Lambert's cosine law of emission.

The answer is yes.   Any surface can be investigated in small segments.   When the entire surface has been analyzed, the rating of it will be an "average."

Suppose we place a piece of frosted glass in front of a light source in such a way that it is perfectly obvious to our eyes that the glass has bright areas and dark areas. Prepare a black mask to more than cover the whole piece of glass, but cut in it a small hole, 1 sq in. in area. Move the mask until the hole is over one of the darker areas of the glass. We now measure, by suitable means, the brightness of that piece of glass and find it to be 100 ft-L. What does this tell us? Simply that this 1-in. square of glass is emitting light at such a rate that 1 sq ft of it would emit 100 lm.

We continue to move the mask, measuring the brightness of each square inch of surface. Some spots may show a brightness of 1,000 ft-L, others 50 ft-L, and so forth. When every square inch has been investigated the *average* brightness is, let us say, 500 ft-L. By this we mean that the piece of glass we have measured will emit an *average* of 500 lm per sq ft. A perfectly diffusing piece of glass of 500 ft-L brightness emits exactly the same number of lumens per square foot but does so in a uniform manner.

## 2.5. Light from a Single Surface

Assume now a surface $ES$ emitting light according to Lambert's law, Fig. 2-4. With that surface as a center construct a sphere of unit radius (1 ft). Only one-half this sphere will receive light from $ES$. For ease in calculation assume that the candlepower normal to the surface is 100. Then the candlepower at any angle from the normal will be $100 \times \cos \theta$.

Referring to Fig. 2-1 and the derivation of the lumen it is seen that

$$F = IA \text{ in unit sphere}$$

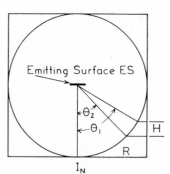

Fig. 2-4. Derivation of flux from a single surface.

We can subdivide the area of one-half the sphere (Fig. 2-4) into suitably small areas and multiply each area by the candlepower directed to it. This will give us the flux on each area. By adding these flux increments we obtain the total flux output of the emitting surface.

Describe around the sphere of unit radius a cylinder of unit radius. The area of the cylinder is equal to the area of the sphere. The area of any zone on the sphere such as between $\theta_1$ and $\theta_2$ will be equal to an area on the cylinder of altitude $H$ or $2\pi r^2(\cos \theta_2 - \cos \theta_1)$.[1]

The illumination on that zone will be the product of area and candlepower. If the zone is narrow in width, it may be assumed safely that the average candlepower striking the surface is equal to the candlepower at the mid-point of the zone.

Take 10° zones beginning at nadir. Calculate the area of each zone by the above formula. Multiply that area by the mid-zone candlepower. For the 0° to 10° zone the mid-zone candlepower is $I_N \cos 5°$, or

$$100 \times .996 = 99.6$$

The area is $2\pi r^2(\cos 0° - \cos 10°)$ or 0.10 sq ft.
Then since

$$F = IA$$

$$F = 99.6 \times 0.10 \text{ or } 9.96 \text{ lm.}$$

---

[1] Proof of the expression is as follows:

$$OB = r \cos \theta_2 \quad \text{and} \quad OA = r \cos \theta_1; \quad H = OB - OA;$$

substituting,                    $$H = (r \cos \theta_2 - r \cos \theta_1)$$

$$H = r(\cos \theta_2 - \cos \theta_1)$$

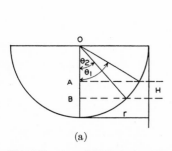    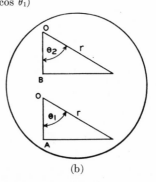

(a)                                        (b)

Fig. 2-5.  (a and b) Relationship between areas on a sphere and areas on a circumscribed cylinder.

The area of a cylinder of height $H = H \times$ circumference (circumference $= 2\pi r$); therefore area of zone $= 2\pi r^2(\cos \theta_2 - \cos \theta_1)$.

This process is repeated for each 10° zone up to 90°, at which limit there is no further candlepower emission from the surface source.

The sum of the lumens so calculated will be 314 plus. We know from eq. (2-1) that if the source had radiated uniformly in all directions, the lumens would have been 1257. Therefore, since the surface in question emits one-quarter of that amount,

$$F_{\text{surface}} = \pi I_N \qquad (2\text{-}5)^1$$

We know from the discussion in Section 2.3 that the candle-power of an emitting surface 1 in. square can be designated as candles per square inch. Conversely, if we state a brightness value in candles per square inch we are saying in effect that this is the candlepower of 1 sq in. of surface. Therefore, if we substitute for $I_N$ in eq. (2-4) a value of candles per square inch, the flux $F$ will be the flux from 1 sq in. of surface. Every square inch of a perfectly diffusing surface such as $ES$ (Fig. 2-4) will have the same normal candlepower and the same brightness in candles per square inch. Therefore a square foot of such a surface will produce 144 times as much flux as a square inch. Hence

$$F_{\text{sq ft}} = 144\pi I_{\text{c/sq in.}} = 452 I_{\text{c/sq in.}}$$

-----

[1] By the calculus the proof is as follows: The element $xy$ of the surface of the sphere will be considered instead of the subtended area of a circumscribed cylinder. Select an angle of infinitesimal size, $d\theta$. The width of the zone on the surface of the sphere subtended by this angle is $xy$ and is $rd\theta$. This zone forms a band around the sphere, this band having a length of $2\pi r \sin\theta$. The area of the band is $2\pi r \sin\theta\, rd\theta$, or $2\pi r^2 \sin\theta\, d\theta$. Since by definition in *unit* sphere

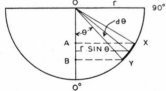

Fig. 2-6. Deriving areas on a sphere by the calculus.

$$F = \frac{I}{r^2} \times \text{area}$$

the flux on this portion of the sphere is

$$F = 2\pi I_\theta \sin\theta\, d\theta$$

The number of zones $xy$ which will be found in the distance from 0° to 90° will be that distance divided by the width of the zone. This distance is $2\pi r/4$ and in unit sphere is $\pi/2$. Also,

$$I_\theta = I_N \cos\theta$$

Then
$$F_{\text{total}} = \int_0^{\pi/2} 2\pi I_N \cos\theta \sin\theta\, d\theta$$

$$= 2\pi I_N \left(\frac{\sin^2\theta}{2}\right)_0^{\pi/2} = \pi I_N$$

One candle per square inch will produce 452 lm per sq ft. A foot-lambert is defined as *one* lumen per square foot, so

$$1_{c/\text{sq in.}} = 452 \text{ ft-L} \tag{2-6}$$

It should be noted that if our units in the above example had been centimeters, our results would have been expressed in lamberts.

### 2.6. Light from a Double Surface

For a source emitting according to the cosine law, from one surface only, the relationship is, from eq. (2-4),

$$F = \pi I_N$$

If the surface source emits from both sides, obviously

$$F = 2\pi I_N \tag{2-7}$$

### 2.7. Light from a Cylinder

In the case of a cylindrical light source,

$$F = \pi^2 I_N \tag{2-8}$$

in which $I_N$ is the candlepower measured normal to the axis of the cylinder. A simple derivation is as follows:

Consider a cylindrical source of flux of radius $r$ and a unit height $h$ (Fig. 2-7). The projected area of the cylinder will emit light in

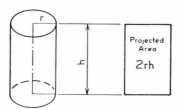

Fig. 2-7. A cylindrical light
source.

the same manner as a single surface, namely, $F = \pi I_N$. This area is $2rh$. The entire cylinder, however, emits light, and its area is $2\pi rh$, or $\pi$ times the projected area. Therefore the flux emission from the cylinder is $\pi$ times the emission from its projected area, or $F = \pi^2\, I_N.$[1]

This emission is described as toroidal (Fig. 2-8), and the concept is useful when calculating the coefficient of utilization of a luminaire from an analysis of its candlepower distribution.

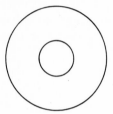

### 2.8. Light from an Infinite Plane

From an infinite plane surface or from a hemisphere of uniform brightness, the illumination in footcandles is

$$E = 452b \qquad (2\text{-}9)$$

when $b$ is measured in candlepower per square inch.

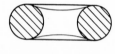

SECTION THROUGH
A TOROID

Fig. 2-8. Toroidal flux distribution.

Understanding of this relationship is made somewhat easier by considering the following (Fig. 2-10). Suppose we are viewing a diffusing sphere whose uniform brightness is 1 ft-L, or 1 lm per sq ft. What we actually see is a projection of the sphere, which is the same as a surface $AB$ cutting through the sphere at its center. Imagine that one-half the sphere is removed and the surface represented by the line $AB$ consists of a diffusing surface of 100% transmission.

---

[1] For proof by the calculus consider an infinitesimally small area of the light-emitting cylinder, this area acting exactly as the single surface in the previous example on page 18. Place the cylinder in unit sphere (Fig. 2-9). The area of the zone $xy$ is again

$2\pi r^2 \sin\theta d\theta$    or    $2\pi \sin\theta d\theta$    when    $r = 1$

The flux on the area is likewise

$$F = 2\pi I_\theta \sin\theta d\theta$$

but        $I_\theta = I_N \cos\theta$

Therefore    $F = 2\pi I_N \cos\theta \sin\theta d\theta$

Integration is now carried from 0 to $\pi$

$$F_{\text{total}} = 2\pi I_N \int_0^\pi \sin^2\theta d\theta$$

$$= 2\pi I_N \left(\frac{\theta}{2} - \frac{\sin 2\theta}{4}\right)_0^\pi = \pi^2 I_N$$

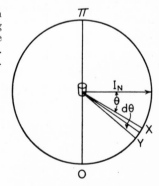

Fig. 2-9. Light flux from a cylindrical source as determined by the calculus.

This surface would have a brightness of 1 lm per sq ft or 1 ft-L.   If we pass from position $P_1$ to position $P_2$, the surface $AB$ having a transmission of 100%, then this surface $AB$ at position $P_2$ must be receiving flux at the rate of 1 lm per sq ft.   By definition the illumination at $P_2$ is then 1 ft-c.   Thus it is apparent that from an infinite plane or the hemisphere of the sky, the illumination on the horizontal plane is equal in footcandles to the brightness of the source in footlamberts.   From the standpoint of practical measurement, brightness is often measured in candlepower per square inch, so

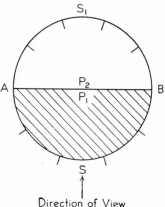

Fig. 2-10.   A light source of any shape is seen as a plane projection.

$E = B$   when $B$ is in footlamberts

or

$E = 452 \, b$   when $b$ is in candles per sq in.

## 2.9. Spherical Reduction Factor

The student will find in the literature references to "spherical reduction factor."   This is simply the ratio of mean spherical candlepower to horizontal candlepower.   When the spherical reduction factor is known for a given shape of light source, it is only necessary to measure its horizontal candlepower and multiply this by the spherical reduction factor to obtain spherical candlepower. The spherical candlepower multiplied by $4\pi$ equals the lumens output of the source.

# PROBLEMS

**1.** (a) If a sphere of 1 ft radius has a light source at the center emitting 1 cp uniformly in all directions, and a hole is cut in the sphere of exactly 1 sq ft in area, how much light, in lumens, streams through the hole?

(b) If the sphere is 2 ft in radius and the hole 4 sq ft in area, how much light is emitted?

**2.** If the sphere in Problem 1 has a light source of 10 mean spherical candles at the center, how much light streams through the opening?

**3.** What is the illumination in footcandles at the opening in Problem 1(a)? At the opening in Problem 1(b)? At the opening in Problem 2?

**4.** An illumination of 20 lm per sq ft is incident on a sheet of paper of 80% reflectance. What is the brightness of the paper in footlamberts?

**5.** The sheet of paper in Problem 4 lies on a desk top of 12% reflectance. What is the brightness of the desk top in footlamberts?

**6.** A light source is found to have a mean spherical candlepower of 300. What is its output in lumens?

**7.** A sheet of diffusing (frosted) glass in a door has 15 lm per sq ft falling on its surface (room side). If the glass absorbs 20% of this light, what is the brightness of the glass on the corridor side?

**8.** A white glass ball globe of 18 in. diameter has a brightness of 3.5 candles per sq in. How many lumens are emitted by the globe?

**9.** A Luckiesh-Taylor brightness meter reading of the ceiling above an indirect luminaire shows, on one scale, 0.25 candle per sq in. What is the brightness in footlamberts?

**10.** A luminaire has a candlepower of 1,200 in direction $A$ measured at 10 ft. What would the candlepower measure at 17 ft?

**11.** A reflector lamp has an end-on candlepower of 7000. What is the illumination in footcandles on a sheet of paper held normal to the beam at a distance of 6 ft? At 9 ft?

**12.** One minute after sunset the perfectly clear blue sky has a brightness of 4 candles per sq in. What is the horizontal illumination in the middle of an airport?

**13.** A fluorescent lamp 60 in. long emits 3,200 lm. A plastic diffusing cylinder of 55% efficiency is to be placed around the lamp, the average brightness to be 250 ft-L. What diameter of cylinder would you specify?

**14.** A diffusing glass surface of uniform brightness has an area of 2 sq ft. At a distance of 1 ft an area of 1 sq in. of this surface produces an illumination of $\frac{1}{2}$ ft-c. What is the brightness of the surface? Calculate in two ways the total light output of the surface.

**15.** At a distance of 100 ft from a searchlight the beam covers a circular spot 10 ft in diameter. The average illumination on this spot is 100 ft-c. The searchlight has an efficiency of 40%. Calculate by two methods the mean spherical candlepower of the source. What is its output in lumens?

**16.** The cover glass of a fluorescent lamp trough measures 10 by 48 in. and has an average brightness of 2.5 candles per sq in. If the glass has a transmission factor of 82% and the light box itself, without glass, returns 78% of the light which strikes it, how many lumens are generated by the source? (Note: The assumption is made that the glass cover, when in place, will not change the value of the internal reflections.)

**17.** A projection lamp emits 22,000 lm. It is placed in a 10-in.-diameter spot light having a beam efficiency of 30% and a beam spread of 10°. What is the average beam candlepower?

**18.** A perfectly diffusing surface 10 by 10 in. has a brightness of $\frac{1}{2}$ candle per sq in., measured at an angle of 45° from the normal. What illumination will it produce on a parallel plane 8 ft away?

**19.** A photographic flash lamp has a maximum intensity of 4,500,000 cp. How much light flux does the lamp radiate when discharged?

## REFERENCES

Barrows, William E., *Light, Photometry, and Illuminating Engineering.* New York: McGraw-Hill Book Co., Inc., 1938.

General Electric Company, *Bulletin LD-2*, October 1948.

Higbie, H. H., *Lighting Calculations.* New York: John Wiley and Sons, Inc., 1934.

Illuminating Engineering Society and University of Pennsylvania Lectures, *Illuminating Engineering Practice.* New York: McGraw-Hill Book Co., Inc., 1917.

Moon, Parry, *The Scientific Basis of Illuminating Engineering.* New York: McGraw-Hill Book Co., Inc., 1936.

# 3

# ELECTRIC LAMPS

---

Light is, of course, produced in many ways and forms, but in North America the illuminating engineer applies his art and science to light which is produced electrically. There is no such thing as artificial light, although the literature dealing with light uses that term exclusively. Light is energy, and energy exists only in pure form— there is no artificial energy. Quite apart from the incorrect use of the term are the negative characteristics associated with the word "artificial." Continued use of the term only adds to the difficulties of the engineer in his work with the public. Therefore, throughout this work, instead of "artificial" light, the term electric light will be used. The light from sun and sky will be called sunlight, skylight, or daylight. Daylight is not "natural" light, as the literature reiterates. Natural implies "good" or "normal," but daylighting can have all the unfavorable attributes of high brightness contrast, insufficient quantity, and nonuniformity usually associated with inadequate electric lighting.

Electric light sources may be grouped into two broad classes:

1. Incandescent:
   a. Tungsten filament.
2. Gaseous Discharge:
   a. Mercury vapor,
   b. Neon,
   c. Sodium,
   d. Fluorescent.

## INCANDESCENT LAMPS

Tungsten is the material most widely used today for producing light by incandescence. Other materials, such as carbon, osmium,

24

and tantalum, have been used in the evolutionary development, but tungsten possesses the best all-around combination of favorable qualities. It has a melting point of 6,120° Fahrenheit, and a positive resistance characteristic. Because the resistance increases with

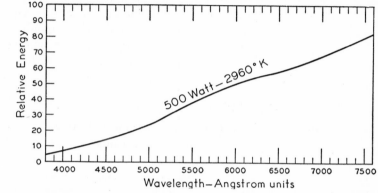

Fig. 3-1. Homogeneous radiation from incandescent tungsten.

temperature, a stable electric circuit is possible. The glowing tungsten emits luminous energy in all wave bands throughout the spectrum. This is called continuous or homogeneous spectral emission, as from a theoretical black body.

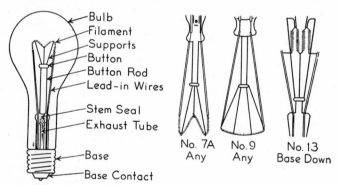

Fig. 3-2. Typical incandescent lamp construction and filaments.

Normally a very brittle metal, tungsten can be processed so that it possesses great strength and ductility.

There are three principal parts of any incandescent lamp: the filament, the enclosing envelope or bulb, and the base (Fig. 3-2).

## 3.1. Filament

The filament assumes various shapes and dimensions depending upon the service for which the lamp is intended. Filament of straight wire has the designation $S$; coiled (as a door spring), it has the designation $C$; and a coiled coil has the designation $CC$. The manner in which the filament is supported depends again upon the intended service. Thus, some lamps are intended to be burned base down, others base up, some in any position, and others within a specified range of angles from the vertical.

### TABLE 3-1

**Theoretical and Actual Current Inrush when Starting**

**Tungsten-filament Incandescent Lamps**

| Lamp watts | Operating amps at 120 volts | Theoretical current inrush | Actual current inrush maximum* |
|---|---|---|---|
| 75 | .625 | 9.38 | 7.2 |
| 100 | .835 | 13.0 | 9.0 |
| 200 | 1.67 | 26.2 | 17.2 |
| 300 | 2.50 | 40.0 | 26.2 |
| 500 | 4.17 | 67.9 | 45.7 |
| 750 | 6.25 | 101.9 | 51.7 |
| 1,000 | 8.33 | 142.4 | 65.2 |

* The current reaches maximum value in .003 sec or less and falls to normal value in 0.2 sec or less.

Most filaments are operated in gas, principally a combination of nitrogen and argon. The gas introduces approximately atmospheric pressure on the filament when hot. This allows higher temperatures and hence higher efficiency without excessive evaporation of the tungsten. Gas is only used with coiled or coiled coil filaments. Otherwise the gas conducts more heat away from the filament than is gained by the higher temperature permitted by the gas pressure, resulting in lower efficiency. Generally, lamps of 40 watts or below are vacuum type, designated by the letter $B$. Larger lamps are gas filled and designated as type $C$.

The cold resistance of tungsten is 1/15 to 1/17 that of the hot resistance. Consequently when the lamp is energized there is an initial inrush of current. The inrush, however, is not 15 times the operating current, because of several limiting factors. In the first place, the filament begins to heat immediately and hence increases in resistance. Also, there is the limiting resistance and reactance of the distribution circuit and of the various switches, fuses, transformers, and the like. Table 3-1 shows the comparison between theoretical and actual test inrush of current. Branch circuit switches must be designed to carry a heavier current than the normal operating value. Even though the time during which the higher current is in existence is only in the nature of tenths of a second, overheating and burning at contact points must be avoided. Thus, branch circuit switches for use with tungsten filament lamps have a *T* rating by the Underwriters Laboratory. Fuses and circuit breakers likewise incorporate time delay features so that the initial rush does not cause them to operate.

## 3.2. Bases

Filament lamps utilize a number of types of bases, depending upon the amperage to be conducted and the physical strength of the glass-to-metal seal (Fig. 3-3). For general use in home and commerce, the Edison screw base predominates. For lamps up to 200 watts, it is known as a medium base; for 300 to 1,500 watts, mogul base. Thus a given lamp socket can accommodate a wide range of lamp wattages. All lamp manufacturers in the United States adhere to the same standards of type and size of base, thus permitting absolute interchangeability.

## 3.3. Bulb

The glass envelope or bulb, often incorrectly referred to as a globe, may be clear, colored, frosted, or coated inside or outside with reflecting metal or diffusing material. Soft glass is commonly used, but for conditions of high temperature or exposure to the weather, hard glass is used. Bulb shapes depend largely upon application, and the maximum diameter is given in number units. The unit is 1/8 of an inch. Thus a pear-shaped bulb is designated by the letters *PS*, and if these are followed by the number 30, the description is of a pear-shaped bulb $3\frac{3}{4}$ in. in diameter. Over-all length is of interest to the designer of luminaires, as is light center length.

Over-all length is measured from the bottom of the base to the top of the bulb; light center length, from the bottom of the base to the center of the filament. Fluorescent lamps are designated by length and diameter. The designated length of the preheat (hot) cathode and Slimline lamps includes the length of the tube and two sockets.

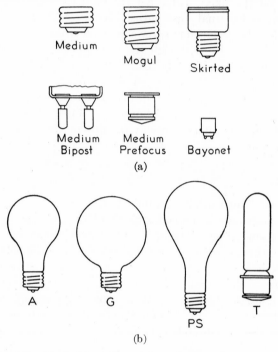

Fig. 3-3. Typical incandescent lamp bases and bulb shapes.

The designated length of iron (cold) cathode lamps includes only the tube.

In recent years the development of metallic, reflective coatings both inside and outside of the bulb has resulted in very useful lamp types. The outside coating is usually of silver and combines a high efficiency reflector with the light source. Principal use is for indirect lighting. The lamp costs more than the standard line, but superior maintenance characteristics often make it more economical in service.

Inside reflective coatings are generally of aluminum or silver and have made possible such developments as the all-glass sealed beam headlamps, and reflector lamps.

Diffusing coatings are applied both inside and out for purposes of softening shadows and lessening glare. These finishes are not to be confused with the inside frosting, which is an etching process. This etching diffuses the light with a loss of less than 1% and is widely applied to all types and sizes of bulbs.

## 3.4. Characteristics

In Fig. 3-4 is shown the general class of characteristic curves for gas-filled tungsten lamps. It will be noted that within approxi-

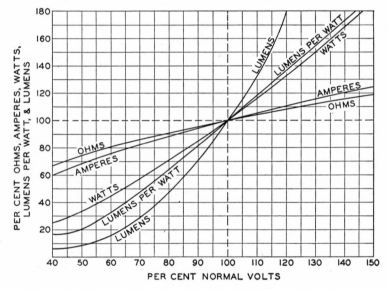

Fig. 3-4. Characteristic curves for tungsten-filament incandescent lamps.

mately 10% of normal design volts, all curves are essentially straight lines. This gives rise to certain rule-of-thumb relationships which are useful for quick appraisals.

With respect to voltage, a 1% change from design point causes a 3% change in light output. Thus 1% *overvoltage* produces a 3% increase in light output. Conversely, 1% *undervoltage* produces a 3% decrease in light output.

With respect to lamp life, a 1% *increase* in voltage reduces lamp life by 8%. A 1% *decrease* in voltage increases lamp life by 20%.

The manufacturers' aim is a combination of lamp life and light output that will be most economical for a given class of service. They must, of course, work from averages. A study of any specific application may indicate the desirability of overvoltage or undervoltage operation. For example, in the lighting of baseball stadiums, the high cost of installation and comparatively few hours of yearly operation make it more economical to operate lamps at 10% overvoltage in order to get maximum light from a minimum of luminaires. For more precise calculations than the rule-of-thumb expressions given above, filament lamp equations and their exponents are given in Table 3-2.

**TABLE 3-2**

**Relationships between Tungsten-filament Lamp Operating Voltage and Various Lamp Characteristics**

$$\frac{\text{life}}{\text{rated life}} = \left(\frac{\text{rated volts}}{\text{volts}}\right)^{13.1}$$

$$\frac{\text{lumens}}{\text{rated lumens}} = \left(\frac{\text{volts}}{\text{rated volts}}\right)^{3.38}$$

$$\frac{\text{rated efficiency}}{\text{efficiency}} = \left(\frac{\text{volts}}{\text{rated volts}}\right)^{1.84}$$

$$\frac{\text{watts}}{\text{rated watts}} = \left(\frac{\text{volts}}{\text{rated volts}}\right)^{1.54}$$

$$\frac{\text{rated volts}}{\text{volts}} = \left(\frac{\text{rated filament temperature}}{\text{filament temperature}}\right)^{2.7}$$

These exponents are valid within voltage range of 10% from design voltage.

The tungsten filament dissipates energy by radiation beyond the bulb, conduction and convection of the surrounding gas (if used), by conduction of supports and lead-in wires, and by absorption in the bulb and base. So little radiation occurs in the shorter (ultraviolet) wavelengths beyond the visible that this percentage is included in the infra-red (heat) radiation (see Table 3-3).

While the incandescent lamp is operating, tungsten is being driven from the filament by molecular excitation. The particles drift to the bulb surface and are deposited there as a dark film. The

**TABLE 3-3**

**Luminous and Thermal Characteristics of Filament Lamps**

| Watts | Initial lumens | Mean lumens | Life, hr | % Energy distribution | | | |
|---|---|---|---|---|---|---|---|
| | | | | Light, % | Infrared, % | Gas loss, % | Bulb and base loss, % |
| 25 | 260 | 220 | 1,000 | 8.7 | 85.3 | .. | 6.0 |
| 60 | 835 | 785 | 1,000 | 7.5 | 73.3 | 13.5 | 5.7 |
| 100 | 1,630 | 1,530 | 750 | 10.0 | 72.0 | 11.5 | 6.5 |
| 200 | 3,700 | 3,250 | 750 | 10.2 | 67.2 | 13.7 | 8.9 |
| 300 Mogul | 5,650 | 5,050 | 1,000 | 11.1 | 68.7 | 11.6 | 8.6 |
| 500 | 9,900 | 8,700 | 1,000 | 12.2 | 70.3 | 8.8 | 8.9 |
| 1,000 | 21,500 | 18,000 | 1,000 | 12.1 | 75.3 | 6.0 | 6.6 |

presence of gas in gas-filled lamps retards this drift but does not prevent it. Eventually enough tungsten has been driven off to weaken the filament to the point where it breaks, and the lamp fails. The blackening, of course, absorbs light so there is a steadily

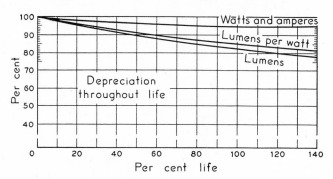

Fig. 3-5.   Loss of light due to use, of incandescent lamp.

decreasing light output as the lamp ages.   This is shown in Fig. 3-5. There is also a falling off in watts consumed because of increasing resistance and resulting lower amperage.

Many lamps continue to operate even after considerable blackening has taken place.   The reduction in light output may be uneconomic, depending upon an appraisal of lamp cost, electric energy charges, and lamp renewal labor cost.

In summation, tungsten filament lamps have a number of favorable characteristics that make them valuable as lighting tools:

1. Unity power factor.
2. Operation directly from standard distribution circuits.
3. Wide range of filament shapes and light distribution.
4. Wide range of interchangeability in standard sockets.
5. Favorable radiation characteristics within the luminous range.
6. They are not affected by surrounding air temperature.

Technical data supplied by the manufacturers is unusually complete and accurate.   No engineer should undertake the design of lighting installations without a thorough understanding of such data.

## GASEOUS DISCHARGE LAMPS

All gaseous discharge lamps possess certain characteristics in common, although they vary quantitatively.

1. Production of radiation is by electronic activity within the gas.
2. Electrodes are necessary to initiate and maintain electronic flow.   The electrodes are usually coated with barium or strontium oxide which has high electron emissive characteristics.
3. The arc column has a negative resistance characteristic, thus requiring ballasting to maintain a steady flow of current.
4. Starting voltage and operating voltage are not the same, thus requiring high-leakage types of transformers.
5. On alternating current the electron flow is interrupted at each cycle change, thus producing rapid flicker or stroboscopic effect.

### 3.5. Neon

Probably the most familiar form of gaseous discharge is found in neon tubing.   The electrodes are iron shells, coated on the inside. The flow of current between these electrodes depends upon the passage of electrons.   Electrons can be thought of as minute particles of negative electricity.   To start the flow of electrons from a cold material requires a high voltage.   When the flow of electrons has been established the current flowing will heat the electrodes and allow electrons to pass with a lower voltage.   The characteristic color of neon gas is pinkish-red.  Its efficiency of light production is not high, so its principal use is for electrical advertising.  While ambient or surrounding temperature affects the light output, the high starting voltage assures operation in very cold weather even in exposed locations.  Helium gas is often substituted for neon, giving a pinkish-white light.  These two gases in combination with colored glass tubing produce a range of colors for variety and effect.

### 3.6. Sodium

Electric discharge lamps using sodium vapor produce pure monochromatic light in the $598\mu$ band, which is orange-yellow.  A fundamental of glowing gases is that the light does not consist of all of the wavelengths of the visible spectrum.  This is known as a discontinuous spectrum.  Sometimes only one wavelength is present, as with sodium.  The effect of monochromatic light upon objects whose color is not that of the light is to make them appear as various shades of gray.  This limits sodium lamps to applications where color is of little importance.  Their commercial use is principally for highway lighting.

Sodium at temperatures below 140° Fahrenheit is in solid form. The electric discharge is initiated through neon gas; then as the temperature builds up, the sodium vaporizes and the typical yellow sodium arc is established.  This arc is contained in a tubular bulb, enclosed by a double-walled vacuum flask to maintain a sodium vapor temperature of around 480° Fahrenheit.  When starting, the cathodes are preheated for approximately 1/2 min.; then upon opening of the preheat switch, an inductive kick of about 300 volts initiates the neon discharge.  After about 10 min., the characteristic red of the neon is gradually displaced by the yellow sodium color. In about 30 min. the lamp reaches full output.  Each lamp requires as auxiliary equipment a transformer, cathode-heater shunts, electric cathode-heater timer, choke coil, and capacitor for the suppression of radio interference.  The primary of the transformer can be arranged for either constant-current series or constant-voltage multiple supply.

Luminous efficiency of the lamp, including auxiliary losses, is about 40 lm per watt.  It may be burned either horizontally or vertically, base up.  The arc fills the entire bulb, approximately

3 in. in diameter by 9 in. long, thus providing a large light source of low brightness. Because application is largely confined to highway lighting, the lamps are rated in lumen output, rather than the customary wattage input. Two sizes are commercially available: the 10,000-lm lamp, consuming 180 lamp watts plus from 40 to 80 watts auxiliary loss, and the 6,000-lm lamp, consuming 145 lamp watts, plus from 30 to 70 watts auxiliary loss. Life of the lamp is affected by the frequency of turn-on and turn-off. In street lighting practice the useful life is 3,000 hr.

## 3.7. Mercury

The older form of mercury-vapor lamp was tubular, much like the fluorescent lamp of today. Known as the Cooper-Hewitt lamp, it operated at a mercury pressure of about .025 mm and an efficiency of about 15 lm per watt. The distribution of spectral energy was discontinuous, there being a small amount of energy in the violet range, and large amounts in the green and yellow. Being deficient in the red, colors of many common objects were distorted.

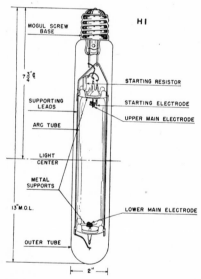

This lamp has been superseded by the high-pressure mercury arc designated as the $H$ lamp in which pressures from $\frac{1}{2}$ to 8 atmospheres are maintained. The arc is short, thus providing a light source that allows for accurate redirection of flux. An exception is a 3 kw tubular lamp $1\frac{1}{4}$ in. in diameter and $54\frac{7}{8}$ in. long. With a light output of 120,000 lm and corresponding high brightness, this lamp is suitable for high mounting and large area lighting. The tube is operated in a horizontal position.

Fig. 3-6. Essential parts of the high-pressure mercury lamp.

Lamps of 100-, 250-, and 400-watt size are in use in industry, having an efficiency of about 40 lm per watt.    The 1,000-watt lamp is very small, operates at 110 times atmospheric pressure and must be water-cooled.    Its principal use is in searchlights and motion picture studio lighting.

The temperature and pressure of conducting gases have important bearing upon the light output.    In order to reduce the effect of surrounding air temperature upon the temperature and pressure of the mercury arc, the arc enclosure of 100-, 250-, and 400-watt lamps is surrounded by a glass bulb in which is placed about 1/2 atmosphere of nitrogen.    Lamps come up to full output in from 4 to 14 min.    If extinguished, they require about the same time to restart, because the pressure of mercury must reduce to allow the design voltage to initiate the electron discharge.    The characteristic line spectrum consists of four wavelengths in the blue, green, and yellow regions of the spectrum.    Because of the deficiency in red and the slow restarting, filament lamps are often used in combination with mercury-vapor lamps to correct for color deficiencies and provide light for safety.

Correct voltage and ballasting is obtained by means of auto-transformers.    For low ambient temperatures, single lamp transformers should be used; otherwise two lamps may be operated from one transformer.    The power factor of lamp and transformer if uncorrected is around 50%, but can be brought up to 90%.

The mercury arc produces large amounts of ultra-violet radiation.    Ordinary glass does not transmit such radiation below $360\mu$. If special glass is used, mercury lamps become efficient producers of ultraviolet for therapeutic purposes, skin tanning, and special fluorescent effects.

Mercury-vapor lamps cannot be dimmed.    As line voltages decrease from the design point, lamp starting becomes unreliable and adversely affects the cathode.    At about 20% under design line voltage the lamps extinguish.    Transformers are equipped with taps to allow for expected line voltage departure from normal.    However, if line voltages are consistently 5% above or $2\frac{1}{2}$% below the tap setting, poor lamp performance is to be expected.

The 100-watt, 1,000-watt water-cooled, and 3,000-watt lamps may be burned in any position.    The 400-watt lamp may not be operated in a position more than 10° from the vertical, base up, unless the arc enclosure is of quartz, because the deflection of the arc stream will melt the glass. In the horizontal burning there is a loss of 4% to 6% in luminous efficiency because of greater heat loss through the arc tube wall. This is sometimes overcome by straightening the arc stream by means of a magnetic field, the energy loss of the magnetic field being less than the gain in luminous efficiency.

### TABLE 3-4

#### Mercury Lamp Data

| Characteristics | Type of lamp | | | | | | |
|---|---|---|---|---|---|---|---|
| | A-H4 | A-H5 | A-H1 | A-H6 | A-H9 | E-H1 | A-H12 |
| Lamp watts.......... | 100 | 250 | 400 | 1,000 | 3,000 | 400 | 1,000 |
| Transformer watts | | | | | | | |
| Single lamp........ | 20 | 40 | 52 | 95 | 220 | 52 | 85 |
| Double lamp........ | | 72 | 80 | | | 80 | |
| Lumens at 100 hr..... | 3,000 | 11,200 | 15,000 | 65,000 | 120,000 | 21,000 | 60,000 |
| *Rated life (hr)....... | 1,000 | 2,500 | 4,000 | 75 | 5,000 | 3,000 | 3,000 |
| Bulb................ | T-10 | T-14 | T-16 | T-2 | T-9½ | T-20 | T-28 |
| Burning position...... | any | any | base up | hor. | any | any | any |
| Over-all length (in.)... | 5⅝ | 8 | 11 | 3¼ | 54⅞ | 11 | 14 |
| Starting time to full output............ | 3 min. | 10 min. | 14 min. | 4 sec | 7 min. | 8 min. | 4 min. |
| Restarting time....... | 3 min. | 4 min. | 14 min. | 2 sec | 8 min. | 5 min. | 6 min. |

* Five hours burning per start.

In common with all mercury-vapor discharge sources, lumen output falls rapidly during the first 100 hr of use. The practice is to rate the source for initial lumens at the 100-hr value. The user, therefore, has a "bonus" during this period. Any measurements of illumination from such sources will show higher than design values, if the measurements are made before the installation has seasoned for 100 hr.

Characteristic curves for typical *H* lamps are shown in Fig. 3-7. Luminous and physical data are given in Table 3-4.

### 3.8. Fluorescent Lamps

It was noted that the mercury arc produces large quantities of ultraviolet radiation. The fluorescent lamp is simply a device for converting this ultra-violet radiation, which is of course invisible, to visible radiation. The transforming agent is known as a phosphor, which is a chemical distributed over the inside of the tube. These phosphors produce certain basic, fixed colors, but an infinite range of colors is obtainable by mixing them.

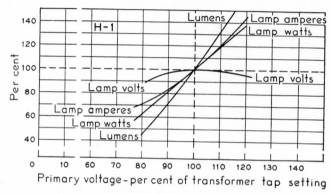

Fig. 3.7. Characteristic curves for H-1 mercury lamp. These are typical of all high-pressure lamps suitable for general lighting application.

The bulb shape is tubular, and except for limited special uses, the commercial lamps are straight tubes.

The arc stream is through mercury vapor. Argon or krypton gas is used in small quantity to help start the arc. These gases have a lower resistance than the cold mercury vapor and hence will start

**TABLE 3-5**

**Data on Iron- (Cold-) cathode Fluorescent Lamps**

| Lamp* | Watts† | Life, hr | Current, ma | Lumens and brightness | | | |
|---|---|---|---|---|---|---|---|
| | | | | Warm white | Soft white | 3500° white | Daylight |
| 93 in., 25 mm | 43 | 15,000 | 120 | 2,300 (1,310) | 1,600 (904) | 2,150 (1,220) | 1,950 (1,085) |
| 93 in., 25 mm | 22 | 15,000 | 50 | 1,150 (633) | 800 (452) | 1,100 (588) | 1,000 (542) |
| 76 in., 25 mm | 40 | 15,000 | 120 | 1,750 (1,220) | 1,200 (860) | 1,650 (1,075) | 1,500 (1,040) |
| 64 in., 25 mm | 38 | 15,000 | 120 | 1,350 (1,130) | 950 (814) | 1,250 (1,040) | 1,150 (950) |
| 52 in., 25 mm | 33 | 15,000 | 100 | 1,100 (1,490) | 750 (1,000) | 1,050 (1,400) | 900 (1,220) |

* Luminous length of lamps is 4 in. less than over-all length.
† Add auxiliary watts for total.

at a lower voltage. The heat from the argon discharge vaporizes the mercury and normal operation occurs. The aim is to maintain an arc stream that produces the maximum of ultraviolet at the maximum phosphor exciting point of 2,537 angstroms. The arc should produce a minimum of visible radiation because the phosphors are nearly opaque to light.

The result is a light source of high efficiency—starting at about 40 lm per watt for commercial "white" light and extending to 200 lm per watt for green light.

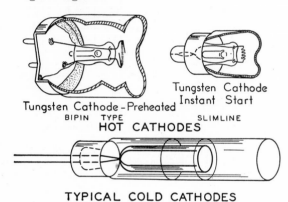

Tungsten Cathode-Preheated
BIPIN TYPE
HOT CATHODES

Tungsten Cathode
Instant Start
SLIMLINE

TYPICAL COLD CATHODES

Fig. 3-8. The three cathode designs used in various types of fluorescent lamps.

The electron stream is maintained through cathodes of varying design, there being three in common use (Fig. 3-8):

1. Iron cathode.
2. Tungsten cathode—preheated.
3. Tungsten cathode—cold.

**a. Electron emission.** Electron emission is produced in two ways —thermionic and electric field. Iron-cathode lamps, popularly called "cold" cathode, depend upon a voltage-differential electric field to start the electron stream. The circuit is so arranged that, upon closing it, between 750 and 900 volts are impressed across the cathodes to develop the necessary electric field strength. The lamp starts instantly. The voltage drop at each cathode is about 50. The drop across the arc stream is about 450 volts. The current density is limited by characteristics of the cathode to about 120 milliamps. Efficiency increases with tube length. The power loss at the electrodes is practically a constant for any length of lamp. In a long lamp, therefore, a greater percentage of input power goes to produce light. For a given wattage input the efficiency also increases as the current density decreases. Therefore larger diameter lamps are favored. However, the diameter cannot be increased to the point where the temperature of the tube wall will fall below the point of the maximum production of ultra-violet radiation of 2,537 angstroms. It is possible to increase the light output by

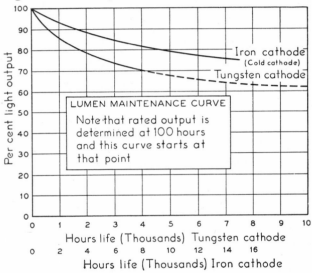

Fig. 3-9. Depreciation in light due to hours use of fluorescent lamps.

increasing the current density but the increase is at the expense of efficiency. Hence there is a nice balance to be maintained. Watts loss at the cathodes is roughly equal to the loss in one foot of tubing. Table 3-5 gives characteristic data.

Iron-cathode lamps can be dimmed and are not affected by the number of starts in relation to operating hours. The electrons are emitted from a relatively larger area of the cathodes as a glow-discharge. This does not cause emitting material to be dislodged. They possess very long life, subject to the usual depreciation in light output as the hours of use increase (Fig. 3-9). Operation may be multiple from ballasts, or in series from transformers.

**TABLE 3-6**

**Fluorescent Lamp Lumens and Brightness**

| Lamp | Lumens | Brightness (footlamberts) |
|---|---|---|
| 40-watt 60-in. 3,500° instant-start........ | 2,450 | 1,000 |
| 40-watt 48-in. preheat cathode: | | |
|   3,500° white........................ | 2,450 | 1,830 |
|   Soft white........................ | 1,800 | 1,375 |
|   Daylight........................ | 2,070 | 1,585 |
|   Standard warm white................ | 2,450 | 1,830 |
|   Standard cool white................ | 2,300 | 1,765 |
|   Deluxe warm white................ | 1,835 | 1,380 |
|   Deluxe cool white................ | 1,725 | 1,335 |
| 96-in. Slimline lamp: | | |
|   Standard warm white................ | 200 ma—3,200 | 1,750 |
| | 300 ma—4,150 | 2,300 |
| | 425 ma—4,500 | 1,700 |
|   Deluxe warm white................ | 200 ma—2,400 | 1,315 |
| | 300 ma—3,110 | 1,725 |
| | 425 ma—2,970 | 1,275 |
|   Standard cool white................ | 200 ma—3,100 | 1,700 |
| | 300 ma—4,000 | 2,200 |
| | 425 ma—4,400 | 1,650 |
|   Deluxe cool white................ | 200 ma—2,330 | 1,275 |
| | 300 ma—3,000 | 1,650 |
| | 425 ma—3,300 | 1,235 |

Average life of all tungsten-cathode lamps when the lamps operate for an average of 6 burning hours per start: 7,500 hr for the preheated cathode, 5,000 hr for the instant-start cathode.

Output of Slimline lamp is approximately the same per foot regardless of length. Brightness is the same for any length.

Output and brightness for any white fluorescent lamp may be computed by means of the following multipliers:

$$deluxe = standard \times 0.75$$
$$soft\ white = standard\ cool \times 0.75$$
$$3,500° \ white = standard\ cool \times 1.05$$
$$standard\ warm\ white = standard\ cool \times 1.05$$
$$daylight = standard\ cool \times 0.90$$

Tungsten-cathode lamps, when preheated, produce electrons chiefly through thermionic emission. Thus a lower starting and operating voltage is required. For the 48-in. lamps, the operating voltage is about 108 volts, of which 17 volts is for electrode drop. As explained previously for the iron-cathode lamps, the efficiency of tungsten-cathode lamps increases with length of tube and increase in tube diameter. Lumen output per foot increases with the increase in current density.

When the circuit is closed for starting, a "starter" energizes the cathodes for a brief heating cycle and then automatically opens, allowing an inductive kick or high-voltage transient of 300 to 600 volts to start the arc stream. The cathodes are treated with emitting salts and some of this is sputtered off at each start. The

**TABLE 3-7**

**Physical and Electrical Data on Tungsten-cathode Fluorescent Lamps**

| Type | Pre-heat | Pre-heat | Slim-line | Slim-line | Slim-line | Slim-line | Slim-line |
|---|---|---|---|---|---|---|---|
| Nominal length (in.) | 48 | 60 | 48 | 72* | 96* | 72† | 96† |
| Luminous length (in.) | $46\frac{1}{2}$ | 57 | $44\frac{1}{2}$ | $68\frac{1}{2}$ | $92\frac{1}{4}$ | $68\frac{1}{4}$ | $92\frac{1}{4}$ |
| Diameter | T-12 | T-17 | T-12 | T-8 | T-8 | T-12 | T-12 |
| Lamp watts | 39 | 82 | 36 | 48 | 66 | 54 | 72 |
| Two-lamp ballast watts | 17.5 | 37 | 28 | 37 | 39 | 38 | 45 |
| Starting volts | 200 | 150 | 450 | 600 | 750 | 525 | 625 |
| Operating volts | 102 | 53 | 95 | 190 | 255 | 142 | 190 |
| Operating amps | 420 ma | 1.65 amps | 425 ma | 300 ma | 300 ma | 425 ma | 425 ma |

\* These lamps may be operated at 120 ma and 200 ma, with corresponding changes in electrical and luminous characteristics.

† These lamps may also be operated at 600 ma, with corresponding changes in electrical and luminous characteristics.

current flows from a small spot on the cathode. This is an arc discharge. The temperature is high and the electron bombardment knocks the salts from the cathode. Eventually so little remains that the electron stream cannot be initiated and the lamp becomes inoperative. Thus the lamp should not be started at frequent intervals, the life being proportional to the total number of starts. Accepted practice is to rate the lamp life in terms of "burning hours per start." The lamp cannot be dimmed very much, nor operated in a series circuit. Physical and electrical data are given in Tables 3-6 and 3-7 and in Fig. 3-10.

Tungsten-cathode lamps for instant starting are known as "Slimline" lamps. They require about the same voltage as the iron-cathode lamps. The electrodes suffer loss of emitting salts with each start, so operating hours per start affect the total lamp life. No starter is required. Current density is lower than for preheat cathode types so tube length is greater for a given lumen output. Since single-pin contacts are used, a rugged socket and tube end-assembly results.

In general, iron-cathode and instant-start tungsten lamps are in 6- and 8-ft lengths. Preheat-cathode lamps are popular in 3- and 4-ft lengths. Fluorescent lamp lengths are stated in "nominal" inches. For iron- (cold-) cathode lamps this means the distance between electrode caps, or the over-all length of the lamp only. For all other fluorescent lamps this means the over-all length of the lamp and two sockets. Tables 3-6 and 3-7 give characteristic data.

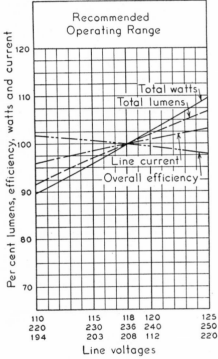

Fig. 3-10. Typical characteristic curves for tungsten-cathode fluorescent lamps.

**b. Temperature and pressure.** The mercury-vapor pressure in any fluorescent lamp has an important bearing upon the efficiency. The light output of fluorescent lamps is proportional to the amount of energy at 2,537 angstroms produced by the mercury arc. This energy is at a maximum for any lamp at a given bulb-wall temperature. Since pressure changes with temperature, the thermal surroundings are important (Fig. 3-11). Low temperatures reduce output more than high temperature. For efficient light production, fluorescent lamps of the preheat- and tungsten-cathode variety should not operate in a surrounding air temperature of less than 50°. The rather critical relationship between bulb-wall temperature and current density requires that the lamp designers choose some surrounding air temperature as a point of departure. They have taken 80° Fahrenheit as this point. Lamps can be built to operate at low temperatures but the current density will be so high as to produce light very inefficiently. Conversely, lamps for high-temperature operation will have current densities so low as to be poor light producers. With 80° Fahrenheit chosen as the design point, low surrounding temperatures cause heat to be dissipated too fast, while high surrounding temperatures cause higher arc temperatures. The net effect is to reduce the amount of energy at the 2,537-angstrom

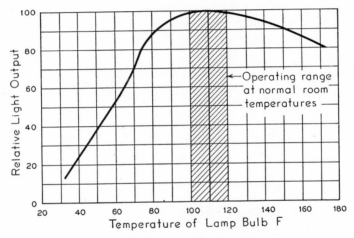

Fig. 3-11.    Effect of bulb wall temperature on light output of fluorescent lamps.

band, and hence the amount of light. The iron-cathode lamp has better starting characteristics in low temperatures because of the higher voltage allowable at the cathode.

c. Energy dissipation. The energy dissipation of fluorescent lamps is about as shown in Fig. 3-12. By comparison with Table 3-3, it will be noted that the efficiency of light production is about twice that of large filament lamps, radiant heat dissipation about one-third, and sensible heat dissipation about five times as great. This has an important bearing upon the correlation of lighting and air conditioning, particularly since ballast losses are all by conduction and convection to the surrounding air.

The lower radiant component of energy has caused the term "cool" to be applied to fluorescent lighting. Actually, 1 kwhr of electrical energy produces 3,414 Btu per hour regardless of the source. It is true that for equal footcandles the amount of radiant energy is less for fluorescent sources than for filament sources. On the other hand, levels of illumination are generally higher with fluorescent lamps than with filament lamps so that the net heat effect upon the user of light is about the same.

It was stated that argon was introduced as a gas to facilitate starting. In certain sizes, krypton is coming into use as its production allows. A 40-watt preheat lamp loses about 7 watts in inevitable electron loss, 1 watt in visible radiation, 24 watts in ultraviolet radiation, and 8 watts in gas loss (electronic collisions). Krypton reduces gas loss by more than 50%; thus by the introduc-

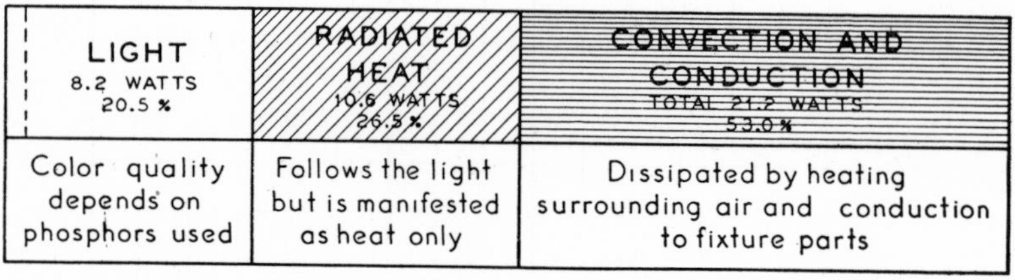

| LIGHT<br>8.2 WATTS<br>20.5 % | RADIATED<br>HEAT<br>10.6 WATTS<br>26.5% | CONVECTION AND<br>CONDUCTION<br>TOTAL 21.2 WATTS<br>53.0 % |
|---|---|---|
| Color quality depends on phosphors used | Follows the light but is manifested as heat only | Dissipated by heating surrounding air and conduction to fixture parts |

Fig. 3-12. Typical energy dissipation of a fluorescent lamp.

tion of this gas the former 100-watt white lamp producing 4,200 lm has been reduced to a rating of 85 watts for the same output.

d. Flicker. In common with all gaseous-discharge lamps, fluorescent lamps are extinguished 120 times a second when operated on 60-cycle alternating current. The resulting flicker or stroboscopic effect is minimized by ballast circuits, using pairs of lamps in split-phase circuits. Single lamps cannot be flicker-corrected. It is observed that the iron-cathode lamps, probably because of higher arc voltage, exhibit the least stroboscopic effect.

Direct-current operation of fluorescent lamps is not recommended because of the high loss in the series resistance—equal to lamp watts—and the excessive blackening at one cathode. This blackening can be equalized by reversing line current every 24 hours —a troublesome remedy. Lamp life and lumen maintenance are not favorable.

Radio interference is experienced with any gaseous-discharge lamp. Direct radiation from the lamp is not noted if the aerial is

9 ft or more from the lamp. Line radiation and line feedback can be corrected by means of suitable filters at each lamp ballast.

At the instant of starting of tungsten-cathode fluorescent lamps without preheat, it is believed that capacitive current is necessary to initiate the electron discharge. Under conditions of high humidity this capacitive effect is maintained by a coating of transparent, non-melting conducting material, such as a silicon, or a narrow conducting strip from end to end. If the lamp is placed in a metal reflector, and this is grounded, the same effect is obtained. If relative humidity exceeds 65%, however, this will not be effective. The conducting strip should not make electrical contact with the lamp or ground.

*Changes in fluorescent and mercury lamps are continual and rapid. The engineer must be supplied with the latest data in order to design intelligently. Planning for the future requires a good knowledge of basic lamp characteristics and their principles of operation, as well as design trends, in order to insure against unreasonable obsolescence.*

Fluorescent and mercury lamps require transformers or transformers and ballasts for their operation. It is obvious that lamp and ballast must be designed as a unit, hence there is no interchangeability of lamp sizes as is common with filament lamps. Application design must therefore be of higher order. The subject of ballasts and starters is treated in the next chapter.

## PROBLEMS

**1.** (a) An incandescent lamp is designated as PS-35. What is its shape and diameter?

(b) A fluorescent lamp is designated as T-12. What is the diameter of the tube?

**2.** Why does a 1,000-watt general service PS-52 incandescent lamp have a mogul screw base instead of a medium screw base?

**3.** An incandescent lamp rated at 500 watts at 120 volts is operated on a 115-volt circuit.

(a) What is the mean lumens output of the lamp?

(b) What are the watts?

(c) What is the average life?

**4.** Why is it good practice to combine type-*H* mercury-vapor lamps and incandescent lamps for lighting of factories?

**5.** Why do instant-start fluorescent lamps require a higher starting voltage than preheat types of lamps?

**6.** State the two outstanding advantages of iron-cathode lamps not possessed by tungsten-cathode lamps.

**7.** Calculate the lumens output of a T-12 fluorescent lamp 96 in. long if the average brightness is:

1. 1,600 ft-L.
2. 2.25 candles per sq in.

**8.** What are the advantages of operating two fluorescent lamps on one auxiliary?

# REFERENCES

Amick, Charles L., *Fluorescent Lighting Manual.* New York: McGraw-Hill Book Co., Inc., 1942.

Campbell, J. H., "Special Circuits for Fluorescent Lamps," *Trans. Illum. Eng. Soc.*, Vol. 45, page 235, April 1950.

Evans, G. S., "Low Temperature Performance of Krypton-filled Fluorescent Lamps," *Trans. Illum. Eng. Soc.*, Vol. 45, page 175, March 1950.

*Fluorescent Lighting Association Bulletin*, "Cold Cathode Fluorescent Lighting Guide," June 1948.

General Electric Company, *Bulletin LD-1*, May 1946.

"Guide Posts for Selecting the Proper Fluorescent Lamp," *Trans. Illum. Eng. Soc.*, Vol. 45, page 303, May 1950.

Lowry, E. F., and E. L. Mager, "Some Factors Affecting the Life and Lumen Maintenance of Fluorescent Lamps," *Trans. Illum. Eng. Soc.*, Vol. 44, page 99, February 1949.

Noel, E. B., "Mercury Lamp Redesigned for Improved Light Output and Appearance," *Trans. Illum. Eng. Soc.*, Vol. 43, page 1044, November 1948.

Thayer, R. N., and A. Brownell, "Performance of Fluorescent Lamps on Leading Power-factor Circuits," *Trans. Illum. Eng. Soc.*, Vol. 44, page 567, September 1949.

West, Eugene S., "The Characteristics of Cold Cathode Lamps," *Trans. Illum. Eng. Soc.*, Vol. 44, page 487, August 1949.

Current bulletins of electric lamp manufacturers.

# 4

# BALLASTS, TRANSFORMERS AND STARTERS

As pointed out in Chapter 3, gaseous-conductor light sources possess negative resistance characteristics, that is, as the arc temperature rises the resistance falls. This allows an increased current to flow. This current in turn increases the temperature, further reducing the resistance and increasing the current. Thus a sequence is introduced which eventually destroys the lamp. It was also pointed out that the voltage necessary to maintain the arc was seldom the same as standard supply voltages. Arc-starting voltages are also of a higher order than arc-maintenance voltages. Thus auxiliary equipment is necessary for the successful operation of most gaseous-conductor lamps such as neon, mercury, sodium, and fluorescent. While much ingenuity has been exercised in the design and assembly of this auxiliary equipment, it introduces elements of cost and maintenance that must always be evaluated. Furthermore, this equipment must be designed for specific sizes and types of lamps. Hence lighting application problems should be thoroughly analyzed in advance because there is little opportunity for interchange of lamp sizes and auxiliaries after the installation is completed.

The auxiliary equipment also consumes electrical energy and this must be accounted for in calculations of operating cost and supply circuit capacity. Discharge lamps are rated in lamp watts alone. To this must be added the watts lost in the auxiliaries necessary for its operation. For example, an auxiliary for operating two 40-watt fluorescent lamps will consume 17 watts. The 3,500° white lamp produces 2,300 lm. Lamp efficiency alone is 2,300/40 or 57.5 lm per watt. The lamp cannot produce these lumens without an auxiliary, therefore the actual efficiency is 2,300/48.5 or 47.5 lm per watt. Supply circuits must be designed to carry 48.5 watts per lamp, not 40 watts. Literature on gaseous-conductor lamps usually, but not always, carries the notation on lamp watts, "Add auxiliary watts for total."

Basically, an auxiliary for gaseous-conductor lamps must accomplish three things:

1. Supply proper starting and operating voltage for the arc.

2. Maintain the arc current at steady operating design value. The means for doing this result in low power factor. This imposes undue penalties on circuit capacity and operating costs, hence the auxiliary has a third duty, namely:

3. Maintain a power factor in excess of 90% for the combined circuit of lamp and auxiliary.

### 4.1. Neon

The electron stream in a neon tube is initiated at the cathodes by voltage differential, or electric field discharge. A simple autotrans-

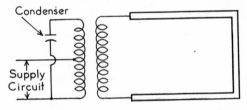

Fig. 4-1.   Typical neon electrical circuit.

former with high leakage characteristics is used. The inductive effect of the transformer windings is sufficient to maintain the arc current at rated value. Open-circuit voltage of the transformer is limited to 15,000 volts.

### 4.2. Iron-cathode Fluorescent

This type of lamp is popularly called the cold-cathode fluorescent lamp. Instant starting is accomplished by electric field electron discharge. At the start the voltage between electrodes may be as high as 900 in the 8-ft lamp. Operating voltage is approximately 500. Many lighting applications permit the use of numbers of these lamps connected in series, in which case the simple high-leakage-reactance autotransformer can be used.  Open-circuit voltage is

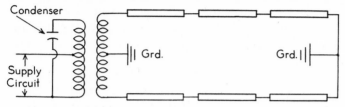

Fig. 4-2.   Typical iron-cathode fluorescent electrical circuit.

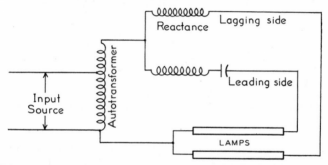

Fig. 4-3.   Typical split-phase electrical circuit.

limited to 15,000 volts.  Voltage to ground in the external circuit can be held to one-half terminal value by grounding the mid-point of the transformer secondary winding and the mid-point of the lamp circuit.

When conditions require the use of two lamps, operated as a unit, they may be connected to one transformer.  The autotransformer is then reduced in size, and inductance coils are introduced to stabilize the arc current.  It is then known as a ballast (Fig. 4-3).  Condensers are used in one lamp

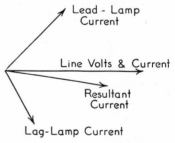

Fig. 4-4.  Vector diagram of power-factor-corrected gaseous-conductor lamp circuit.

circuit to introduce leading current, thus offsetting the lagging effect of the inductance.  Stroboscopic effect is also reduced.  The overall power factor of the auxiliary is raised to above 90% (Fig. 4-4).

33822

### 4.3. Type-H Mercury Lamps

Type-$H$ mercury lamps have a starting voltage 1/4 to 1/6 the operating voltage and a starting current about twice the value of operating current.  A simple autotransformer of the high-leakage-reactance type, with condenser for power factor correction, will maintain the arc at rated values.

Transformers for operating two type-$H$ lamps are available, utilizing the same split-phase circuit as described for iron-cathode lamps.  However, the lamp on the leading circuit requires about double the time for arriving at full brilliancy as the lag lamp.[1]  In low surrounding air temperature it may never come to full brightness.  Hence, for any use where low temperatures may be encountered the single lamp transformer should be used.  Inasmuch as type-$H$ mercury lamps are unstable in operation except within a few per cent of design voltage, the transformer primary has a number of taps to allow for a close setting to line voltage.

### 4.4. Sodium-vapor Lamps

Sodium-vapor lamps are designed for two current ratings: 6.6 amp for constant-current street lighting circuits, and 5.2 amp for 115-volt constant-voltage circuits.  External insulating transformers are generally used on series street lighting circuits to protect the luminaire against the high voltage.

Auxiliary devices within the lamp housing include a thermal switch for cathode preheating, capacitor and choke for suppression of radio frequency, and, in the case of a constant-voltage lamp, a transformer.  The cathodes of the lamp are in series with the arc, so that operating current maintains cathode temperature after the preheating period.

### 4.5. Slimline Fluorescent Lamps

Slimline lamps are instant-starting, with electron emission at start due to voltage gradient or electric field discharge.  Starting voltage is in the 400 to 700-volt range and operating volts around 140 to 200 volts, depending upon lamp length.

---

[1] While not in resonance, the inductive and capacitive reactances tend to neutralize each other, causing the circuit to follow roughly Ohm's law, that is, $I = E/R$; hence $I$ is relatively constant.

The auxiliary or ballast for a single lamp is an autotransformer
and choke-coil combination (Fig. 4-5).    For operation of two lamps
from one ballast the split-phase principle is applied (Fig. 4-3).

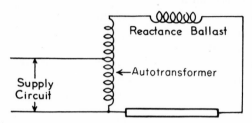

Fig. 4-5.    Typical electrical circuit for a single
fluorescent lamp.

### 4.6. Preheat Cathode Fluorescent Lamps

Electron flow at starting is accomplished principally by thermionic emission, which affords lower starting voltages.    By means of
a suitable switch, the cathodes are heated for about four seconds.
After this period, the switch, called a starter, opens and the accom-
panying inductive "kick" starts the lamp.    Lamps up to 20 watts in
size can be operated through a simple choke coil connected to a

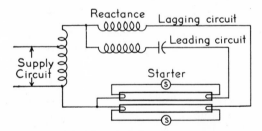

Fig. 4-6.    Typical split-phase electrical circuit
for preheat fluorescent lamps.

120-volt supply circuit.    For larger lamps the usual circuit voltage
will not suffice and an autotransformer in combination with a choke
coil is used.    If two lamps are operated from one auxiliary, the
familiar split-phase principle is used (Fig. 4-6).    With lamps of 40
watts and below it has been found that the lamp connected to the

lead circuit is supplied with about half the heating current of the lag lamp. This is due to the constant-current effect of inductance and capacitance in series. This low value of current causes slow starting and shorter lamp life. The difficulty is removed by adding a compensator winding to the lead circuit reactor, thus in effect producing a lag circuit at start. This winding is in series with the lamp starter and hence draws current only during the 2- to 4-second starting period. When cut out of the circuit, the lead characteristic of the circuit is re-established (Fig. 4-7). Lamps above 40 watts have cathodes of such size that adequate preheating takes

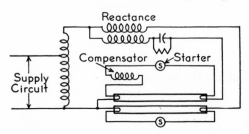

Fig. 4-7. Typical split-phase electrical circuit with compensator, for preheat fluorescent lamps.

place on the amount of current available through either lag or lead circuit.

It is a general rule that each size and type of gaseous-conductor lamp must have an auxiliary (ballast or transformer) designed specifically for its operation. An exception occurs in the case of the 100-watt, 60-in., T-17 preheat lamp. This may be operated from a standard 40-watt instant-start lamp ballast, producing less light and hence having a lower brightness. In fact, it is popularly called a "low-brightness lamp."

The characteristics of auxiliaries described in this chapter extend to the specialty lamps such as circline, germ-killing, ultra-violet generator, indicator, and the like. They vary in size and shape, but the underlying principles are unchanged.

### 4.7. Direct-current Operation

Direct-current operation of fluorescent lamps is possible by substituting a resistance for the autotransformer. The objection is that the resistance consumes about the same power as the lamp. In addition, lamp life is shorter because of less reliable starting conditions. Lumen maintenance is poorer. Due to one-way current flow, one end of the lamp will show excessive blackening unless line reversing switches are utilized to reverse current flow once each day. The drawbacks to such a procedure are obvious. Fortunately the use of direct current for lighting purposes is limited to the transportation field.

### 4.8. Flicker or Stroboscopic Effect

Gaseous-conductor lamps go out completely 120 times each second on 60-cycle current. While this rate of flicker is above the

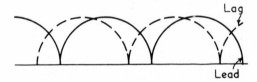

Fig. 4-8. The split-phase electrical circuit reduces stroboscopic effect by allowing one lamp to be lighted while the other is at zero voltage.

threshold of visual perception, it will produce a stroboscopic effect on moving objects. On 25-cycle current the flicker is noticeable at the cathodes and the effect upon moving objects most pronounced. The effect on 60-cycle current is considerably reduced through the use of the two-lamp auxiliary. The lag and lead lamps are 120° out of phase and consequently one lamp is always lighted when the other is out (Fig. 4-8).

With fluorescent lamps, certain phosphors exhibit some afterglow, so strictly speaking some fluorescent lamps do not go fully out, but appear to insofar as the visual effect is concerned.

### 4.9. Transformer Hum

Characteristic transformer hum, caused by magnetic action on the laminated core, is generally present. It varies, depending upon quality of materials and workmanship, and size of ballast. The vibrations are transmitted to surrounding metal parts of luminaires and accentuated.  Use of vibration-absorbing pads and rigid construction will reduce the effect, but often in quiet surroundings the only solution is to place the ballasts in an area isolated from the lighted space.  This may be a costly remedy.

The larger transformers associated with the type-$H$ mercury lamp, and series-operated iron-cathode lamps exhibit little hum. The large-cross-section or "brick" ballasts, for preheat-cathode, Slimline, and iron-cathode lamps operated in pairs, produce less noise than the narrow-cross-section ballasts.

### 4.10. Radio Interference

The gaseous arc acts like a small radio transmitter.  There are three ways in which these waves may interfere with radio reception:

1. Direct radiation from the bulb to the radio receiver.  This diminishes rapidly with distance and beyond 9 ft is negligible.

In case it is not possible to isolate by distance, connect the aerial to the receiver by means of shielded wire with the shield grounded, or a "doublet" aerial with twisted pair leads.  Also provide a good ground for the radio.

2. Direct radiation from the electric supply line to the aerial.

3. Line feedback from lamp to receiver through the electric supply.  Direct radiation and feedback are best minimized by the use of filters at each lamp or luminaire.  These are available commercially.

Very often radio interference is caused by poor contact between lamp holder and lamp base pins, or a faulty starter.

### 4.11. Starters

With the preheat type of fluorescent lamps, a means must be provided for allowing the cathodes to heat before the starting voltage is applied.  To do so manually is feasible only with single, easily accessible lamps such as those at desks, wall brackets, and so forth.

Several types of automatic switches or starters have been developed.  The first was a magnetic vibrator type that repeatedly opened and closed, each closing allowing the cathode to gain heat, until the electron flow was sufficient to start the arc.  The operating current then produced sufficient magnetic flux to hold the vibrator contacts open. This starter produced swift and positive starting but it consumed 1 to 2 watts all the while the lamp was in operation. The many small moving parts gave rise to maintenance troubles.

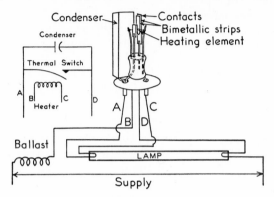

Fig. 4-9.  Schematic diagram of a thermal starter and lamp circuit.

The next development was a thermal starter in which a bimetallic contact strip allowed current to pass through a heater coil until sufficient heat was generated to open the contact switch (Fig.

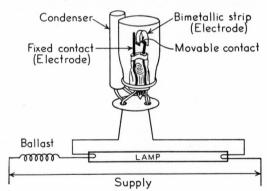

Fig. 4-10.  Schematic arrangement of a glow starter and lamp circuit.

4-9). The normal lamp operating current flowed continuously through the heater coil in order to hold it open. The power consumption varied from $\frac{1}{2}$ to $1\frac{1}{2}$ watts.

Another development is known as the glow-switch starter. (Fig. 4-10). This consists of a small glass bulb containing a gas such as neon, helium, or argon, depending upon the lamp size to be controlled. Upon closing the circuit, the voltage at the starter produces a glow discharge in the gas. This discharge is sufficient to heat a bimetallic strip and close a circuit, putting lamp cathodes and ballast in series across the line. The voltage available for the glow discharge is then reduced and while cathode preheating begins, the glow discharge dies out and cools the bimetallic strip. When the strip shrinks sufficiently to open the circuit, the cathode preheating is complete and the inductive kick starts the lamp. The contacts remain open while the lamp is in operation, because the voltage available will not maintain a glow discharge. There is no continuous power consumption by the starter.

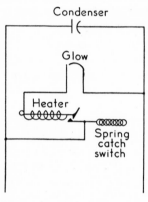

Fig. 4-11. Schematic diagram of a lockout starter.

A thermal or glow switch will attempt to start a lamp after the electron-emissive material is no longer effective. The repeated blinking is annoying and also heats the ballast. The switch is likely to destroy itself. By placing a heater-coil-operated switch in series with the glow discharge, the circuit can be opened after the

**TABLE 4-1**

**Ballast and Transformer Losses**

| Type of lamp | % of lamp watts |
|---|---|
| Iron-cathode—series transformer................. | 35 |
| Iron-cathode—twin lamp....................... | 20–25 |
| Type-$H$ mercury............................... | 10 |
| Sodium—10,000 lm: | |
|    Series, without insulating transformer.......... | 15 watts |
|    Series, with insulating transformer............ | 40 watts |
|    Multiple................................... | 75 watts |
| Slimline: | |
|    Single lamp................................ | 40–50 |
|    Twin lamp................................. | 20–40 |
| Preheat (hot-cathode)........................ | 25–30 |

starter has attempted to light the lamp a sufficient number of times to have passed the requisite heating current.  If a spring-operated latch is brought to the outside of the switch, the switch can remain inoperative until the deactivated lamp is replaced.  At this time manual resetting of the spring catch again places the starter in normal operating condition (Fig. 4-11).

It is apparent that starters are ingenious devices but subject to replacement.  Hence they are treated as separate component parts of the circuit, readily accessible for replacement.

To shunt out line harmonics which cause radio interference, it is common practice to place a small condenser across the line switch.

## PROBLEMS

**1.** A branch circuit has a capacity of 2,000 watts.  How many 96-in. 300-ma Slimline fluorescent lamps can be operated from it?  Assume ballast loss at 30% of lamp watts.

**2.** State reasons for and against the use of:

(a) Two 48-in. T-12 Slimline lamps in place of one 96-in. T-12 Slimline lamp.

(b) Two 52-in. 100-ma iron-cathode lamps in place of one 93-in. 100-ma iron-cathode lamp.

**3.** List three advantages of a dual lamp ballast as compared with a single lamp ballast.

**4.** Why is a compensator necessary in the lead lamp circuit of a dual lamp ballast?

**5.** Name three advantages of instant-start fluorescent lamps over preheat types of fluorescent lamps.

## REFERENCES

Amick, Charles L., *Fluorescent Lighting Manual.*  New York: McGraw-Hill Book Co., Inc., 1942.

General Electric Company, *Bulletin LD-1*, October 1950.

Miller, E. A., "Transformers and Ballasts for Cold Cathode Lighting Installations," *Trans. Illum. Eng. Soc.*, Vol. 40, page 697, September 1945.

Thayer, R. N., and Brownell, A., "Performance of Fluorescent Lamps on Leading Power-factor Circuits," *Trans. Illum. Eng. Soc.*, Vol. 44, page 567, September 1949.

Catalog data from manufacturers of transformers and ballasts.

# 5

## CONTROL OF LIGHT

---

The control of light from modern sources is an important aspect of illuminating engineering. Light from low-power sources such as candles and kerosene flames can be allowed to pass to the surrounding space with little interference, because there is so little of it. Light from filament and gaseous sources must often be modified and controlled in order to achieve the results inherent in their characteristics. In considering this subject the matter is simplified by referring to light as rays.

A ray of light travels in a straight line until it encounters some object. The ray is then absorbed, reflected, or transmitted. In general, any two or all three of these phenomena may occur.

### 5.1. Absorption

Very few materials in engineering use absorb all of the light that strikes them, but all absorb some light. Some is reflected, some refracted, some transmitted, and some is polarized. By definition, *absorption factor*, symbol $a$, is the ratio of light absorbed by a body to the incident light.

### 5.2. Reflection

There are five classes of reflection.

1. Regular or specular reflection.
2. Diffuse reflection.
3. Spread reflection.
4. Mixed reflection.
5. Scattered reflection.

1. *Regular or specular reflection* is the most familiar phenomenon. It is that in which the angle of reflected light is equal to the angle of incident light. All polished surfaces reflect light in this manner. The *regular reflection factor* is the ratio of the regularly reflected light to the incident light.

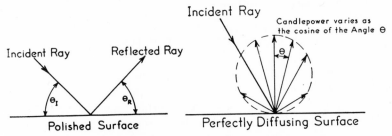

Fig. 5-1. The law of regular reflection states that the angles of reflection and incidence are equal.

Fig. 5-2. Diffuse reflection is common. Perfect diffusion, obeying Lambert's cosine law, is rarely found.

2. *Diffuse reflection* is that in which the light is reflected in all directions. Perfect diffusion is that in which the light is scattered uniformly in all directions. A plate of such diffusing material would appear equally bright from any angle of view. It would obey Lambert's cosine law of emission. No material is perfectly diffusing. A block of magnesium carbonate is a close approach, and in addition has the very high reflection factor of 98.3% for tungsten light. The *diffuse reflection factor* is the ratio of the diffusely reflected light to the incident light.

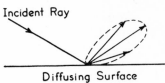

Fig. 5-3. Spread reflection.

3. *Spread reflection* is that in which the reflected light is so diffused that a clear image of the incident ray cannot be seen, yet the general direction of the reflected ray obeys the law of regular reflection. Many of the practical reflecting surfaces, known as mat surfaces, reflect light in this manner.

4. *Mixed reflection* occurs when part of the light is diffusely reflected and part regularly reflected. Porcelain enamel, calendered paper, and shiny paint surfaces reflect light in this manner. At the critical angle of view, the image of the incident ray can be clearly seen as in a mirror.

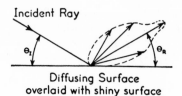

Diffusing Surface
overlaid with shiny surface

Fig. 5-4.   Mixed reflection.

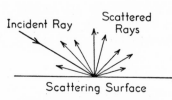

Scattering Surface

Fig. 5-5.   Scattered reflection.
Tiny portions of the surface act
like mirrors.

5. *Scattered reflection* takes place when the incident ray is broken up into a multiplicity of separate rays. Rippled glass and crinkled metal foil are good examples. The surface sparkles because at many angles of view the incident beam is seen as though it were coming from a series of small mirrors.

## 5.3. Transmission

There are five classes of transmission bearing the same names as the five classes of reflection.

      1. Regular or direct transmission.
      2. Diffuse transmission.
      3. Spread transmission.
      4. Mixed transmission.
      5. Scattered transmission.

1. *Regular or direct transmission* occurs in clear glass or plastic. The incident rays pass through with a loss due to absorption by the

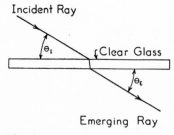

Fig. 5-6.   Regular transmission.

material and reflection from the surfaces. The angle at which the ray leaves is the same as that at which it entered, but a shift in position occurs because of refraction. The *regular transmission factor* is the ratio of the regularly transmitted light to the incident light.

2. *Diffuse transmission* is that in which the transmitted light is emitted in all directions. If the emerging light obeyed Lambert's law, the material would appear equally bright from any angle of

view. No material possesses this characteristic. Many of the milky or white glasses obey Lambert's law over a wide angle of view, however. The *diffuse transmission factor* is the ratio of diffusely transmitted light to the incident light.

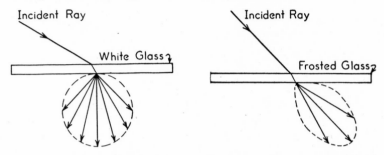

Fig. 5-7.   Diffuse transmission.       Fig. 5-8.   Spread transmission.

3. *Spread transmission* occurs when the emerging ray is so diffused that a clear image of the incident ray cannot be seen, but the general direction of the diffused beam follows the pattern of direct transmission. Frosted and sandblasted glass exhibit this phenomenon. At certain angles of view, the glass will be brighter than at others.

4. *Mixed transmission* occurs when a portion of the incident ray is diffused and a portion passes through as regular transmission.

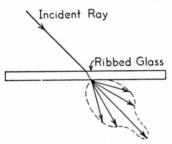

Fig. 5-9.   Mixed transmission.

Diffusing glasses with small, clear areas exhibit this phenomenon. At certain angles of view, the incident ray can be seen in substantially full brightness.

5. *Scattered transmission* takes place when the incident ray is broken up into a multiplicity of regularly transmitted rays. Con-

figurated and ribbed glass exhibit this tendency.  At many angles
of view, the incident ray is seen at substantially full brightness.

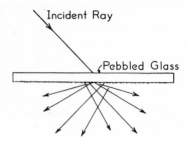

Fig. 5-10.  Scattered transmission.  From some angles of view
the light source can be seen at
nearly full brightness.

Such glass has sparkle but must be used with caution if uncomfortable brightness is to be avoided.

## 5.4. Effect of Angle of Incidence

It is an observed fact that the amount of light reflected by a
surface depends in part upon the angle at which the incident ray
strikes that surface.  A pure metallic surface with no protective
overlay is an exception, but such surfaces are of little interest to the
illuminating engineer.  Specular surfaces protected by a coating,
and diffuse surfaces, with or without a coating, are subject to this
phenomenon.  For angles of incident ray up to 50° there is little
change.  Beyond 50° the reflection factor changes rapidly with
increase in angle.  A glass surface, for example, has a reflection
factor of 10% at 50° from normal but a reflection factor of 60% at
80° from normal.

To be precise, the reflection factor should be stated for a given
angle of incidence.  Published values are usually based upon the
incident ray at an angle of 45° to 55° from the normal to the surface.

The angle of the incident ray influences transmission in the
same way that it affects reflection.  A light ray in passing through
a substance is:

1. Partially reflected from both plane surfaces.
2. Partially absorbed by the material.

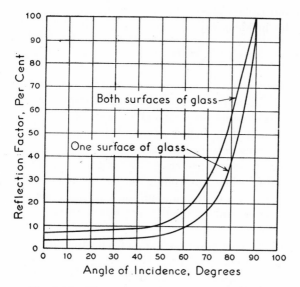

Fig. 5-11. The amount of light reflected by a shiny surface depends in part upon the angle of the incident ray.

The amount transmitted is therefore the incident light minus the reflected light, minus the absorbed light.

Tests for transmission are usually made with the incident ray normal to the surface. In the design of luminaires, the effect of light incident at grazing angles is, however, quite important.

## 5.5. Effect of Color of Light

All light of practical interest is composed of radiation of different wavelengths. The various wavelengths are not treated alike by light control substances. One material will reflect more blue than red. Another will transmit more yellow than blue. There-

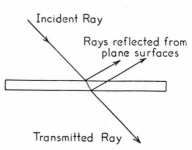

Fig. 5-12. Each boundary surface of a transmitting material will reflect light.

fore the reflection factor or the transmission factor is not a constant. It depends upon the spectral quality of the incident radiation as well as on the spectral reflectance or transmission characteristics of the material. The values for transmission and reflection factors are therefore related to a particular radiation or a particular light source.

These phenomena of selective absorption, selective reflection, and selective transmission are of great practical value. A glass or plastic that absorbs proportionately more of the blue and green wavelengths than of the yellow and red will not be an efficient material for controlling certain fluorescent or mercury-vapor radiation. Similarly, high absorption in the yellow and red end of the spectrum is not desirable when controlling incandescent filament sources. On the other hand, a certain amount of selective reflection or transmission can be useful in modifying certain unfavorable spectral qualities.

Published data on transmission and reflection are usually based upon tungsten filament light. These figures are only useful as guides and indications of magnitude. A spectral analysis is necessary for a clear understanding of the performance of the material.

## 5.6. Characteristics of Materials

Materials of interest in the control of light are:

1. Sheet steel—porcelain-enamelled and paint-enamelled.
2. Stainless steel.
3. Aluminum—polished and mat surface.
4. Glass.
5. Plastic.
6. Plaster and painted surfaces.

1. *Porcelain-enamelled steel* is an interesting material. The reflecting substance is sprayed upon the steel base and then the piece is heated to incandescence, fusing the reflecting surface. The resulting light reflection is mixed, the glass surface reflecting specularly, and the under coating reflecting diffusely. The steel reflector must be in its final shape before the enamelling is done.

The baked paint finishes are less costly than porcelain enamel. There is some specular reflection from the surface, but the majority of the reflection is in the spread classification. These finishes are widely used in fluorescent light control because of their lower cost and the lower heat encountered.

2. *Stainless steel* is used where resistance to corrosion is of paramount importance. The surface may be polished or, as is more often the case, *de*-polished or mat finished.

3. The surface of *aluminum* may be polished to produce regular or specular reflection. It may also be given a mat finish to produce spread reflection. When this finish is protected by a special sealing process, the surface is hard and quite permanent. Such an aluminum sheet is known as Alzak[1] and is widely used.

Aluminum is easily formed by bending or spinning into a variety of shapes and forms. The light weight of finished reflectors is a favorable factor. For light control characteristics of metals, see Table 5-1.

### TABLE 5-1

**Light Control Characteristics of Metals**

(Tested with tungsten light)

| Material | Reflection factor, % |
| --- | --- |
| Alzak aluminum—polished | 85 |
| Alzak aluminum—mat | 80 |
| Rhodium—polished | 70–79 |
| Chromium—polished | 62–66 |
| Stainless steel—polished | 55–65 |
| Stainless steel—etched | 42–47 |
| Nickel | 60–62 |
| Porcelain enamel—shiny | 60–80 |
| Porcelain enamel—mat | 60–83 |
| Baked white enamel | 80 |

4. *Glass* is the oldest light control material. When diffusing material is scattered through it as a homogeneous mixture, it is known as white glass. Flashed white glass consists of a layer of clear glass for strength and a thin layer of white glass for light diffusion. Ceramic-coated glass accomplishes somewhat the same result. A diffusing ceramic coating is sprayed on the clear glass and then baked at high temperature. The diffusion is not uniform and the ceramic coating can be scratched off.

---

[1] Trade-marked by the Aluminum Company of America.

The surface of any glass can be ribbed, patterned, or roughened to alter the transmission, reflection, or diffusion pattern.

Mirrored glass is used where light control by regular reflection is desired. High accuracy of reflection, permanence, and resistance to heat and corrosion are favorable factors.

By means of prisms incorporated in glass of various shapes, the principal of refraction can be utilized to produce luminaires for almost every lighting purpose.

Metallic silver has a high reflection factor but is subject to rapid deterioration. By placing the silver on a glass surface and sealing the silver with copper, a well-protected "sandwich" is achieved.

Glass is available that absorbs radiant energy in the infrared or heat region of the spectrum. It is known as heat-absorbing glass. In the process, light is absorbed too, in amounts greater than usual for clear glass. As would be expected, the glass has a greenish tint. It is used in windows, and as cover-glass for light sources to screen out radiant heat. Light control characteristics of glass are shown in Table 5-2.

TABLE 5-2

**Light Control Characteristics of Glass**

| Material | Thickness | Transmission, % | Reflection, % |
|---|---|---|---|
| Clear glass | .25–.125 | 80–92 | 8–10 |
| Configurated glass* | .12–.23 | 57–90 | 7–24 |
| Satin finish* | .075 | 89 | 8 |
| Acid-etched* | .08 | 82–88 | 7–9 |
| Sandblasted* | .08–.012 | 77–81 | 11–16 |
| White ceramic-coated | .125 | 40–64 | 24–50 |
| Solid white | .07–.14 | 12–38 | 40–66 |
| Flashed white | .08–.11 | 47–66 | 31–45 |
| Mirrored glass | | | 80–90 |

* One side only—this side toward the light.

5. *Plastics* are substances new to the field of light control. They can be made to exhibit a wide range of transmission, reflection, and diffusion characteristics. Light weight and resistance to shattering are favorable physical properties. Low temperature

limits, discoloring due to ultraviolet radiation, and dimensional
instability are negative characteristics which are present in some
types of plastics. Light control characteristics of plastics are
shown in Table 5-3, and classes of plastics used in lighting practice
in Table 5-4.

### TABLE 5-3

**Light Control Characteristics of Plastics**

(Tested with tungsten filament light)

| Material | Thickness | Transmission, % | Reflection, % |
|---|---|---|---|
| Thermoplastic types: | | | |
| Plexiglass........................ | .08 | 64–89 | 34–10 |
| Lumitile........................ | | 38–51* | 39–50 |
| Lumarith...................... | | 75–90* | |
| Lucite........................ | | 90* | |
| Lustron........................ | | 88* | |
| Thermosetting types: | | | |
| Natural Plaskon............. | .05 | 49 | 28 |
| White Plaskon............... | .05 | 28 | 55 |
| Insurok...................... | .06 | 65 | |
| Insurok...................... | .12 | 50 | |

* May be varied over a wide range.

### TABLE 5-4

**Classes of Plastics Used in Lighting Practice**

*Thermosetting*

Urea formaldehydes:
  Plaskon
  Beetle
Cast phenolic resins:
  Catalin
  Durez
  Marblette

*Thermoplastic*

Cellulose acetate:
  Lumarith
  Plastacele
Methyl methacrylate:
  Plexiglass
  Lucite
Polystyrenes:
  Lumitile
  Styron
  Lustron

For simplicity, plastics may be divided into two broad classes: thermosetting and thermoplastic. Thermosetting plastics undergo a fundamental chemical change under heat and retain the shape given them. Thermoplastic plastics do not undergo any fundamental chemical change but simply soften under heat. They can be put into various shapes when soft and will retain that shape when cooled.

6. *Plaster and painted surfaces* are of interest in primary light control because of their use in coves, coffers, and light boxes. White, unpainted plaster with a smooth trowelled finish reflects light diffusely except at high grazing angles. It has a very high reflection factor (See Table 5-5).

**TABLE 5-5**

**Light Control Characteristics of Plaster and Paint**

(Tested with tungsten light)

| *Material* | *Reflection factor,* % |
|---|---|
| White plaster | 90–92 |
| Gloss white paint | 80–85 |
| Flat white water paint | 75–90 |
| Flat white oil paint | 80 |
| Magnesium carbonate | 98.3 |
| Aluminum paints | 38–75 |

Glossy-painted surfaces reflect light in much the same manner as porcelain enamel. Mat or eggshell paints reflect light in a diffuse manner, generally in the manner of spread reflection.

## 5.7. Interpretation of Photometric Data

The information on reflection, transmission, and absorption must be carefully sorted out before correct use can be made of it. Let us start with a simple example of reflection from shiny porcelain-enamelled steel. The total reflection factor includes both the diffuse and the specular reflections, since the pattern is mixed reflection. The only part of the incident light that can be accurately controlled is that which is specularly reflected. Therefore this percentage must be known. The rest of the light is diffusely reflected in all directions and accurate control of it is not possible.

Consider now a reflector made of translucent glass. The incident ray from the lamp is partly reflected from both surfaces of the glass, the percentage depending upon the incident angle. In passing through the glass, a part of the light is lost or absorbed. The amount which emerges from the far side, divided by the incident amount, is known as the transmission factor. This figure by itself is not enough. Suppose this glass is to be used in a semi-indirect reflector (Fig. 5-14). The important data is that which discloses the amount *reflected* from the surface, because the reflector, to be useful, must reflect a high percentage of the incident light. If it were known that the glass had a transmission factor of 10%, this at first thought might lead one to think that 90% of the incident light was lost. Such, of course, need not be

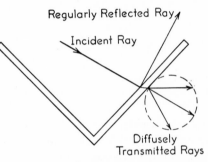

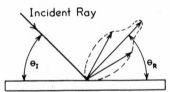

Fig. 5-13. A portion of the reflection from shiny porcelain enamel can be accurately controlled.

Fig. 5-14. A reflector of diffuse translucent material can control the specularly reflected light but not the diffusely emitted light.

the case, because by proper design and a knowledge of the surface reflection factor, perhaps 75% of the incident light can be reflected out into space.

Lighting practice makes increasing use of panels of diffusing translucent material, behind which are placed fluorescent or incandescent light sources. For the diffuser, the transmission factor of the panel might seem to be all that need be known. Let us again follow a ray of incident light (Fig. 5-15). The amount which is reflected from the surfaces of the glass goes back into the "light box." If it is completely absorbed there it is lost and never returns to the surface of the cover. However, the inside surfaces of light boxes are generally of high reflection factor. Therefore some portion of that reflected light will get back to the cover and pass through. Eventually then, more light gets through the cover than the original figure of transmission might indicate. Globes of white diffusing glass are commonly used, the white glass having a transmission factor of 50%. The globe, however, may have an efficiency of 80%. At first thought this seems impossible, but when one analyzes the meaning of transmission and reflection factors, and traces a beam of light, the reason is clear. The rays reflected from the internal glass surfaces are not all trapped but pass out through the glass on repeated reflections.

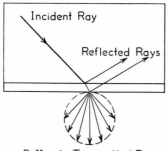

Fig. 5-15. The light reflected from the shiny surfaces in effect increases the transmission of the translucent material.

### 5.8. Basic Reflector Contours

It should be obvious that the character of the reflecting surface determines the degree of light control possible. If a light ray is reflected diffusely, then the reflected ray is so broken up that the shape of the reflecting surface is of little importance. When the light ray is reflected in a spread pattern then the reflected ray can only be given a general direction; the ray will always be fuzzy. If the ray is reflected from a specular sur-

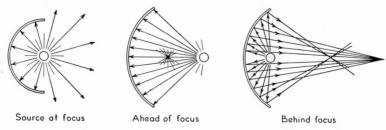

Source at focus          Ahead of focus          Behind focus

Fig. 5-16.   Circular reflector focuses rays upon the source.

face then the laws of regular reflection hold absolutely, and accurate control is possible.

The circular section is the simplest of all contours (Fig. 5-16). When the light source is at the center of the circle, the rays are reflected back to it, greatly increasing the power of the emerging rays. If the source is ahead or behind the center, the effect of reinforcement is lost and the emerging rays are a jumble. The circular section is found in the silvered bowl incandescent lamp, and is widely used in picture projection equipment.

The parabolic section is probably the most useful of all reflector forms (Fig. 5-17). When the light source is placed at the focal

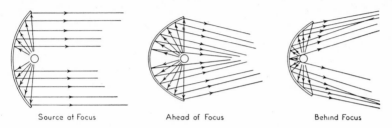

Source at Focus          Ahead of Focus                Behind Focus

Fig. 5-17.   Parabolic reflector produces parallel rays.

point of the parabola, the reflected rays are essentially parallel. The emerging beam is thus strong and subject to precise control. Searchlights use parabolic mirror reflectors.   If the source is ahead of the focal point, the rays converge at some point and then spread out.   When the source is behind the focal point, the rays spread

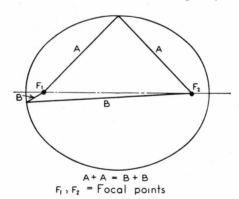

A + A = B + B
$F_1$ , $F_2$ = Focal points

Fig. 5-18.   An ellipse has two focal points.

out immediately. The resulting beams can be defined accurately, but they are useful only for relatively short distances of projection.

An ellipse has two focal points (Fig. 5-18). A light source placed at one will cause the reflected rays to pass through the other. Thus a relatively large amount of light can be made to pass through a small opening accurately before spreading out. This principle is utilized in the design of "pin-hole" spotlights (Fig. 5-19). If the source is not at the focal point, the beam is destroyed and the purpose of the elliptical contour is lost (Fig. 5-20).

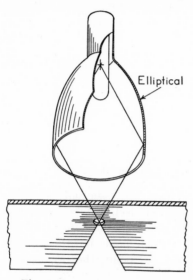

An analysis of a small section of the reflecting surface of any specular contour will show that each incident ray is reflected at an angle equal to the angle of incidence. In essence, then, any specular contour is a series of plane mirrors, subject to the law of regular reflection.

Combinations of basic contours are widely utilized in lighting practice. The circular and plane reflector shown in Fig. 5-21 directs the light upward without glare in any viewing angle below the horizontal.

Fig. 5-19. A light source at one focal point of an ellipse will send the reflected rays through the other focal point. This principle is used for "pin-hole" spotlights.

The parabola and circle are useful partners. As shown in Fig. 5-22, the circular section returns the light to, or near, the source, thereby increasing its power, while the parabola directs the flux in a more or less parallel sheet of light. This arrangement is

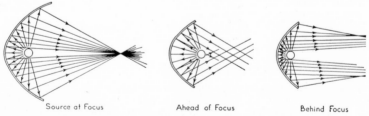

Fig. 5-20.   Effect of light source not at focal point of ellipse.

particularly useful when the light source is a lumiline lamp or a fluorescent lamp.

For concentrated sources, the arrangement shown in Fig. 5-23

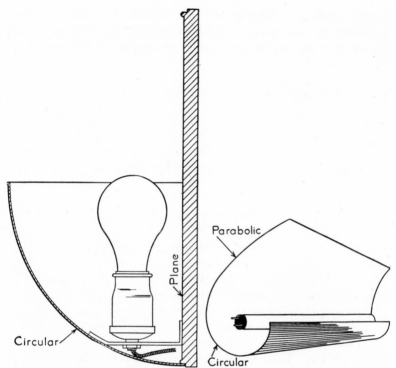

Fig. 5-21. Combined circular and plane reflectors.

Fig. 5-22. Combined circular and parabolic reflectors for line source.

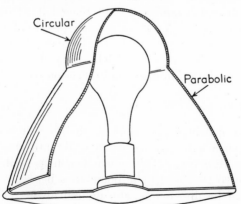

Fig. 5-23. Combined circular and parabolic reflectors for concentrated source.

is often employed. The circle reflects the light back to the source, increasing its power. The parabola reflects the light in a well defined pattern. Floodlights and direct-type luminaires often are constructed in this fashion.

## 5.9. Effect of Light Source upon Performance

According to the principles of optics, the source of light should be very small in relation to the dimension of the contour if accurate results are to be obtained. The tungsten filament lamps can approximate this in varying degree. The glass bulb will transmit light with moderate loss so that rays reflected back to the source are useful.

The phosphors in a fluorescent lamp prevent this simplicity of treatment. They reflect about 65% of incident light in a diffuse pattern. Twenty per cent of the light is absorbed and 15% goes straight through the lamp and out the other side. In effect, such reflections and emissions add to the primary light of the lamp itself. Since this is diffuse emission from a relatively large source, the effectiveness of accurate reflector contours is reduced. In a porcelain-enamelled reflector, for example, an approximate loss of 5% in efficiency occurs for each lamp beyond one, which is incorporated in the reflector. Further, the extended fluorescent source cannot be treated as a point of light. For purposes of design it is divided into small sections, and each section considered as a "point" source, but the final result is a compromise. In general it is considered that light from fluorescent lamps cannot be projected accurately to any distance unless the reflector is very large in relation to the lamp diameter. Thus the control of light from fluorescent lamps is largely in the realm of diffusion and reflection from plane surfaces.

## 5.10. Refraction

The speed of light is greater in air than it is in water, glass, or plastic. When a light ray passes from air into glass it slows up and changes direction. This phenomenon is called *refraction*. It is possible so to arrange the boundaries between air and glass that light can be directed to any desired angle. Thus accurate control of light is possible by means of refraction, just as it is by reflection.

The prism is the classical form of refractor (Fig. 5-24).   It may be so constructed as to direct light back upon itself.   Prisms can be incorporated into the surfaces of various shapes of glass as well as into flat plates.   Any desired distribution of the reflected or, more properly, *refracted* light rays can be accomplished.

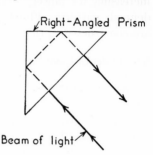

Fig. 5-24.   A prism may be made totally reflecting.

A lens is simply a built-up system of prisms just as a parabola is a built-up system of plane mirrors (Fig. 5-25).   Lenses in common use are shown in Fig. 5-26.

A Fresnel lens is an interesting adaptation of the convex lens (Fig. 5-27).   A large portion of the lens can be cut away so long as the contour of the cut-away pieces is duplicated in the remaining surfaces.   Thus there is a saving in glass and a reduction in weight.

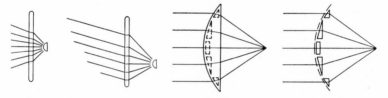

Fig. 5-25.   A lens is a built-up series of prisms.   Lens plates are a combination of prisms.

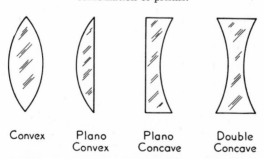

Convex      Plano Convex      Plano Concave      Double Concave

Fig. 5-26.   Types of lenses in common use.

This principle is used in lighthouses, searchlights, and floodlights. If a plano-convex lens is used as the model, a plate lens results which is useful in many interior lighting applications (Fig. 5-28). The vertical surfaces serve no useful lighting purpose, but due to inaccuracies in manufacture a little light is spilled through them. This light is in pleasing contrast to the working lens surface, or if

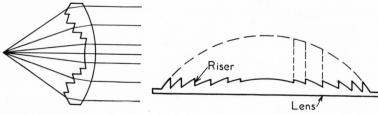

Fig. 5-27. A Fresnel lens is a series of convex lenses contrived to save glass and weight.

Fig. 5-28. Many plate types of lenses are cut-away plano-convex lenses.

the riser is tinted in a suitable color, an interesting decorative touch is achieved. Light on the work plane is not sacrificed.

## 5.11. Polarization

Polarization is a phenomenon that has limited application in lighting practice but is of considerable interest to the layman.

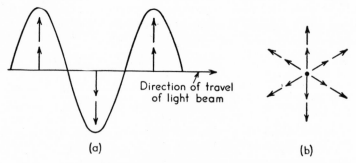

(a)　　　　　　　　　　　　　　　　(b)

Fig. 5-29. Schematic light beam.

According to the wave theory of light, the vibrations in the wave are at right angles to the direction of travel. Fig. 5-29a represents a side view of a light beam and Fig. 5-29b an end view. Through certain combinations of reflection and refraction the vibrations in a light beam can be absorbed so that only a portion of the beam, vibrating in one plane, is left (Fig. 5-30). The beam is then said to be polarized and the material accomplishing this is called a polarizer. It is obvious that a suitable polarizing filter can be placed in such a position that this beam will pass through it, or that the filter can be rotated so that the beam will not pass through it. Such a filter is called an analyzer. A homely example would be to think of two brass plates with a slot cut in each. If the two plates are arranged with the slots in line the light will pass through. If the slots are not in line the light will not pass through.

Practical polarizing screens called "Polaroid" are commercially available. They are in film form and are sometimes used in that state, or sandwiched between glass. A beam of light passed through a single film will be polarized. A second identical film parallel to the first will either pass the light or absorb it depending upon how the second film is rotated. A single polarizing film will absorb from 60% to 75% of the light. Windows of Polaroid are sometimes seen in airplanes and railway club cars.

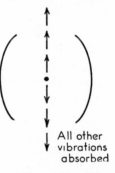

Fig. 5-30. Schematic polarized light beam.

Daylight is partially polarized. So also is sunlight when reflected from shiny surfaces. Thus a single film of Polaroid will serve as an analyzer and reduce the brightness of the reflections. Sun glasses and camera filters are good examples of the use of this phenomenon.

## PROBLEMS

**1.** Daylight of 3,000 lm per sq ft is incident on a clear glass window pane. How many lumens per square foot are available inside the window if the glass absorbs 12% of the incident light?

**2.** A light source of 200 ft-L brightness is seen in a silvered mirror. What is the brightness of the image to an observer? The silver surface reflects 98% and the glass has a transmission of 92%.

**3.** A recessed light box without a cover emits 900 lm. If an acid-etched glass plate, with etched surface inside, is used as a diffuser, how many lumens are available? Neglect loss due to internal reflections.

**4.** A reflector is to be made of glazed white porcelain enamel on steel, reflection factor 78%. Thirty-five per cent of the lamp flux is not intercepted by the reflector. Neglecting losses due to internal reflection, what is the maximum efficiency of the luminaire?

**5.** A phototube is adjusted to operate at 10 ft-c incident. The activating light beam is to be reflected from a polished Alzak aluminum mirror of 40% reflectance set 10 ft from the tube and 5 ft from the primary light source. What candlepower must be provided in the light beam?

**6.** A fluorescent trough is 1 by 4 ft. Two 2,300-lm lamps are installed in it. If the reflector is white enamel of 80% reflection factor and intercepts 60% of the lamp flux, what is the brightness in footlamberts of the uniformly diffusing cover glass of 70% transmission? What is the efficiency of the luminaire? Neglect internal interreflections.

**7.** Is the diffuse reflection factor of a surface a constant? Give reasons for your answer.

**8.** A material is said to have a transmission factor of 85%. What has become of the other 15%?

# REFERENCES

Bigelow and Howard, "Translucent Urea-Formaldehyde Plastics in Artificial Illumination," *Trans. Illum. Eng. Soc.*, Vol. 31, page 414, April 1936.

Committee Report, "Measurements of Diffusion," *Trans. Illum. Eng. Soc.*, Vol. 34, page 109, January 1939.

Edwards, Junius D., "Aluminum for Reflectors," *Trans. Illum. Eng. Soc.*, Vol. 29, page 351, May 1934.

———, "Aluminum Reflectors," *ibid.*, Vol. 34, page 427, April 1939.

Gamble, D. L., "The Influence of the Reflecting Characteristics of Wall Paints upon the Intensity and Distribution of Artificial and Natural Illumination," *Trans. Illum. Eng. Soc.*, Vol. 28, page 326, April 1933.

General Electric Company, *Bulletin LD-2*, 1948.

Meacham, James A., "Light Reflection from Painted Surfaces," *Trans. Illum. Eng. Soc.*, Vol. 34, page 87, January 1939.

Paul, M. Rea, "Surfacing Materials for Light Wells," *Trans. Illum. Eng. Soc.*, Vol. 28, page 315, April 1933.

Paulus and Woodside, "Illumination Characteristics of Organic Plastics," *Trans. Illum. Eng. Soc.*, Vol. 28, page 749, November 1933.

Report of Joint Committee on Illuminating Glasses, *Trans. Illum. Eng. Soc.*, Vol. 29, page 677, September 1934.

Taylor, A. H., "Light and Ultraviolet Reflection by Various Materials," *Trans. Illum. Eng. Soc.*, Vol. 30, page 563, July 1935.

Warner, Frank E., "Plastics in Lighting," *Trans. Illum. Eng. Soc.*, Vol. 33, page 244, March 1938.

# 6

# LUMINAIRES

A luminaire is defined as "a complete lighting unit consisting of a source, together with its direct appurtenances." These appurtenances are a globe, reflector, refractor, housing, and such support as is an integral part of the housing. Through long usage a luminaire is commonly known as a fixture. However, the term is too generally used, as plumbing "fixture," store "fixture," and the like, to express adequately its true function.

The majority of electric lighting is accomplished by means of luminaires attached to walls or ceilings. They are "packaged" articles and carry designations of the manufacturer, usually by copyrighted names and catalog numbers. The purpose of the luminaire is first to introduce the source of luminous flux into the area, and then to diffuse, modify, or redirect this light flux to establish the desired lighting result. Unfortunately, in all too many instances, the true function of the luminaire is subordinated and it is considered instead an end in itself.

There is a commendable growing tendency to incorporate the luminaires into the building structure. In some rooms "packaged" equipment can be utilized, but in others the design must be made by the engineer or architect and the equipment built to a specification. In such cases a considerable knowledge of light sources and light-control media is necessary for a successful result. However, one should always bear in mind that a luminaire possesses inherent lighting qualities that are modified, or accentuated, by the surroundings. Rarely can the descriptive adjectives "good" or "bad" be applied, because the over-all lighting result depends heavily upon environmental conditions. The engineer must select or design the luminaire to achieve the desired result. An obviously extreme example would be the use of an indirect luminaire in a room with a black ceiling. No matter what inherent good qualities had been built into the luminaire, the result would be disappointing.

## 6.1. Component Parts

Parts of a luminaire are quite simple. Fig. 6-1 shows the parts for concentrated light sources such as incandescent and mercury lamps, and Fig. 6-2 shows them for the extended fluorescent sources.

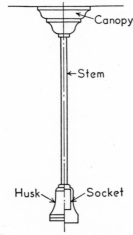

Fig. 6-1. Supporting elements of an incandescent lamp luminaire.

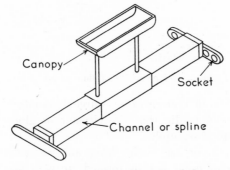

Fig. 6-2. Supporting elements of fluorescent lamp luminaires.

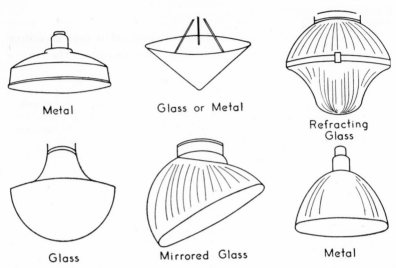

Metal

Glass or Metal

Refracting Glass

Glass

Mirrored Glass

Metal

Fig. 6-3. Light-control elements of incandescent lamp luminaires.

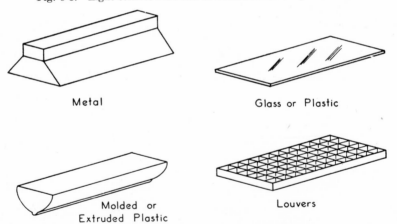

Metal

Glass or Plastic

Molded or Extruded Plastic

Louvers

Fig. 6-4. Light-control elements of fluorescent lamp luminaires.

The majority of concentrated-source luminaires are equipped with light-control media that are circular or globular. Fig. 6-3 shows some typical examples.

Fluorescent luminaires, being large and essentially rectangular in shape, depend upon flat or formed surfaces for light control, as shown in Fig. 6-4.

## 6.2. Types of Luminaires

It is fitting that luminaires should be classified by type according to arbitrary assignment of light flux distribution. The Inter-

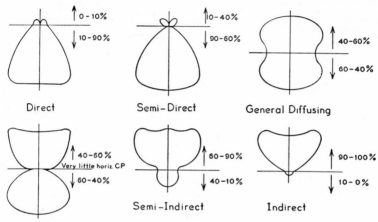

Fig. 6-5. Basic luminaire flux distribution according to I.C.I. classifications.

national Commission on Illumination (I.C.I.) classification is shown in Table 6-1. The direct-indirect subdivision of the general

**TABLE 6-1**

**Types of Luminaires**

| Classification | Distribution in percentage of total luminaire output | |
|---|---|---|
| | Upward, % | Downward, % |
| Direct | 0–10 | 100–90 |
| Semi-direct | 10–40 | 90–60 |
| General diffusing | 40–60 | 60–40 |
| Direct-indirect | 50 | 50 |
| | | (very little horizontal candlepower) |
| Semi-indirect | 60–90 | 40–10 |
| Indirect | 90–100 | 10–0 |

diffusing type is an outgrowth of the fluorescent lamp. Through shielding media the light flux at angles near the horizontal is sharply restricted. Flux passes upward and downward with little modification. It is not recognized officially as a luminaire type, but is widely used and referred to in lighting literature.

Candlepower distribution curves representing the I.C.I. classifications are given in Fig. 6-5. Note that the percentages of upward and downward distribution total 100%.

## 6.3. Efficiency

The efficiency of a luminaire is the ratio of total output of luminous flux to input of luminous flux. The input of luminous flux is, of course, the lamp lumens. If a luminaire is equipped with a 500-watt general service incandescent lamp (initial output, 9,900 lm), and the photometric test shows it to emit 8,160 lm, the luminaire efficiency is 8,160/9,900 or $82\frac{1}{2}\%$.

If, of this 8,160 lm, the distribution curve shows 7,507 lm in the upper half, then 7,507/8,160 or 92% is in the 90° to 180° zone. The luminaire is therefore classified as *indirect*.

There is a tendency to overemphasize the importance of luminaire efficiency. A polyphase induction motor of 92% efficiency is generally a better buy at the same price than a polyphase induction motor of 88% efficiency. A luminaire, however, emits light which in turn activates human vision. Both the quantity of light and the manner of its distribution are vital to the visual function. Since luminaire efficiency relates only to quantity of flux, it is only one criterion of luminaire worth.

The most efficient luminaire is a socket holding a bare lamp, but the resulting illumination in most cases would be glaring and uncomfortable. It would hinder vision and reduce visual efficiency.

Luminaires of each classification should be compared not only for efficiency, but for candlepower distribution and brightness. If the latter two are matched, then the luminaire with the higher efficiency should be favored.

Mechanical strength, facility in maintenance, and quality of light-control surfaces are also important. There is no single point of judgment, but rather a careful weighing of several factors against the illumination desired and the service conditions encountered.

## 6.4. Selecting the Luminaire

A luminaire should be analyzed from four points of view:

1. Mechanical.
2. Electrical.
3. Illuminating.
4. Esthetic.

1. *Mechanical.* A luminaire should have the mechanical strength to enable it to be shipped, assembled, and installed, without breakage or warping. It should be so made that it can be cleaned, repaired, or parts replaced without complete removal from the outlet. Filament and high pressure mercury lamps, being light in weight and compact in size, may be fitted with luminaires that are strong, yet light, rigid, and moderate in size. In most instances, the body of the luminaire incorporates all the light-control media. Conventional fluorescent luminaires incorporate the lamp auxiliary within the luminaire. This adds considerable weight. Lamp sockets must be kept in alignment and the large surfaces devoted to light control properly supported. The better designs incorporate auxiliaries, sockets, and supporting devices into a central spine or channel of sufficient strength to hold all parts in alignment. Light-control elements are removable and provision is made to replace auxiliaries easily.

The limitation of temperatures at certain critical points is of importance. With filament lamps, the socket is probably the most critical point. With fluorescent lamps, the auxiliary is the vital point, although air temperature around the lamp affects light output. Losses as high as 70% in light output can result from lack of attention to heat dissipation. In general, the upper limit of socket temperatures is 345° Fahrenheit for medium base sockets and 390° Fahrenheit for mogul base sockets. Safe temperature for enclosed fluorescent lamp auxiliaries is 221° Fahrenheit. Heat dissipation is accomplished by ventilation, radiation, or both. Only with specialized equipment such as picture projectors or searchlights is forced air circulation necessary.

2. *Electrical.* The provisions for the safe conduction of electrical energy are so well codified that a certificate of approval by

the National Board of Fire Underwriters provides assurance against all but willful hazard. A luminaire should not be specified or accepted unless it carries the Underwriters' label. With fluorescent auxiliaries, additional desirable features are: (1) low noise level or hum; (2) power factor above 85%; (3) minimum flicker or stroboscopic effect; and (4) compound-leak-proof casings.

3. *Illuminating.* *Direct lighting* is characterized by generally high utilization of light flux on the work plane, but accompanied by high contrast with surroundings, sharp shadows, and direct and reflected glare. For specialized applications, direct and reflected glare can be controlled by means of location with respect to the work, or by providing large luminous areas on the luminaire. Direct luminaires are used principally for the lighting of industrial areas, show windows, and floodlighting. Some use of fluorescent direct luminaires of the recessed trough type is made in the lighting of stores, offices, and schools. Such systems are not free of the negative attributes of high contrast and direct and reflected glare. Completely luminous ceilings become, by definition, direct luminaires. If the ceiling is of the grid louver type, all of the negative factors associated with direct lighting *can* be eliminated. The usual practice of placing bare fluorescent lamps above the grids does not eliminate reflected glare. When the ceiling is composed of diffusing material all the negative factors disappear if the surface brightness is low.

*Semi-direct lighting,* by providing for some upward distribution of flux, eliminates to a degree the high contrasts associated with direct lighting. The brightening of the upper portions of the space makes the room look larger and this is generally pleasant. The other attributes of direct lighting are present.

*General diffuse lighting* distributes light more evenly throughout the space and hence creates a pleasant environment. Direct and reflected glare is present in a large degree. Principal uses are in commercial interiors, large assembly areas, and corridors, where visual tasks are not dominant. Because large amounts of light flux are directed to ceilings and walls, the utilization is considerably improved if these surfaces are light in color. Light-colored finishes greatly improve brightness ratios as well. General diffuse luminaires are generally completely enclosed and hence there is opportunity for making the equipment relatively dust-tight.

*Direct-indirect lighting* arises from the characteristics of the fluorescent lamp. Possessing high diffusing qualities and much lower brightness than filament lamps, there is less need for diffusion and shielding. Furthermore, the exact control of fluorescent lamp flux is difficult, hence the tendency is to rely more upon diffusion and less upon reflection and refraction.

Upward flux serves to improve the room appearance and reduce contrasts. The downward flux, if allowed to pass unrestricted to the work plane, is efficiently utilized but may contribute to reflected glare. Grids and louvers serve to shield only against direct viewing of the light source.

Direct-indirect lighting is widely used in commercial interiors, and in schools and offices where factors of economics and maintenance preclude the use of higher quality lighting.

*Semi-indirect lighting* provides for better brightness control in the lower hemisphere and reasonable freedom from shadows. Utilization of light depends more heavily upon light ceilings and sidewalls, inasmuch as 70% of the total luminaire flux may be directed upward. This type of lighting is an improvement over general diffuse lighting. It has less direct and reflected glare, but is often not suitable for the lighting of areas where close and prolonged eye work is done.

*Indirect lighting* allows for the greatest control of brightness in the direct and reflected glare zones.[1] Efficient utilization of light depends absolutely upon light ceilings and walls. Of course, there are many applications where utilization is of little moment, esthetic effect being paramount. Indirect lighting is very effective in such instances.

For offices and schools, or wherever visual tasks are exacting, this is the finest type of lighting. Luminaires can be very efficient. By design the luminaire can have a luminous surface which is pleasing and of low contrast with the background.

Dirt and dust have a very detrimental effect upon the efficiency of indirect lighting. Periodic maintenance is important. However, if luminaires and surroundings are not well maintained, the brightness ratios within the area stay fairly constant, hence visual comfort remains high.

---

[1] A discussion of these factors will be found in Chapter 9.

4. *Esthetic considerations.* The principal function of a luminaire is to control the luminous flux from a lamp. There are many places where the appearance of the luminaire is not important. It may appear frankly for what it is, with no attempt to disguise the materials or modify the shape.

On the other hand there are many places where a luminaire must have form and finish to harmonize with the surroundings. It is not easy to accomplish this without undue sacrifice of the primary function of light control. There is no basic reason why esthetic function and lighting function cannot be accomplished harmoniously.

Unfortunately too many luminaires of basically pleasing design are either unduly glaring, or annoyingly dim. Likewise many luminaires have neither pleasing appearance nor good lighting qualities.

On the other hand, the designer of a lighting system has the responsibility of making appropriate selections. Luminaires which are eminently suited for a given function may appear quite out of place if improperly applied.

When the lighting is incorporated into the structure, the problems are somewhat different. When only the luminous portions of the luminaire are visible, the size, shape, and brightness of it are important. When the luminaires are concealed behind structural or decorative elements the problem is usually one of size and optical control. The lighting designer must have a sound knowledge of the basic decorative and architectural forms. Likewise a sense of fitness, proportion, and balance is necessary for successful designing.

## 6.5. Luminaire Brightness and Glare

The brightness of the luminaire in certain angular zones below the horizontal has an important bearing upon glare. In rooms of average ceiling height the zone from 45° to 90° is considered the *direct glare zone.* In rooms with high ceilings this zone is considered to be 30° to 90° (Fig. 6-6).

In the average luminaire using an incandescent or mercury lamp the brightness in these zones should not exceed 800 ft-L if it is to be just comfortable and 300 ft-L if it is to be very comfortable. In industrial areas the higher figure can be accepted. In schools, offices, and similar areas, the lower figure should be adopted.

Research has disclosed that direct glare depends upon the area of the bright source as well as the brightness in footlamberts. A large light-emitting area must have a lower brightness than a small area. Fluorescent luminaires are larger than incandescent luminaires. Consequently a lower brightness is necessary. For "just comfortable" it is wise to adopt 600 ft-L as the upper limit. For "very comfortable" 250 ft-L or less is recommended. When fluorescent luminaires are combined into long rectangles or "continuous runs" the luminous area increases. The brightness limits

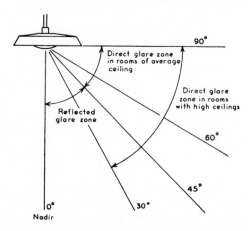

Fig. 6-6.    Zones of brightness on a luminaire, which affect eye comfort and visibility.

should be decreased to 400 ft-L for "just comfortable" and 175 ft-L to be "very comfortable."

The brightness in the zone from 0° to 30° or 0° to 45° determines to a large extent the degree of reflected glare. This is a difficult factor to assess. Much experimental work remains to be done. Reflected glare may be uncomfortable, and it always reduces the visibility of the seeing task. If the luminaire brightness is less than 400 ft-L in the zone from 0° to 30° or 45° reflected glare will be minimized. A brightness of 225 ft-L or less is desirable.

The brightness limits here described apply to installations where visual comfort and efficiency are important. They are based upon illumination levels of the order of 30 to 50 ft-c.

### 6.6. Light Flux Control

To redirect light flux and control luminaire brightness, the familiar principles of reflection, refraction, and transmission are employed.

For accurate reflection of flux, refraction and specular reflection are utilized. Luminaires utilizing the refracting principles are generally of the direct type, embodying enclosing glassware, or plates.

The prisms are so formed and dimensioned as to bend the light rays in the desired directions. The glass is usually pressed out by mold. To effect a slight diffusion, one surface may be lightly etched.

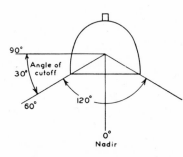

Fig. 6-7. Angle of cutoff may be stated in degrees below the horizontal or at a certain degree from nadir.

Specular surfaces used in reflectors are generally polished aluminum or mirrored glass. Contours may be parabolic, hyperbolic, circular, plane, or combinations of these. Each portion of the surface obeys the law of regular reflection, that is, the angle of incidence and the angle of reflection are equal. The angles through which light is to be controlled are determined by the luminaire type and the design proceeds from that point. In Fig. 6-7, for example, the absolute cutoff of light from the lamp is set at 30° below a horizontal line through the light center. A considerable portion of the lamp flux may pass to the room without interference.

If the control surface is etched or roughened so that it produces spread reflection, the degree of control is considerably lessened. The reflected light rays tend to radiate in all directions. If the surface is absolutely diffuse, no control is possible because every emitted ray obeys the law of cosine emission. All the control surface does is to shield the lamp; it can be practically any shape.

A porcelain-enamelled metal surface produces mixed reflection. The specular "glass" surface will control light by the law of regular reflection, but the porcelain body reflects light according to the cosine law of emission. The specular surface can control only a relatively small amount of flux. Thus the shape of the surface has only moderate effect, serving principally to control the degree of cutoff. Thus, as shown in Fig. 6-8, both luminaires cut off at 30° below the horizontal. Although the reflectors are quite different in size and shape, the form of the candlepower curve is approximately the same in both cases.

Translucent materials are frequently used in globes and basins. If the transmission is completely diffuse, the brightness can be

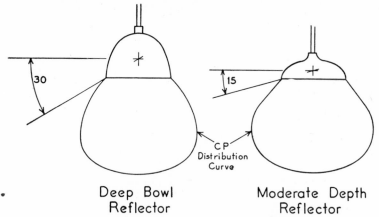

Deep Bowl
Reflector

Moderate Depth
Reflector

Fig. 6-8. A reflecting surface that is essentially diffuse cannot redirect light in a predetermined pattern.

well controlled. If the transmission is mixed, the lamp may be seen from some angles of view. This is often deliberately done to introduce highlights. Sometimes, however, as a result of careless design the luminaire exhibits objectionable brightness at important viewing angles.

Glass and plastic are the materials most commonly used. One or both surfaces are ordinarily shiny or specular. Thus the light can be both reflected and diffused. Open basins and troughs utilize this principal. By choice of contour the specular surface can redirect a certain percentage of the light, while the remainder is diffusely transmitted (Fig. 6-9).

The classical concept in dealing with light control is to consider the light source as a point. This is only approximately so with filament sources but the deviation is not beyond control. Fluorescent lamps, on the other hand, have length and breadth and by no stretch of the imagination can be called point sources. Further, the lamp acts as an effective barrier to the passage of light. This complicates the design with respect to efficiency. In general, luminaires for fluorescent lamps seek to shield the source so as to control brightness, but to attempt little in the way of accurate flux redirection.

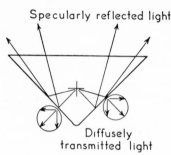

Fig. 6-9. The specular surface of a diffusely transmitting material can be utilized to reflect light flux in a specified direction.

The effect of temperature upon fluorescent lamp output must be carefully considered in the design of fluorescent luminaires. Maximum lamp output occurs at bulbwall temperatures of between 100° and 120° Fahrenheit. At 80° Fahrenheit, the output is 85% of normal; at 140° Fahrenheit it is 95% of normal; at 175° Fahrenheit it is 80% of normal.

TABLE 6-2

**Effect of More than One Row of Fluorescent Lamps on Luminaire Efficiency**

| *Type of luminaire* | *Multiplier* |
|---|---|
| Cove lighting: | |
|     One row of lamps.............................. | 1.00 |
|     Two rows of lamps............................. | 0.93 |
|     Three rows of lamps........................... | 0.85 |
| Open industrial reflector: | |
|     Two rows of lamps............................. | 1.00 |
|     Three rows of lamps........................... | 0.92 |
|     Four rows of lamps............................ | 0.87 |
| Open louvered troffer: | |
|     One row of lamps............................. | 1.00 |
|     Two rows of lamps............................ | 0.92 |
|     Four rows of lamps........................... | 0.85 |
| Glass-covered troffer: | |
|     One row of lamps............................. | 1.00 |
|     Two rows of lamps............................ | 0.92 |
|     Four rows of lamps........................... | 0.85 |
| Glass-enclosed luminaire: | |
|     One row of lamps............................. | 1.00 |
|     Two rows of lamps............................ | 0.96 |
|     Three rows of lamps.......................... | 0.87 |

When more than one fluorescent lamp is used in a single luminaire the increase in light output is not directly proportional to the
number of lamps. The extra lamps produce more heat and this
is not always easy to dissipate. If the lamp bulb-wall temperature
exceeds 120° the light output decreases. These extra lamps also
shield each other or inevitably absorb light. Thus the efficiency
of multiple fluorescent lamp luminaires is lower than single lamp
luminaires of similar design (Table 6-2).

The reflecting surfaces in most luminaires form the body of the
luminaire. Luminaires subject to rough handling, such as floodlights and some industrial luminaires of silvered glass or refracting
glass, are enclosed in protective metal covers or frames. The
reflectors in spotlights and searchlights are required to deliver
accurate beam patterns, and are usually firmly mounted and
protected by sturdy metal housings.

## PROBLEMS

**1.** A reflector is to be made of glazed white porcelain enamel on steel,
reflection factor 78%. Assume that 70% of the lamp flux is intercepted
by the reflector. Neglecting losses due to internal reflection, what is the
maximum efficiency of the luminaire?

**2.** A 500-watt lamp producing 10,000 lm is used in a floodlight having
a polished aluminum reflector of 80% reflectance and a stippled cover glass
of 85% transmission. Sixty per cent of the lamp lumens are intercepted
by the reflector. How many lumens are available in the floodlight beam?

**3.** A 300-watt lamp emits 5,600 lm. What diameter sphere must be
used to reduce brightness to one candle per square inch if 60% transmission
opal glass is used? Ignore internal reflections.

**4.** An indirect luminaire cuts off lamp flux at 5° above the horizontal.
If 9% of the intercepted flux is diffusely transmitted by the basin, the
area of which is 1.5 sq ft, what is the basin brightness when a 5,400-lm
lamp is used?

**5.** An Alzak aluminum reflector cuts off direct light from the lamp at
20° below the horizontal. Assuming average reflectivity of aluminum of
72%, what will be the light output and luminaire efficiency if a lamp of
9,800 lm output is placed in the luminaire? Ignore internal reflections.

**6.** A 1,000-watt, 21,500-lm incandescent lamp is mounted inside a 2-ft
translucent sphere. The brightness of this sphere is 1,000 ft-L. What is

the transmission factor of the material (neglect losses due to interreflections within the sphere)?

**7.** A tracing table illuminated from beneath by four 2,300-lm fluorescent lamps is covered by acid-etched glass 3 by 4 ft in size and of transmission factor equal to 75%. If 80% of the total lumens are incident on the glass cover, what is the brightness of a piece of tracing paper, transmittance 60%, placed upon the table?

**8.** A fluorescent industrial-type luminaire has an efficiency of 55% when equipped with one lamp. What is the efficiency if three lamps are used in it?

**9.** A fluorescent luminaire is equipped with two 96-in., T-12 300-ma, warm white Slimline lamps. How many 25-mm, 93-in., 100-ma, warm white iron-cathode lamps would be necessary in the same luminaire to produce about the same light output?

# REFERENCES

Barnes, R. B., and Stock, C., "Properties of Urea Plastics in Lighting Fixtures," *Trans. Illum. Eng. Soc.*, Vol. 37, page 89, February 1942.

Darley, W. G., "An Analysis of Reflected Glare," *Trans. Illum. Eng. Soc.* Vol. 48, page 85, January 1948.

Douglas and Adams "Design of Reflectors for Fluorescent Lamps," *Trans. Illum. Eng. Soc.*, Vol. 38, page 141, March 1943.

Harrison, Ward, "Fluorescent Luminaires of Today—How Will They Seem in '45," *Trans. Illum. Eng. Soc.*, Vol. 36, page 752, July 1941.

———, "Indirect Luminaires—Efficient and Inefficient," *ibid.*, Vol. 34, page 255, March 1939.

Illuminating Engineering Society *Lighting Handbook.*

Ketch and Gianini "Engineering Aspects of Direct Lighting, Part I," *Trans. Illum. Eng. Soc.*, Vol. 33, page 545, December 1938.

———, "Engineering Aspects of Direct Lighting, Part II," *ibid.*, Vol. 34, page 411, April 1939.

Potter, W. M., and Darley, W. G., "Design of Luminaires for Fluorescent Lamps," *Trans. Illum. Eng. Soc.*, Vol. 35, page 759, November 1940.

Report of Quality and Quantity Committee, "Brightness and Brightness Ratios," *Trans. Illum. Eng. Soc.*, Vol. 39, page 713, December 1944.

Severence, D. P., "Design of Plane-mirror Reflectors for Fluorescent Lamps," *Trans. Illum. Eng. Soc.*, Vol. 39, page 45, January 1943.

———, "Design of Reflectors for Fluorescent Lamps," *ibid.*, Vol. 36, page 1341, December 1941.

Winkler, F. C., "Fundamental Facts of Fluorescent Fixture Design," *Trans. Illum. Eng. Soc.*, Vol. 37, page 229, April 1942.

# 7

# MEASUREMENTS OF LIGHT
# AND LIGHTING

---

The determination of the candlepower and luminous flux of light sources and luminaires is a laboratory function. Instruments associated with such measurements are the Ulbricht or integrating sphere, the bar photometer, and candlepower distribution photometers of various forms. Examples are shown in Figs. 7-1, 7-2, and 7-3. The science of photometry is beyond the scope of this text. The results of this science in the form of lumens rating of light sources and candlepower distribution curves for luminaires are, however, of great value to the engineer. They are tools which help him bridge the gap between natural forces and beneficial human use.

The emphasis in this text is upon application engineering. Measurements in this field are chiefly directed to the determination of footcandles and brightness. Discussion will therefore be restricted to the instruments and methods associated with "field measurements."

## 7.1. Comparison Instruments

The human eye is not capable of quantitative light measurements. Even highly trained technicians cannot state by observation how many lumens per square foot (footcandles) are incident upon a surface. Nor can they state how bright a given surface may be. Estimates based upon experience are possible, but they are in the class of educated guesses.

The eye is, however, quite capable of accurately bringing into

Fig. 7-1.   Ulbricht sphere.

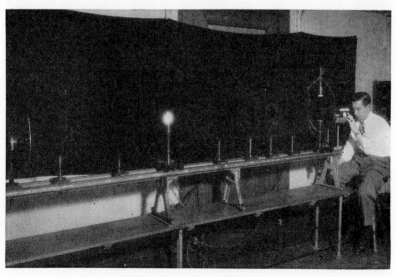

Fig. 7-2.   Bar photometer.

Fig. 7-3.   Goniophotometer for determining candlepower distribution
of lamps and luminaires.

balance the brightness of two adjacent lighted surfaces if they are
substantially the same color.   If the brightness of one surface is
known, then by comparison the other may be known also.   Two
portable instruments utilizing this principle are available to the
engineer.

**a. The Macbeth Illuminometer.** The Macbeth Illuminometer is shown assembled in Fig. 7-4. A cross section of the measuring tube is shown in Fig. 7-5. A test plate of white diffusing material of known reflection factor is placed upon the surface at which the illumination is to be measured. The sighting tube is held a foot or so away from this plate. The light reflected from the plate is received on one part of a Lummer-Brodhun cube. A small comparison lamp of known candlepower lights the other part of the cube. The cube is fixed in position while the lamp is moved back and forth by means of a rack and pinion. This varies the light on the cube until a balance is reached. The rack is marked off in footcandles ranging from 1 to 25 and when the two patterns in the cube appear equal in brightness, the footcandle value is read directly. Suitable filters can be placed in the instrument to extend the range from 0.02 to 1,200 ft-c.

The sighting tube should be pointed toward the test plate at an angle not greater than 40° from the vertical. It will be recalled that a perfectly diffusing surface is of equal brightness at any angle of view, that is, obeys Lambert's cosine law of emission. Although the test plate is highly diffusing, it conforms to Lambert's cosine law only within the angle stated. If the test plate is viewed at angles greater than 40° the footcandle values will be in error.

The Macbeth Illuminometer actually reads the brightness of the test plate in lumens per square foot. The reflection factor of the plate is nominally 85%. Each plate is calibrated and carries an exact designation of reflection factor. Therefore the illumination *on* the test plate in footcandles (or lumens per square foot) is this measurement divided by the reflection factor. This calculation is incorporated in the calibration of the footcandle scale of the instrument.

If the sighting tube is held near any surface which is reflecting or emitting light, the brightness of that surface in footlamberts may be determined. The reading of the footcandle scale is simply *multiplied* by the reflection factor of the plate.

To determine the candlepower of a light source, the test plate is placed in position at right angles to the light rays, and at a known distance from the source. The footcandles are measured, and this value divided by the square of the distance between light source and test plate gives the candlepower of the source in that direction.

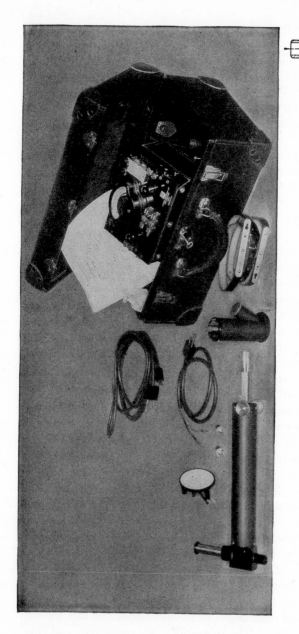

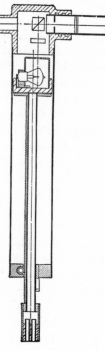

Fig. 7-4. (*Above.*) Macbeth Illuminometer.
Fig. 7-5. (*Right.*) Cross section of
sighting tube of Macbeth Illuminometer.

The Illuminometer can be supplied with color screens so that light from fluorescent, sodium, and mercury-vapor sources can be measured with high accuracy.

**b. Luckiesh-Taylor brightness meter (Fig. 7-6).** This meter also utilizes the comparison field principle. The object to be observed is focused either between or around the trapezoid. The inner portion of the field (trapezoid) is illuminated by a small lamp. The light from this lamp is filtered through a graded density film rotated by the observer to vary the brightness on the comparison screen. This screen is observed through an eyepiece. When a balance has been reached, the brightness of the test object is read on a scale which is viewed through another eyepiece. The scale extends from 2 to 50 ft-L and from 0.0045 to 0.11 candles per sq in. By means of easily manipulated filters the scale may be extended to 0.002 to 50,000 ft-L or 0.0000045 to 110 candles per sq in.

Provision is made to light the comparison lamp with flashlight cells within the instrument case. For extended readings, external dry cells can be used, connected through jacks. The instrument can also be mounted on a tripod for ease in taking measurements over an extended period of time.

Footcandles are easily determined by simply measuring the brightness of a surface of known reflection factor. The scale reading in footlamberts is then divided by the reflection factor to yield footcandles.

Magnesium carbonate is much favored as a test surface. It is easily cleaned, has the highest reflection factor of any practicable surface (98.3% for tungsten filament light), and obeys Lambert's cosine law over a wide angular range.

The object whose brightness is to be measured should appear in the photometer field at approximately the same color as the comparison lamp field. A color difference introduces considerable error because of the inability of the eye to separate brightness difference from color difference.

The average brightness of a surface of varying reflection factors cannot be measured. The object lens system is so designed that only a small portion of a test object is observed. Thus the edge grain in a piece of fir plywood, part of the pattern in a square of linoleum, or a spot on a glass block will be measured. These measurements may be useful but they do not tell us what the

Fig. 7-6.  Luckiesh-Taylor brightness meter.

average is. If the surface is uniform in reflectance then the brightness of a small portion is a good average.

The brightness of very small objects can be measured readily. It is not necessary that the object fill the entire space around the trapezoids. If it can be viewed *between* the trapezoids a photometric balance can be obtained (Fig. 7-7). When the brightness to be measured is a slender line in a vertical position the meter can be turned so that the object lies across the trapezoid.

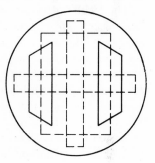

Fig. 7-7. Object whose brightness is desired need fill only a portion of the space between the trapezoids.

## 7.2. Direct Reading Instruments

The photo-voltaic or barrier-layer cell is well suited to the measurement of luminous flux. As constructed for this purpose it consists of a sandwich of three materials (Fig. 7-8). The base usually is of steel, next is a layer of selenium, over that is sputtered a semi-transparent metallic film, usually of silver. This film is the negative pole and the metal base is the positive pole. A clear glass cover is placed over the sandwich to protect it from the elements.

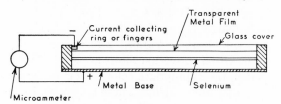

Barrier Layer Cell
Components

Fig. 7-8. Schematic diagram of photo-voltaic or barrier-layer cell.

Radiant energy is converted directly to electrical energy. The electric current is very small but quite sufficient to actuate a microammeter. Therefore a combination of barrier-layer cell and microammeter can be calibrated to read directly in footcandles.

The selenium cell converts radiant energy between approximately 300 and 850 millimicrons. The human eye converts radiant energy too, its conversion giving us the sense of sight. The limits of this conversion are approximately 400 to 760 millimicrons.

The result is that the cell and the eye do not make equal evaluations of luminous energy. Two methods of equalizing them are possible. The first is to calibrate the cell for a certain light source and then determine correction factors which will be applied to scale readings when light from other sources is measured. The second method is to place a filter over the cell which screens out radiation beyond that perceived by the eye. The cell response will then be approximately the same as the eye response, and no correction factors are necessary (Fig. 7-9).

This second method is better because it relieves the user of the mathematics involved in correction. It also eliminates the error which inevitably arises when light from mixed sources is measured, because the observer can then only estimate which correction factor to apply.

Two manufacturers supply the majority of barrier-layer cells for light measurement, the Weston Electrical Instrument Corporation and the General Electric Company (Fig. 7-10). Popularly such instruments are known as light meters, sight meters, or footcandle meters. For simplicity, the term "light meter" is used in this text. The Weston Corporation market their product under the copyrighted name of "Photronic cells." Their visual correction filter is known as "Viscor," a registered trade mark.

Cells without visual correction filters are grayish in appearance. When using them, the appropriate color correction factors supplied by the manufacturer are needed. These are shown in Table 7-1.

Cells with visual correction filters are yellow-green in appearance. No color correction factors need be applied to readings taken with them.

There are, however, other sources of error in the combination of cell and microammeter which are very large. Unless the observer is aware of these and makes due allowance for them, the footcandle values may be inaccurate.

a. Error due to angle of incidence.   The well known "Cosine Law of Illumination" tells us that the illumination in footcandles will vary as the cosine of the angle between the plane normal to the

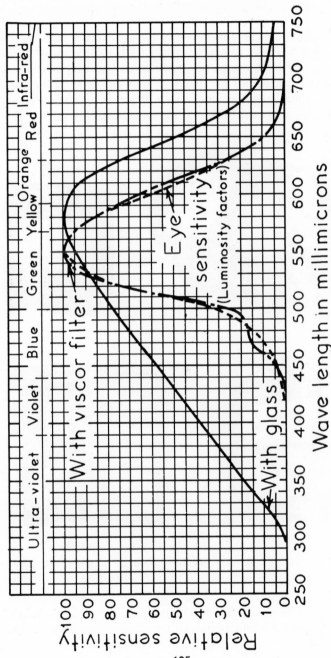

Fig. 7-9.　Barrier-layer cells can be corrected to respond to radiation as does the human eye.

light rays and the plane of measurement. This relationship is plotted in Fig. 7-11. When a light meter is rotated away from the normal to the light beam, the readings do not vary as the cosine of the angle. They are *less* than we would expect from the application of the mathematical law. This difference is often referred to as "the cosine error." This is an unfortunate term. It is per-

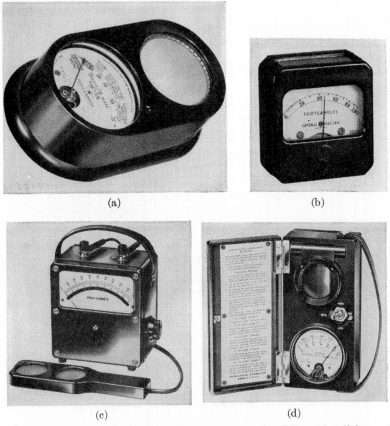

(a)                                         (b)

(c)                                         (d)

Fig. 7-10.  (a) Weston 703 light meter.  (b) G.E. pocket light meter.  (c) Weston 756 light meter.  (d) Weston 614 light meter.

fectly normal to expect the illumination to vary as the cosine of the angle. The error could better be known as "the departure from the cosine."

This error arises from two factors: the shiny or specular surface of the cell, and the projecting rim of the cell case.   In Chapter 5, it was pointed out that light striking a polished surface at wide angles from the normal is reflected from the surface in a greater amount than light striking at small angles from the normal.   Therefore, light which strikes the cell at an oblique angle is not as effective in creating electric current as the same light striking the cell at angles near the normal.   The cell does not have an opportunity to measure all of the light which is available, hence it reads low.

In some light meters the case has a pronounced rim around the cell edge.   This rim will cast a shadow when light rays approach from a wide angle.   The response of the cell is therefore less than would be expected.

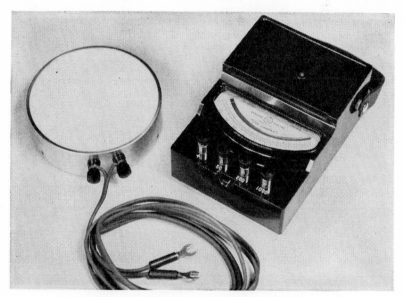

Fig. 7-10(e).   G.E. cosine- and color-corrected light meter.

When measuring illumination from sources which have strong direct radiation, such as concentrating reflectors, spot lamps, projectors, and the like, this procedure is suggested: Hold the light meter cell at right angles to the dominant light rays, and multiply the scale reading by the cosine or the sine of the appro-

## TABLE 7-1

**Correction Factors for Selenium Photovoltaic Cells under Various Light Sources**

(Calibrating Source is Tungsten Filament at 2,700° K)

| Source | Color | G.E. cell | Weston cells | |
| | | | Type 1* | Type 3 |
|---|---|---|---|---|
| Incandescent | 2,700 K | 1.00 | 1.00 | 1.00 |
| | 2,800 | 0.99 | | |
| | 2,848 | | 1.01 | 1.00 |
| | 2,900 | 0.98 | | |
| | 3,000 | 0.97 | | |
| | 3,200 | 0.95 | | |
| | 3,400 | 0.94 | | |
| Fluorescent | Std. warm white | 1.10 | | |
| | Deluxe, warm white | 0.93 | | |
| | Deluxe, cool white | 0.82 | 1.06 | |
| | Std., cool white | 0.89 | | |
| | Daylight | 0.82 | 1.06 | 0.92 |
| | Soft white | 0.90 | | |
| Mercury vapor | DH–1 | 0.84 | | |
| | EH–1 | 0.94 | | |
| | AH–4 | 0.86 | 1.35 | 1.20 |
| | H–9 | 1.02 | | |
| Sodium | NA–9 | 1.36 | 1.43 | 1.44 |
| Neon | 15-mm tubing at 30 ma | 0.85 | | |
| Daylight | Direct sunlight | 1.18 | | |
| | Overcast sky | 1.31 | 0.97 | 0.77 |

* Commonly used in light meters.

## TABLE 7-2

**Correction Factors for Light Meter Due to Diffusion of Incident Light**

| *Type of lighting* | *Multiplying factor* |
|---|---|
| Strong direct light............................. | 1.00 |
| Semi-direct lighting: | |
| Moderately light surroundings.................. | 1.05 |
| General diffuse lighting: | |
| Light surroundings............................ | 1.10 |
| Indirect lighting: | |
| All surfaces light............................ | 1.15 |
| Light ceiling—dark walls...................... | 1.10 |
| Overcast or clear sky.......................... | 1.25 |
| Overcast or clear sky through side-wall windows.... | 2.00 |

priate angle to convert to footcandles on the horizontal or vertical plane (Fig. 7-12).

The majority of field measurements are under diffused light. Correction factors for such conditions are only approximate because

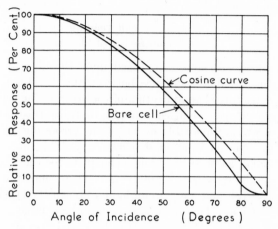

Fig. 7-11.  The response of barrier cells departs from the basic cosine law.

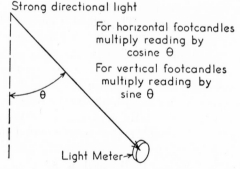

Fig. 7-12.  Method of light measurement for strong directional rays.

of the wide variation in light distribution from luminaires and reflections from surrounding surfaces. The figures in Table 7-2 are useful as a guide.

A fairly accurate check for error due to diffusion can be made. Select a piece of blotting paper and determine its reflection factor (described in Section 7.3). Measure the illumination at the desired point in the usual way. Now place the blotting paper at the position where the illumination was measured. Face the cell to the blotter and move it forward and backward until the scale reading is constant. Then

$$E = \frac{1.25 \times \text{scale reading}}{\text{reflection factor of blotter}}$$

The constant 1.25 is empirical, based upon the diffusion of light from the blotter. The difference between the direct reading and the reflected reading is an indication of the error. The cell and the light meter scale must be at right angles to utilize this procedure.

Light meters are available in which the errors due to angle of incidence are reduced to a small percentage. The rim of the cell is made as small as possible. The cover plate for the barrier cells is made of highly diffusing material. These measures reduce shadow on the cell and allow more light to reach the cell at angles nearer the normal. The diffuse cover absorbs a large percentage of the incident light. A single barrier-layer cell does not generate enough current for accuracy, so several cells are placed in parallel. This increases the size of the light meter and its cost, thus limiting its use for general field measurements.

b. **Error due to temperature.** The cell itself must not be subjected to temperature beyond 140° Fahrenheit. When measuring illumination above 500 ft-c from sunlight or incandescent sources, the cell should be exposed just long enough to obtain a reading.

The temperature of the surroundings affects the resistance of the electrical circuit. This in turn affects the response of the cell. The light meter should be at the temperature of the room before readings are taken. Within a range of 60° to 90° Fahrenheit, the error is only about 2%.

c. **Error due to fatigue.** If the cell is used continuously its response will drop about 5% in the first hour. After that the readings are constant. When the cell is first exposed there is a quick drop in sensitivity, so the meter should be exposed for two or three minutes before readings are taken.

d. **Calibration and ammeter error.** A small microammeter is not an instrument of high precision. At best, an error of plus or minus

5% is to be expected.   As in all electrical indicating instruments, the readings at both ends of the scale are in error.   With multi-range instruments, therefore, every effort should be made to get mid-scale indications.   The meter should be checked frequently for zero setting, and at least once a year should be calibrated against a good standard.

## 7.3. Measurement of Reflectance and Transmission

For the measurement of reflectance the cell and meter scale must be at right angles.   The sample to be measured should be at least one foot square.   Face the cell toward this surface and

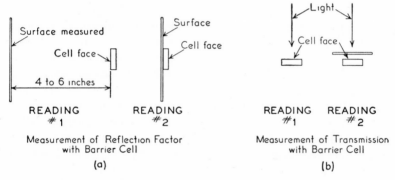

Fig. 7-13.    Using light meter to measure reflectance and transmission.

move it back and forth until a constant reading is noted (Fig. 7-13).   Then face the cell toward the light with meter against the surface.   The reflection factor is

$$\text{R.F.} = \frac{\text{reading No. 1}}{\text{reading No. 2}}$$

A more accurate method utilizes a one-foot square of diffuse white material of which the reflection factor is known.   Place this piece against the surface whose R.F. is to be measured.   Face the cell toward it and move back and forth until a constant reading is obtained.   Hold the cell in this position, remove the standard, and read again. The reflection factor will be

$$\text{R.F.} = \frac{\text{reading No. 2}}{\text{reading No. 1}} \times \text{R.F. of standard}$$

The test lighting should be diffuse in character for both methods. It is obvious that the barrier-layer cell measures average reflection factor.

To measure the transmittance of transparent materials simply place the meter on a horizontal surface, read the scale, place the material over the cell, and read again. The transmission factor is the ratio of

$$\frac{\text{reading No. 2}}{\text{reading No. 1}}$$

To find the transmission factor of translucent, diffusing material, certain precautions are necessary. If the test light is strongly directional and little diffused, proceed as before, but multiply reading No. 2 by 1.25. If the test light is well diffused, the multiplying factor is unnecessary.

Quite accurate readings of diffuse reflectance and transmittance can be made with a modified Taylor reflectometer (Fig. 7-14). This instrument can be considered portable in that it can be taken into the field to make certain measurements. Essentially, however, it is a laboratory device.

The two spheres are little integrating spheres. The upper sphere is independent of the lower and is used alone for measuring reflectance. Two barrier-layer cells are set into the sphere walls and connected to a microammeter. This ammeter has a scale divided equally into one hundred divisions.

The sphere rests on a flat bottom plate in which there is a circular opening. The sample whose reflectance is desired is placed at this opening. A light beam is directed to the sphere wall and adjusted in intensity until the microammeter indicates some desired value up to 100. The light beam is then directed to the sample, and the scale again observed. Since the only light in the sphere is now reflected from the sample, the ratio of the two scale readings is obviously the reflection factor of the sample. Field measurements of reflectance can be made if the sphere can be held to the surface.

In measuring transmittance the upper sphere is placed over the lower, a small hole in the lower being centered with the hole in the upper.  A lamp in the lower sphere is lighted and a convenient scale reading established.  The sample is now slid between the two spheres and the meter scale reading observed.  Since the light

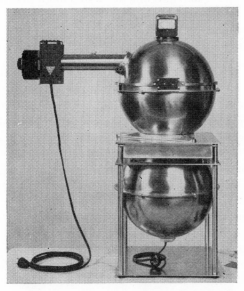

Fig. 7-14.  Modified Taylor reflectometer for accurate measurement of transmission and diffuse reflectance.

in the upper sphere has been reduced by passing through the sample, the ratio of scale readings is the transmittance of the sample.

## 7.4. Measurement of Brightness

For these measurements the cell and meter faces should be at right angles.  The method is the same as that described for measuring reflectance.  By definition a footcandle is one lumen per square foot.  When the cell is facing a surface, the reading of the footcandle scale is an indication of the lumens per square foot coming from that surface.  By definition then, that reading is also the brightness of the surface in footlamberts.  If the surface is diffuse, the reading should be multiplied by 1.25.     It makes no difference whether the surface measured is reflecting light or transmitting light.

These methods of measuring reflectances and transmission are not highly accurate, but are adequate for rough appraisal.  A discussion of precision instruments and laboratory techniques is beyond the scope of this work.

### 7.5. Field Measurements of Footcandles

There are a number of factors which affect the accuracy of field measurements of footcandles and brightness.  Some relate to the installation itself, others to the techniques of measurement.

**a. Relation between socket voltage and rated lamp voltage.**  This has been discussed in Chapter 3.  If the rated lamp voltage does not coincide with the socket voltage, a correction should be made to bring the lumen output of the lamps to rated value.  This is not necessary if the test is to disclose conditions as they are.  It is necessary if the test is for comparative purposes, or for measuring performance against design calculations.

**b. Warm-up period for lamps and auxiliaries.**  Sodium lamps, mercury-vapor lamps, and fluorescent lamps do not come up to rated output for periods varying from 10 min. to 1 hr.  Therefore any installation of these lamps under test should be turned on at least 1 hr before readings are taken.

**c. Depreciation of lamps during first 100 hours of burning.**  All gaseous conductor lamps depreciate about 10% during the first 100 hrs of burning.  Therefore the manufacturers consider as "initial lumens" that value which applies after 100 hrs of burning.  If tests are necessary at first turn-on, the 10% must be deducted if comparisons are to be made against design calculations.

**d. Color of light.**  If the cells are equipped with color-correcting screens, no additional correction is necessary.  If the cells are not so corrected, a suitable multiplying factor, as in Table 7-1, should be applied.

**e. Allowance for depreciation factor.**  If the measurements are made at what is considered the initial period, the values will be higher than the "in-service" value by the per cent depreciation factor used in the design calculations.  Owners of lighting installations are often misled as to average performance by tests made at the initial turn-on, if the factor of depreciation is overlooked.

f. Shielding of cell by observer.  A common fault when reading the scale is to lean over the instrument.  Obstruction of light results, even though no obvious shadow is cast.  The clothing of the observer may also affect the cell by reflection or absorption.

g. Selection of test stations.  Common practice in the measurement of horizontal footcandles delivered by a lighting system is to read a high and low value and average them.  This is meaningless. The footcandle value at specific work points is, of course, of interest. The average footcandles are of value in checking performance against design, in deriving coefficients of utilization, and in comparing one system of lighting with another.

A true average would be obtained by marking off the entire area in 1-ft squares and taking readings in the center of each square. The average of all readings would be a measure of the horizontal footcandles.  This is a tedious task, so short cuts have been devised that weight a few representative readings instead of averaging many readings.  The Illuminating Engineering Society has published a "Standard Method for Measuring and Reporting Horizontal Footcandles."  To simplify the use of this material it has been subdivided to conform with the lighting systems usually encountered in practice.  The test stations for these installations and the simple mathematics necessary have been clearly outlined in Figs. 7-15 to 7-22.

Experience indicates that the accuracy of this weighted method is within 5% of the accuracy of the "1-foot squares" measurements.  This is quite acceptable for field measurements, particularly in view of the time saved.

It should be clearly recognized that an appraisal of footcandles is no measure of the visual effectiveness of a lighting system.  Footcandles are only a step in the mathematics of design.  Visual effectiveness depends upon brightness and brightness distribution.

# INSTRUCTIONS FOR DETERMINING AVERAGE
# HORIZONTAL FOOTCANDLES

$M$ = number of rows of luminaires.
$N$ = number of luminaires per row.

1. Room with single luminaire (Fig. 7-15):

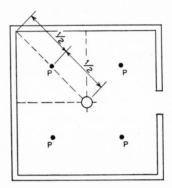

Fig. 7-15.

Horizontal ft-c = $P_{av}$
$P_{av}$ = average of 4 $p$ readings

2. Room with one row of luminaires (Fig. 7-16):

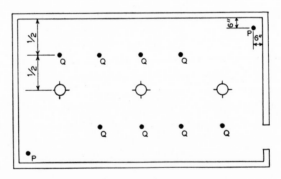

FIG.   7-16.

Horizontal ft-c = $[Q_{av}(N-1)] + P_{av}$
where $Q_{av}$ = average of 8 $q$ readings
$P_{av}$ = average of 2 $p$ readings

*Note:* If there are only 2 luminaires in the row, take 6 $q$ readings instead of 8.

3. Room with two rows of luminaires (Figs. 7-17a and b):

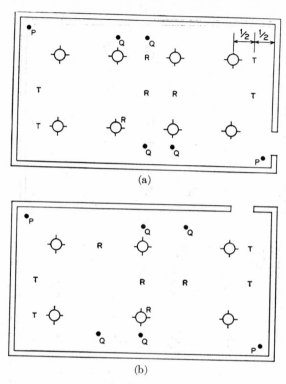

(a)

(b)

Fig. 7-17.

$R_{\text{av}}$ = average of 4 $r$ readings
$Q_{\text{av}}$ = average of 4 $q$ readings
$T_{\text{av}}$ = average of 4 $t$ readings
$P_{\text{av}}$ = average of 2 $p$ readings

$$\text{Horizontal ft-c} = \frac{[R_{\text{av}}(M-1)(N-1)] + [Q_{\text{av}}(N-1)] + [T_{\text{av}}(M-1)] + P_{\text{av}}}{MN}$$

4. Room with three rows of luminaires (Figs. 7-18a and b):

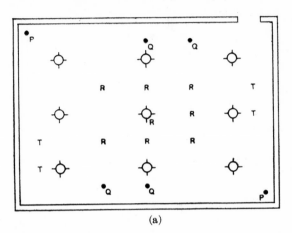

(a)

(b)

Fig. 7-18.

$R_{av}$ = average of 8 $r$ readings
$Q_{av}$ = average of 4 $q$ readings
$T_{av}$ = average of 4 $t$ readings
$P_{av}$ = average of 2 $p$ readings

$$\text{Horizontal ft-c} = \frac{[R_{av}(M-1)(N-1)] + [Q_{av}(N-1)] + [T_{av}(M-1)] + P_{av}}{MN}$$

5. Room with four or more rows of luminaires (Fig. 7-19):

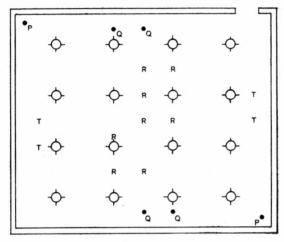

Fig. 7-19.

$$R_{av} = \text{average of 8 } r \text{ readings}$$
$$Q_{av} = \text{average of 4 } q \text{ readings}$$
$$T_{av} = \text{average of 4 } t \text{ readings}$$
$$P_{av} = \text{average of 2 } p \text{ readings}$$

$$\text{Horizontal ft-c} = \frac{[R_{av}(M-1)(N-1)] + [Q_{av}(N-1)] + [T_{av}(M-1)] + P_{av}}{MN}$$

*Note:* If each row has only three luminaires the plan then is the same as (7-18b) above. If there are more than 4 rows of luminaires the plan then becomes similar to some one of those previously described.

6. Room with one continuous row of luminaires (Fig. 7-20):

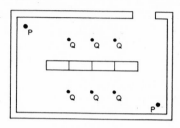

Fig. 7-20.

*Note:* Divide row into 4 equal divisions.

$$Q_{av} = \text{average of 6 } q \text{ readings}$$
$$P_{av} = \text{average of 2 } p \text{ readings}$$

$$\text{Horizontal ft-c} = \frac{[Q_{av}N] + P_{av}}{N + 1}$$

7. Room with two continuous rows of luminaires (Fig. 7-21):

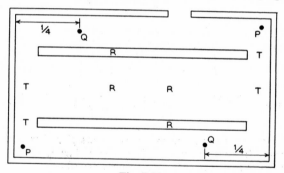

Fig. 7-21.

$$R_{av} = \text{average of 4 } r \text{ readings}$$
$$Q_{av} = \text{average of 2 } q \text{ readings}$$
$$T_{av} = \text{average of 4 } t \text{ readings}$$
$$P_{av} = \text{average of 2 } p \text{ readings}$$

$$\text{Horizontal ft-c} = \frac{[R_{av}N(M - 1)] + [Q_{av}N] + [T_{av}(M - 1)] + P_{av}}{M(N - 1)}$$

8. Room with three continuous rows of luminaires (Fig. 7-22):

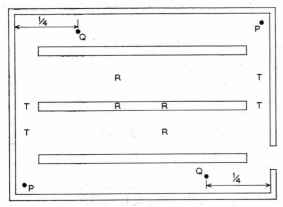

Fig. 7-22.

$$R_{av} = \text{average of 4 } r \text{ readings}$$
$$Q_{av} = \text{average of 2 } q \text{ readings}$$
$$T_{av} = \text{average of 4 } t \text{ readings}$$
$$P_{av} = \text{average of 2 } p \text{ readings}$$

$$\text{Horizontal ft-c} = \frac{[R_{av}N(M-1)] + [Q_{av}N] + [T_{av}(M-1)] + P_{av}}{M(N-1)}$$

*Note:* If a room has more than 3 rows of luminaires, the location of readings then becomes similar to either Fig. 7-21 or Fig. 7-22 above.

## PROBLEMS

**1.** A Luckiesh-Taylor brightness meter indicates 24 ft-L brightness of a piece of magnesium oxide. What are the footcandles at the point of measurement?

**2.** Why should the material whose reflection factor is to be measured by a light meter be at least 1 ft square?

**3.** A block of magnesium carbonate has a brightness of 1,000 ft-L under an overcast sky. A light meter reads 800 at the same time and location. List the possible reasons for the difference.

**4.** Does a barrier-layer cell as normally constructed measure light? Why not? What steps can be taken to convert the response to a true light measure?

**5.** What three precautions are necessary to insure high accuracy of measurement with a Macbeth Illuminometer or a Luckiesh-Taylor brightness meter?

**6.** Why cannot average reflection factors of non-uniform surfaces be measured with either the Luckiesh-Taylor brightness meter or a Macbeth Illuminometer?

# REFERENCES

Buck, G. B., "Correction of Light-sensitive Cells for Angle of Incidence and Spectral Quality of Light," *Trans. Illum. Eng. Soc.*, Vol. 44, page 293, May 1949.

Committee Report on Measuring and Reporting Illumination, *Trans. Illum. Eng. Soc.*, Vol. 38, page 75, February 1943.

Committee Report on Photoelectric Photometers, *Trans. Illum. Eng. Soc.*, Vol. 32, page 379, April 1937.

Dows, C. L., "Illumination Measurements with Light-sensitive Cells," *Trans. Illum. Eng. Soc.*, Vol. 37, page 103, February 1942.

Dows, C. L., and Allen, C. J., "The Light Meter and Its Uses," *Trans. Illum. Eng. Soc.*, Vol. 31, page 675, July 1936.

Fogle, Marlin E., "New Color Corrected Photronic Cells for Accurate Light Measurement," *Trans. Illum. Eng. Soc.*, Vol. 31, page 773, September 1936.

Goodwin, W. N., Jr., "The Photronic Illumination Meter," *Trans. Illum. Eng. Soc.*, Vol. 27, page 825, December 1932.

"Lighting News," *Trans. Illum. Eng. Soc.*, Vol. 32, page 235, March 1937.

Photometers and accessories, Leeds and Northrup Company, *Cat. E-72-1940*.

Taylor, A. H., "Brightness and Brightness Meters," *Trans. Illum. Eng. Soc.*, Vol. 37, page 19, January 1942.

Technical data on Weston Photronic cells, Weston Electrical Instrument Corporation, *Cir. B-20-B-10/44*.

# 8

# CANDLEPOWER DISTRIBUTION CURVES

---

The candlepower distribution curve provides the engineer with data for determining the illuminating characteristics of a light source or a luminaire. From it, the candlepower at various angles, brightness, total luminous flux, and the luminous flux in any zone may be ascertained. Following are some standard definitions which apply.

**Curve of vertical distribution:** "A curve of vertical distribution is a curve, usually polar, representing the luminous intensity of a lamp or luminaire at various angles of elevation in a vertical plane passing through its light center. Unless otherwise specified, a vertical distribution curve is assumed to be an average vertical distribution curve, such as may, in many cases, be obtained by rotating the unit about its axis, and measuring the average intensities at different angles of elevation. It is recommended that in vertical distribution curves, angles of elevation shall be counted from the nadir as zero to the zenith at 180°."

**Symmetrical distribution:** A symmetrical light distribution is one in which the curves of vertical distribution are substantially the same for all planes about the axis.

**Asymmetrical light distribution:** An asymmetrical light distribution is one in which the curves of vertical distribution are not the same for all such planes.

Luminaires for general lighting purposes are almost exclusively symmetrical in candlepower distribution. Show window reflectors and certain refracting lens luminaires emit flux in an asymmetrical pattern.

A candlepower distribution curve represents a kind of diagnosis of illumination characteristics. The methods of testing and the form of presentation of data should be standardized so that comparable data and conclusions can be derived.

## 8.1. Desirable Form for Presentation of Data

The Illuminating Engineering Society has prepared testing specifications for many types of luminaires commonly employed in lighting practice. Unfortunately, not all candlepower distribution curves presented by manufacturers are prepared according to these specifications. Therefore, the user must scrutinize all data carefully. A knowledge of the experience and equipment of the laboratories which prepared the data will be very helpful.

Figure 8-1 represents a candlepower distribution curve which includes all of the necessary data in a standard form. Figures 8-8 and 8-9 are likewise representative of standard curves prepared by a testing laboratory. Note that the names of the laboratory, the luminaire tested, and the manufacturer of the luminaire are included. A description of the test lamp, a dimensioned sketch of the luminaire, and other pertinent data follow. In the example the test does not conform to Illuminating Engineering Society Standards because only one sample was submitted. According to I.E.S. Standards the luminaire would have been selected at random by the laboratory from six representative pieces as passed by the factory inspector. The intent of this random sampling is to insure a selection from average production. Otherwise the test might be made of a specially good sample not representative of what would be found on the open market. Figures 8-10, 8-11, 8-12, 8-13, and 8-14 represent types of candlepower distribution curves prepared in the laboratories of manufacturers.

Luminaires for filament lamps will usually accommodate more than one size of lamp. The candlepower and light flux values shown on the distribution curve are valid only for the lamp shown in the test. However, the efficiency of the luminaire when equipped with lamps of other sizes will be substantially constant if the light center is not changed. The candlepower and zonal flux can be considered to vary in proportion to the lumens rating of the lamp. This is not rigidly true but the error is so small that it may be neglected.

The candlepower at selected angles and the lumens for various

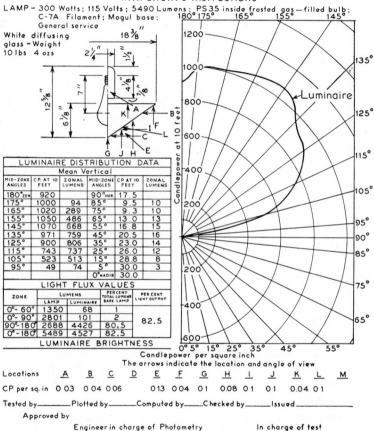

NAME OF TESTING LABORATORY
NAME OF MANUFACTURER
**CANDLEPOWER DISTRIBUTION**

One unit submitted for test   Lamp positioned in accordance
with client's instructions

LAMP – 300 Watts; 115 Volts; 5490 Lumens; PS 35 inside frosted gas–filled bulb;
C-7A Filament; Mogul base;
General service

White diffusing
glass – Weight
10 lbs 4 ozs

**LUMINAIRE DISTRIBUTION DATA**

Mean Vertical

| MID-ZONE ANGLES | CP. AT 10 FEET | ZONAL LUMENS | MID-ZONE ANGLES | CP. AT 10 FEET | ZONAL LUMENS |
|---|---|---|---|---|---|
| 180° ZEN | 920 | | 90° HOR | 17.5 | |
| 175° | 1000 | 94 | 85° | 9.5 | 10 |
| 165° | 1020 | 289 | 75° | 9.3 | 10 |
| 155° | 1050 | 486 | 65° | 13.0 | 13 |
| 145° | 1070 | 668 | 55° | 16.8 | 15 |
| 135° | 971 | 759 | 45° | 20.5 | 16 |
| 125° | 900 | 806 | 35° | 23.0 | 14 |
| 115° | 743 | 737 | 25° | 26.0 | 12 |
| 105° | 523 | 513 | 15° | 28.8 | 8 |
| 95° | 49 | 74 | 5° | 30.0 | 3 |
| | | | 0° NADIR | 30.0 | |

**LIGHT FLUX VALUES**

| ZONE | LUMENS | | PER CENT TOTAL LUMENS BARE LAMP | PER CENT LIGHT OUTPUT |
|---|---|---|---|---|
| | LAMP | LUMINAIRE | | |
| 0°- 60° | 1350 | 68 | 1 | |
| 0°- 90° | 2801 | 101 | 2 | 82.5 |
| 90°-180° | 2688 | 4426 | 80.5 | |
| 0°-180° | 5489 | 4527 | 82.5 | |

**LUMINAIRE BRIGHTNESS**

Candlepower per square inch
The arrows indicate the location and angle of view

| Locations | A | B | C | D | E | F | G | H | I | J | K | L | M |
|---|---|---|---|---|---|---|---|---|---|---|---|---|---|
| CP per sq. in | 0 | 03 | 0 04 | 0 06 | | 0 13 | 0 04 | 0 1 | 0.08 | 0 1 | 0 1 | 0.04 | 0 1 |

Tested by_____Plotted by_____Computed by____Checked by_____Issued_____

Approved by

Engineer in charge of Photometry      In charge of test

Fig. 8-1.   A standard candlepower distribution curve for an incandescent luminaire, as prepared by a testing laboratory.

zones are tabulated.  The method of derivation will be discussed later.

## 8.2. Points of Brightness Measurement

Brightness values are determined for various lettered locations (Fig. 8-2).  These locations represent angles of view that have a bearing upon visual comfort and glare.  The angles are prescribed by the various I.E.S. Standard Test Procedures. Values are determined for those locations which are pertinent to the luminaire.  For example, no measurements need be taken at angles above 90° if the luminaire is of the direct type. The description of the observed angles and the test procedure will be found in the various testing specifications listed in the references at the end of the chapter.

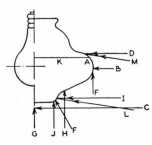

Fig. 8-2. Directions in which brightness measurements are taken on luminaires.

## 8.3. Test Conditions for Filament and Fluorescent Lamps

A candlepower distribution curve of a luminaire is plotted to polar coordinates and may or may not include the candlepower distribution of the lamp itself.  For symmetrical luminaires utilizing filament and mercury-vapor lamps, the luminaire is tested while being rotated.  Thus candlepower values need only be taken in one vertical plane because these values will be averaged by virtue of the rotation.

Fluorescent luminaires must be tested in a stationary position because rotation will produce cooling of the lamp wall and affect the light output in unpredictable ways.  The luminaire is held stationary and the candlepower determined in various planes.  If the luminaire is placed in any position other than the normal position for field service, corrections are applied to compensate for uneven heat distribution.  Ideally, five planes are suggested but generally only three are selected: plane $A-A$ normal to the lamp axis; plane $B-B$ parallel to the lamp axis; plane $C-C$ at 45° to the

lamp axis.   The candlepower at any angle is then the average of
the reading in planes *A–A*, *B–B*, and twice *C–C*.

It will be noted from a study of Fig. 8-1 that the candlepower
was measured at a distance of 10 ft from the luminaire.   The
fluorescent luminaire shown in Fig. 8-8 was measured at a distance
of 25 ft.   These are standard distances for filament lamps and
4-ft fluorescent lamps.

In Chapter 2 it was pointed out that the basic concepts apply to
substantially "point" sources.   It can be shown that a source is
substantially a "point" when the distance of measurement exceeds
five times the maximum dimension of the source.[1]

For concentrated beam searchlights the test distance is around
100 ft because of unusually high candlepower and peculiarities of
beam pattern.

## 8.4. Calculating Light Flux

In Chapter 2 it was stated
that in unit sphere, $F = IA$.
Let us then surround the curve
of candlepower distribution
with an imaginary sphere of 1
ft radius as in Fig. 8-3.   The
area of the zone $Z$ is
$A_Z = 2\pi R^2(\cos \theta_2 - \cos \theta_1)$.
The flux on that zone is
$F = I_{55°}2\pi R^2(\cos 50° - \cos 60°)$.
The usual practice is to assume
zones that are 10° in width.
The surface of the sphere is then

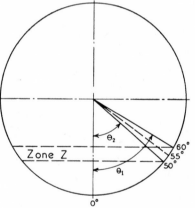

Fig. 8-3.   Zonal areas on unit sphere
for deriving lumen constants.

composed of 18 zones, each zone having a definite area in square feet.
The average candlepower emitted in that zone is assumed to be the
candlepower at its midpoint.   Thus the average candlepower in the
zone from 50° to 60° is the candlepower at 55°.   In some cases
where the change in candlepower over a given zone might not be
linear, or when greater accuracy is desired, the zones are taken at 5°
widths instead of 10°.

---

[1] Moon, Parry, *The Scientific Basis of Illuminating Engineering,* page 183.
New York: McGraw-Hill Book Co., Inc., 1936.

The total flux is then determined by multiplying the area of each of the 18 zones by the mid-zone candlepower and adding the products arithmetically. Obviously these zonal areas are constant, hence they are labeled "zonal constants" or "lumen constants" and placed in convenient tables (see Tables 8-1 and 8-2).

The zones which occur near the horizontal are greater in area

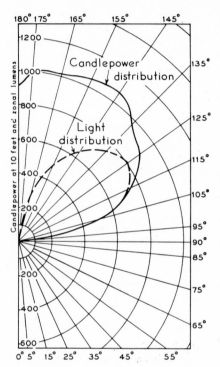

than those which occur near the nadir or zenith. Therefore, candlepower emitted in those zones is more effective in producing flux than candlepower emitted in zones near zenith or nadir. In Fig. 8-4 is shown the curve of *candlepower distribution* taken from Fig. 8-1 and the curve of *light distribution* calculated from those candlepower values. The difference is quite marked. This illustrates the fallacy of calling a candlepower distribution curve a *light distribution* curve. It is apparent that the area or "volume" enclosed by the candlepower distribution curve cannot be taken as an indication of light output.

Fig. 8-4. Curve of light distribution derived from curve of candlepower distribution.

In the case of asymmetric distributions of candlepower as in show window reflectors, the basic theory of determining lumens from candlepower is the same as described above. The presentation of data, however, is in a form better calculated to serve the purposes of the user. The lumen values are plotted on both horizontal and vertical lumen distribution diagrams, from which the designer can transfer directly to his particular problem (see Fig. 8-5). For floodlights and spotlights the candlepower is often plotted on rectangular coordinates as isocandle curves, and the lumens calculated

## TABLE 8-1

### Zonal Factors for Determining Lumens for 10° Zones

| Lower hemisphere | | Upper hemisphere | | Lumen constant |
|---|---|---|---|---|
| Zone | Mid-zone cp | Zone | Mid-zone cp | |
| 0°–10° | 5° | 170°–180° | 175° | 0.0954 |
| 10°–20° | 15° | 160°–170° | 165° | 0.283 |
| 20°–30° | 25° | 150°–160° | 155° | 0.463 |
| 30°–40° | 35° | 140°–150° | 145° | 0.628 |
| 40°–50° | 45° | 130°–140° | 135° | 0.774 |
| 50°–60° | 55° | 120°–130° | 125° | 0.897 |
| 60°–70° | 65° | 110°–120° | 115° | 0.992 |
| 70°–80° | 75° | 100°–110° | 105° | 1.058 |
| 80°–90° | 85° | 90°–100° | 95° | 1.091 |

## TABLE 8-2

### Zonal Factors for Determining Lumens for 5° Zones

| Lower hemisphere | | Upper hemisphere | | Lumen constant |
|---|---|---|---|---|
| Zone | Mid-zone cp | Zone | Mid-zone cp | |
| 0°–5° | 2.5° | 175°–180° | 177.5° | 0.0239 |
| 5°–10° | 7.5° | 170°–175° | 172.5° | 0.0715 |
| 10°–15° | 12.5° | 165°–170° | 167.5° | 0.118 |
| 15°–20° | 17.5° | 160°–165° | 162.5° | 0.165 |
| 20°–25° | 22.5° | 155°–160° | 157.5° | 0.210 |
| 25°–30° | 27.5° | 150°–155° | 152.5° | 0.253 |
| 30°–35° | 32.5° | 145°–150° | 147.5° | 0.294 |
| 35°–40° | 37.5° | 140°–145° | 142.5° | 0.334 |
| 40°–45° | 42.5° | 135°–140° | 137.5° | 0.370 |
| 45°–50° | 47.5° | 130°–135° | 132.5° | 0.404 |
| 50°–55° | 52.5° | 125°–130° | 127.5° | 0.435 |
| 55°–60° | 57.5° | 120°–125° | 122.5° | 0.462 |
| 60°–65° | 62.5° | 115°–120° | 117.5° | 0.486 |
| 65°–70° | 67.5° | 110°–115° | 112.5° | 0.506 |
| 70°–75° | 72.5° | 105°–110° | 107.5° | 0.523 |
| 75°–80° | 77.5° | 100°–105° | 102.5° | 0.535 |
| 80°–85° | 82.5° | 95°–100° | 97.5° | 0.543 |
| 85°–90° | 87.5° | 90°–95° | 92.5° | 0.548 |

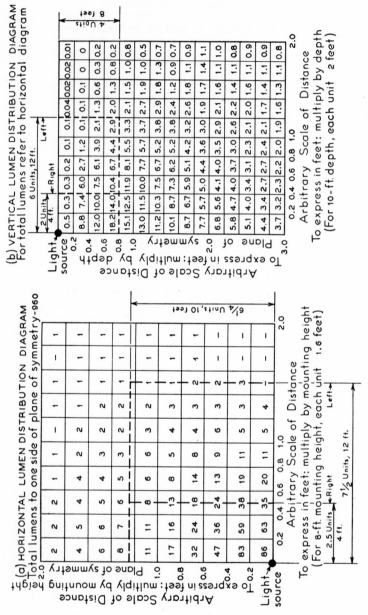

Fig. 8-5. Lumen distribution diagram for an asymmetric show-window reflector.

NAME OF TESTING LABORATORY
NAME OF MANUFACTURER
## CANDLEPOWER DISTRIBUTION

REFLECTOR – Parabolic, matte Alzak aluminum.　Diameter 17 ½ inches
COVER CLASS – Convex colorless glass, 17 ½ inches effective diameter
LAMP – 1500 Watts; 115 Volts; 33000 Lumens;
PS 52 clear gas-filled bulb; C-7A
filament; Mogul base; General service.
Filament dimensions 25.8 mm high
x 34.9 mm wide. Light center length
9 ½ inches

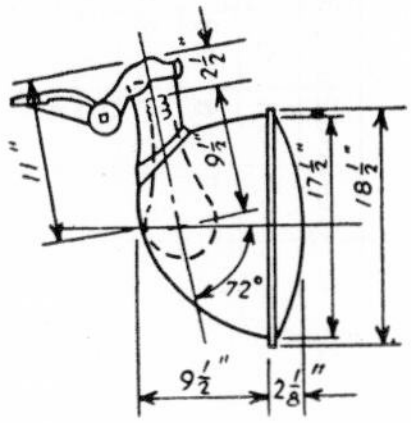

### PROJECTOR DATA

| | |
|---|---|
| Total Lumens | – 25800 |
| Total Efficiency | –  78 % |
| Beam Lumens | – 24908 |
| Beam Efficiency | –  75.5 % |
| Beam Spread Vertical | –  96° |
| Beam Spread Horizontal | –  104° |
| Maximum Beam Candlepower | – 34500 |

| AVERAGE ISOCANDLE CURVES | AVERAGE LUMEN DISTRIBUT'N | | | | | | | Total |
|---|---|---|---|---|---|---|---|---|
| 48° | 79 | 75 | 69 | 47 | | | | 270 |
| 40° | 157 | 141 | 118 | 88 | 59 | | | 563 |
| 32° | 259 | 231 | 187 | 130 | 86 | 43 | 22 | 958 |
| 24° | 417 | 366 | 272 | 185 | 109 | 65 | 30 | 1444 |
| 16° | 592 | 500 | 362 | 223 | 133 | 76 | 35 | 1921 |
| 0° | 640 | 546 | 395 | 245 | 142 | 80 | 35 | 2083 |
| 8° | 539 | 464 | 365 | 223 | 137 | 82 | 35 | 1845 |
| 16° | 386 | 340 | 265 | 192 | 113 | 75 | 23 | 1394 |
| 24° | 258 | 229 | 189 | 139 | 93 | 63 | 17 | 988 |
| 32° | 164 | 151 | 128 | 99 | 71 | 46 | | 659 |
| 40° | 102 | 98 | 87 | 70 | 49 | | | 406 |
| 48° | 68 | 67 | 64 | 47 | | | | 246 |
| Total | 3661 | 3208 | 2501 | 1688 | 992 | 530 | 197 | GRAND TOTAL 12777 |

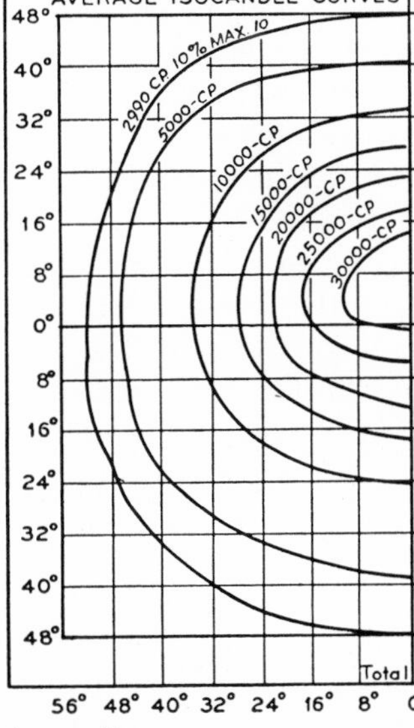

56° 48° 40° 32° 24° 16° 8° 0° 8° 16° 24° 32° 40° 48° 56°

(Curve labels: 2000-CP 10% MAX 10, 5000-CP, 10000-CP, 15000-CP, 20000-CP, 25000-CP, 30000-CP)

Approved by
　　　　Engineer, Photometric Dept.　　　　　In charge of test
Plotted by　　　　　　　　Checked by

Fig. 8-6.　Isocandle curves and lumen distribution diagram for a floodlight.

for any desired subtended areas. This data is easily used by the designer (see Fig. 8-6).

## 8.5. Simple Flux Calculations

There are times when the engineer is confronted with a candle-power distribution curve drawn to some scale but showing no lumen values. If a table of zonal constants is not at hand, a fairly close

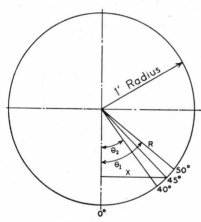

Fig. 8-7. Derivation of simple method of flux computation from candlepower distribution curve.

determination of flux can be made by the following method. Refer to Fig. 8-1. The candlepower scale is 560 candles to the inch. To find the lumens in the 120° to 130° zone, measure in inches the horizontal distance from the vertical to the midpoint of the 120° to 130° zone (125°) where it lies on the candlepower curve. This is 1.31 in. Multiply this value by the candlepower scale of 560 cp to the inch, and again by 1.10; the result is the approximate lumens in this zone, or 806. From the calculated data given on the test report the lumens are 806; thus the approximate method is of high accuracy if careful measurements are taken.

To find the lumens in a group of adjacent zones, measure the horizontal distances to each mid-point, add, multiply by the scale and 1.10. The result will be the total lumens in that group of zones. As an example, refer to Fig. 8-10. It is desired to know the lumens in the 0° to 40° zone. The candlepower scale is 760 to the inch. The horizontal distance to the mid-point of the 0° to 10° zone is 0.18 in.; to the mid-point of the 10° to 20° zone, 0.48 in.; to the mid-point of the 20° to 30° zone, 0.75 in.; to the midpoint of the 30° to 40° zone, 1.0 in. The total is 2.41 in. This, multiplied by the scale of 760 cp to the inch and the constant of 1.1, gives us 2,020 lm in the 0° to 40° zone.

This factor of 1.1 is not empirical but of mathematical derivation

NAME OF TESTING LABORATORY
NAME OF MANUFACTURER
## CANDLEPOWER DISTRIBUTION

LAMPS – Four 40 Watts; 118 Volts; 2300 Lumens; T-12 White fluorescent
UNIT   – Synthetic enamelled metal housing, reflectance 0.84; translucent plastic sides
TEST  – Candlepower distribution in three vertical planes intersecting in the center of the unit,
A–A normal, B–B parallel and C–C 45° to the tube

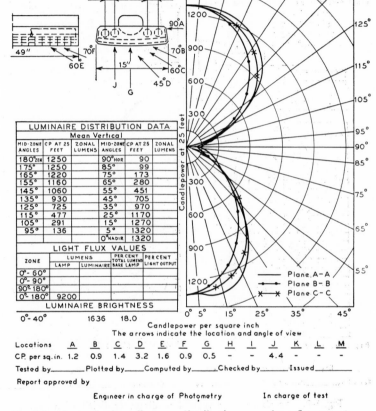

| LUMINAIRE DISTRIBUTION DATA | | | | | |
|---|---|---|---|---|---|
| Mean Vertical | | | | | |
| MID-ZONE ANGLES | CP AT 25 FEET | ZONAL LUMENS | MID-ZONE ANGLES | CP AT 25 FEET | ZONAL LUMENS |
| 180°ZEN | 1250 | | 90°HOR | 90 | |
| 175° | 1250 | | 85° | 99 | |
| 165° | 1220 | | 75° | 173 | |
| 155° | 1160 | | 65° | 280 | |
| 145° | 1060 | | 55° | 451 | |
| 135° | 930 | | 45° | 705 | |
| 125° | 725 | | 35° | 970 | |
| 115° | 477 | | 25° | 1170 | |
| 105° | 291 | | 15° | 1270 | |
| 95° | 136 | | 5° | 1320 | |
| | | | 0°NADIR | 1320 | |

| LIGHT FLUX VALUES | | | | |
|---|---|---|---|---|
| ZONE | LUMENS | | PER CENT TOTAL LUMENS BARE LAMP | PER CENT LIGHT OUTPUT |
| | LAMP | LUMINAIRE | | |
| 0°- 60° | | | | |
| 0°- 90° | | | | |
| 90°-180° | | | | |
| 0°-180° | 9200 | | | |

| LUMINAIRE BRIGHTNESS | | |
|---|---|---|
| 0°- 40° | 1636 | 18.0 |

Candlepower per square inch
The arrows indicate the location and angle of view

| Locations | A | B | C | D | E | F | G | H | I | J | K | L | M |
|---|---|---|---|---|---|---|---|---|---|---|---|---|---|
| C.P. per sq.in. | 1.2 | 0.9 | 1.4 | 3.2 | 1.6 | 0.9 | 0.5 | – | – | 4.4 | – | – | – |

Tested by_____ Plotted by____Computed by_____Checked by_____ Issued_____

Report approved by

Engineer in charge of Photometry       In charge of test

Fig. 8.8.   A standard candlepower distribution curve for a fluorescent luminaire.   Lumen values are omitted here for teaching purposes.

(Fig. 8-7).   Consider the zone 40° to 50°.   The area of unit sphere subtended by this zone is as follows:

$$\text{Area} = 2\pi r^2(\cos \theta_2 - \cos \theta_1) = 2\pi(\cos 40° - \cos 50°)$$
$$= 2\pi(.7660 - .6427) = 0.774 \text{ sq ft}$$

If we assume the candlepower emitted toward the mid-zone 45° to be unity, then the flux on this zone is 0.774 lumens.

NAME OF TESTING LABORATORY
NAME OF MANUFACTURER
## CANDLEPOWER DISTRIBUTION

LAMPS — Two 40 Watts ; 118 Volts ; 2100 Lumens ; T–12 Fluorescent.
UNIT  —  Synthetic enamel reflector, reflection factor 0.82 , white opal plastic cover
TEST  —  Candlepower distribution in three planes intersecting in the center of the unit,
A–A normal, B–B parallel,
and C–C 45° to the tubes.

Light output in per cent of bare lamps

0°- 60°  -  5.0
0°- 90°  -  7.5
90°-180°  - 63.5
0°-180°  - 71.0

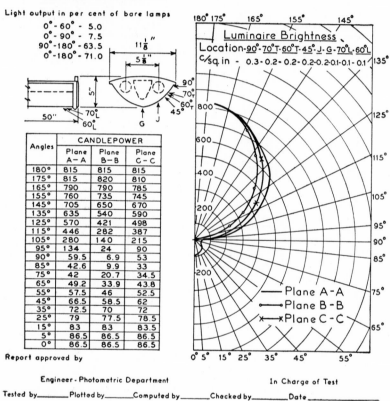

| Angles | CANDLEPOWER | | |
|---|---|---|---|
| | Plane A–A | Plane B–B | Plane C–C |
| 180° | 815 | 815 | 815 |
| 175° | 815 | 820 | 810 |
| 165° | 790 | 790 | 785 |
| 155° | 760 | 735 | 745 |
| 145° | 705 | 650 | 670 |
| 135° | 635 | 540 | 590 |
| 125° | 570 | 421 | 498 |
| 115° | 446 | 282 | 387 |
| 105° | 280 | 140 | 215 |
| 95° | 134 | 24 | 90 |
| 90° | 59.5 | 6.9 | 53 |
| 85° | 42.6 | 9.9 | 33 |
| 75° | 42 | 20.7 | 34.5 |
| 65° | 49.2 | 33.9 | 43.8 |
| 55° | 57.5 | 46 | 52.5 |
| 45° | 66.5 | 58.5 | 62 |
| 35° | 72.5 | 70 | 72 |
| 25° | 79 | 77.5 | 78.5 |
| 15° | 83 | 83 | 83.5 |
| 5° | 86.5 | 86.5 | 86.5 |
| 0° | 86.5 | 86.5 | 86.5 |

Report approved by

Engineer - Photometric Department                    In Charge of Test

Tested by_____Plotted by_____Computed by_____Checked by_____Date_____

**Fig. 8-9.**   An abbreviated type of candlepower distribution curve.

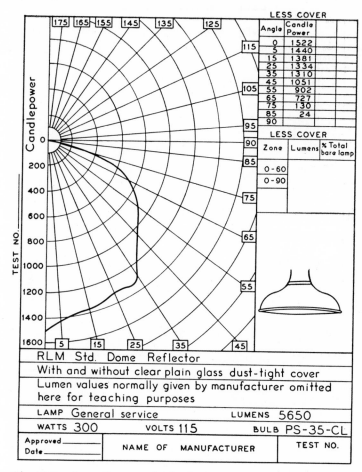

Fig. 8-10. A candlepower distribution curve developed by a manufacturer.

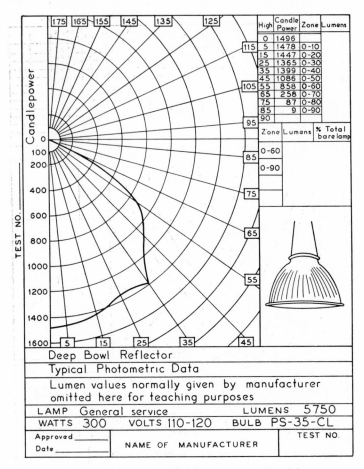

| High | Candle Power | Zone | Lumens |
|------|------|------|------|
| 0 | 1496 | | |
| 5 | 1478 | 0-10 | |
| 15 | 1447 | 0-20 | |
| 25 | 1365 | 0-30 | |
| 35 | 1399 | 0-40 | |
| 45 | 1086 | 0-50 | |
| 55 | 858 | 0-60 | |
| 65 | 258 | 0-70 | |
| 75 | 87 | 0-80 | |
| 85 | 9 | 0-90 | |
| 90 | | | |

| Zone | Lumens | % Total bare lamp |
|------|------|------|
| 0-60 | | |
| 0-90 | | |

Deep Bowl Reflector

Typical Photometric Data

Lumen values normally given by manufacturer omitted here for teaching purposes

| LAMP General service | LUMENS 5750 |
|------|------|
| WATTS 300   VOLTS 110-120 | BULB PS-35-CL |

| Approved_____ Date_____ | NAME OF MANUFACTURER | TEST NO. |

Fig. 8-11.   A candlepower distribution curve developed by a manufacturer.

The horizontal distance $X$ is

$$X = R \sin \theta$$

When $R = 1$ and $\theta = 45°$, then $X = 0.707$. It has been stated that $F = KX$. Therefore

$$0.774 = 0.707K \qquad \text{and} \qquad K = 1.1$$

The constant 1.10 is quite accurate for all engineering computation carried out with the slide rule.

## 8.6. Effect of Lamp Size on Candlepower

A particular type of incandescent lamp luminaire is usually designed to accommodate a wide range of lamp sizes. The shape of

NAME OF MANUFACTURER

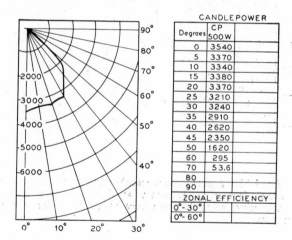

| Degrees | CP 500 W | |
|---|---|---|
| 0 | 3540 | |
| 5 | 3370 | |
| 10 | 3340 | |
| 15 | 3380 | |
| 20 | 3370 | |
| 25 | 3210 | |
| 30 | 3240 | |
| 35 | 2910 | |
| 40 | 2620 | |
| 45 | 2350 | |
| 50 | 1620 | |
| 60 | 295 | |
| 70 | 53.6 | |
| 80 | | |
| 90 | | |
| ZONAL EFFICIENCY | | |
| 0°-30° | | |
| 0°-60° | | |

Fig. 8-12. A candlepower distribution curve such as found in a catalogue of luminaires. The zonal efficiency factors have been omitted for teaching purposes.

the candlepower distribution curve is essentially the same for all lamp sizes. Therefore the value of candlepower at any angle can

NAME OF MANUFACTURER

Diffusing luminaire "D___" and Semi-indirect luminaire "J___" both tested with 500 watt clear lamp, 10050 lumens

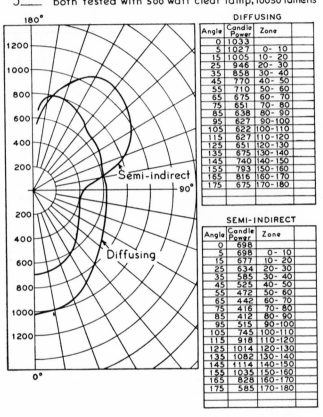

DIFFUSING

| Angle | Candle Power | Zone |  |
|---|---|---|---|
| 0 | 1033 | | |
| 5 | 1027 | 0- 10 | |
| 15 | 1005 | 10- 20 | |
| 25 | 946 | 20- 30 | |
| 35 | 858 | 30- 40 | |
| 45 | 770 | 40- 50 | |
| 55 | 710 | 50- 60 | |
| 65 | 675 | 60- 70 | |
| 75 | 651 | 70- 80 | |
| 85 | 638 | 80- 90 | |
| 95 | 627 | 90-100 | |
| 105 | 622 | 100-110 | |
| 115 | 627 | 110-120 | |
| 125 | 651 | 120-130 | |
| 135 | 675 | 130-140 | |
| 145 | 740 | 140-150 | |
| 155 | 793 | 150-160 | |
| 165 | 816 | 160-170 | |
| 175 | 675 | 170-180 | |

SEMI-INDIRECT

| Angle | Candle Power | Zone |  |
|---|---|---|---|
| 0 | 698 | | |
| 5 | 698 | 0- 10 | |
| 15 | 677 | 10- 20 | |
| 25 | 634 | 20- 30 | |
| 35 | 585 | 30- 40 | |
| 45 | 525 | 40- 50 | |
| 55 | 472 | 50- 60 | |
| 65 | 442 | 60- 70 | |
| 75 | 416 | 70- 80 | |
| 85 | 412 | 80- 90 | |
| 95 | 515 | 90-100 | |
| 105 | 745 | 100-110 | |
| 115 | 918 | 110-120 | |
| 125 | 1014 | 120-130 | |
| 135 | 1082 | 130-140 | |
| 145 | 1114 | 140-150 | |
| 155 | 1035 | 150-160 | |
| 165 | 828 | 160-170 | |
| 175 | 585 | 170-180 | |

Fig. 8-13.  A candlepower distribution curve such as found in a manufacturer's catalogue or available in separate sheets. Lumen values normally given have been omitted for teaching purposes.

be considered as proportional to the lamp output in lumens.  If the engineer has at hand a candlepower distribution curve such as shown in Fig. 8-10, obtained with a 300-watt lamp producing 5,650 initial lumens, the candlepower values for the same luminaire with a 500-watt lamp producing 9,950 initial lumens will be 9,950/5,650 or 1.76 times as great.

NAME OF MANUFACTURER

Tests on Luminaire — Hanger Mounted
and close Ceiling Mounted: four 48" 40 watt white lamps

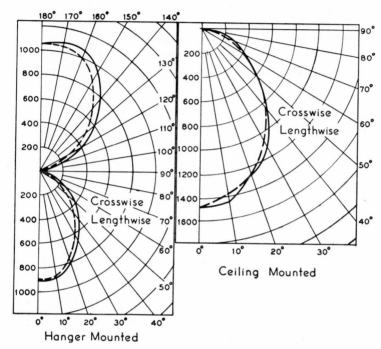

Hanger Mounted

Fig. 8-14. Type of candlepower distribution curves sometimes issued by manufacturers. No candlepower or lumen values are listed; they must be determined by the user. The efficiency, normally stated, is omitted here for teaching purposes.

## PROBLEMS

1. Using the lumen constants for 10° zones, calculate the output in lumens for the luminaires analyzed in Fig. 8-13. What is the efficiency of each? What types are they (I.C.I. classification)?

2. Refer to Fig. 8-12. Calculate the total lumens output and efficiency. What type of luminaire is it? Calculate the ratio of lumens in the 0° to 40° zone to lumens in the 0° to 90° zone.

3. Refer to the distribution curve in Fig. 8-10. Calculate the total lumens output and the efficiency. What type of luminaire is it?

**4.** Refer to the distribution curve in Fig. 8-11. Calculate the total lumens output and the efficiency. If the luminaire was equipped with a 750-watt lamp, plot the candlepower distribution.

**5.** Refer to Fig. 8-14. Calculate the total lumens output and efficiency for each luminaire.

**6.** Calculate the total lumens output and efficiency of the luminaire whose candlepower distribution is shown in Fig. 8-8. What type is it?

**7.** Calculate the total lumens output and efficiency of the luminaire shown in Fig. 8-9. What type is it?

**8.** A candlepower distribution curve of a luminaire discloses the following data (test lamp is 500 watts):

| Angle | cp | Angle | cp |
|-------|------|-------|-----|
| 5° | 1190 | 90° | 156 |
| 15° | 1157 | 95° | 224 |
| 25° | 1068 | 105° | 345 |
| 35° | 920 | 115° | 465 |
| 45° | 735 | 125° | 537 |
| 55° | 527 | 135° | 591 |
| 65° | 334 | 145° | 668 |
| 75° | 224 | 155° | 761 |
| 85° | 162 | 165° | 795 |

(a) What is its efficiency?   (b) What type (I.C.I.) is it?

# REFERENCES

"Guide for Testing Street Lighting Luminaires," *Trans. Illum. Eng. Soc.*, Vol. 43, no. 9, November 1948.

"I. E. S. Guides to Testing Procedures," *Trans. Illum. Eng. Soc.*, Vol. 44, no. 7, July 1949.

"Specifications for Testing Asymmetric Show Window Reflectors," *Trans. Illum. Eng. Soc.*, Vol. 28, no. 6, June 1933.

"Specifications for Testing Diffusing Type Enclosing Glassware," *Trans. Illum. Eng. Soc.*, Vol. 28, no. 6, June 1933.

"Specifications for Testing Semi-indirect and Indirect Luminaires," *Trans. Illum. Eng. Soc.*, Vol. 32, no. 8, September 1937.

"Testing Procedure for Narrow Beam Enclosed Projectors," *Trans. Illum. Eng. Soc.*, Vol. 28, no. 6, June 1933.

# 9

# COEFFICIENTS OF UTILIZATION

---

The basic formula for the calculation of average illumination on a horizontal plane by the lumen method (sometimes called "flux-of-light method") is

$$E = \frac{F_g \times \text{C.U.} \times \text{D.F.}}{A}$$

where $E$ = illumination in footcandles on the horizontal plane,
$F_g$ = luminous flux generated by light sources,
C.U. = coefficient of utilization,
D.F. = depreciation factor,
$A$ = floor area of lighted space.

The coefficient of utilization is defined as "the total flux received by a plane divided by the total flux from the lamps illuminating it." This ratio comprises a chain involving the efficiency and distribution of flux from a luminaire, the shape of the lighted space, and the reflection factors of the various boundary surfaces in the room. All of these factors are interrelated. Let us first consider the room shape.

## 9.1. Room Shape

A room which is wide in relation to height will allow more light flux to reach a horizontal plane with a minimum of intermediary reflections than one which is narrow. If the light flux is directed first to the ceiling, as in Fig. 9-1a, more of it reaches the horizontal plane without reflection from the walls if the room is wide. In a narrow room, Fig. 9-1b, much of the flux will first strike the walls before reaching the work plane.

When the light flux is directed first to the horizontal plane the same considerations hold true, as can be seen from Figs. 9-2a and b.

Light flux emitted in a horizontal direction is toward the walls and must be reflected before reaching the horizontal plane. Room

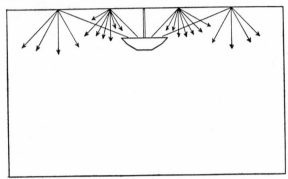

Less total light is absorbed by walls
in large room

(a)

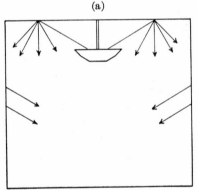

Walls in small room absorb
more of total light

(b)

Fig. 9-1. (a) and (b) Room shape affects loss of light
from surfaces.

width in relation to room height has little effect upon the utilization of this horizontal flux.

It is apparent that rooms in which the ceiling is high in relation to width will utilize light flux less efficiently than rooms whose ceiling height is low compared to the width. It is also apparent that in rooms of any proportion the reflection factor of the various surfaces affects the utilization of light flux.

The factor of room shape is integrated into an expression, Room Index (symbol RI).   The height of the light source above the work

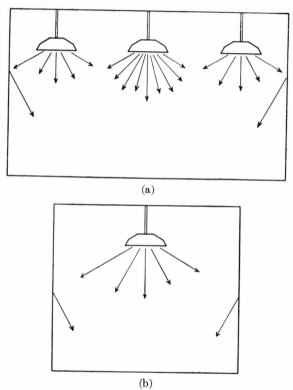

(a)

(b)

Fig. 9-2.   (a) and (b) Direct light suffers less interference in passage to work plane.

plane is an important dimension, so two formulas are in use.   For direct, semi-direct, and general diffuse light distributions,

$$\text{RI} = \frac{LW}{H_s(L + W)} \tag{9-1}$$

where $L$ = room length,
$W$ = room width,
$H_s$ = height of luminaire above work plane.

## TABLE 9-1

### Room Index

| | Ceiling Height—Feet | | | | | | | | | | |
|---|---|---|---|---|---|---|---|---|---|---|---|
| Semi-indirect and indirect lighting | 9 to 9½ | 10 to 11½ | 12 to 13½ | 14 to 16½ | 17 to 20 | 21 to 24 | 25 to 30 | 31 to 36 | 37 to 50 | | |
| | Mounting Height Above Floor—Feet | | | | | | | | | | |
| Direct, semi-direct, general diffuse, and direct-indirect lighting | 7 to 7½ | 8 to 8½ | 9 to 9½ | 10 to 11½ | 12 to 13½ | 14 to 16½ | 17 to 20 | 21 to 24 | 25 to 30 | 31 to 36 | 37 to 50 |
| Room width, ft / Room length, ft | Room Index | | | | | | | | | | |

**Room width 9 (8½–9)**

| Room length, ft | | | | | | | | | | | |
|---|---|---|---|---|---|---|---|---|---|---|---|
| 8–10 | H | I | J | J | | | | | | | |
| 10–14 | H | I | J | | | | | | | | |
| 14–20 | G | H | I | J | J | | | | | | |
| 20–30 | G | G | H | I | J | J | | | | | |
| 30–42 | F | G | H | I | J | J | J | | | | |
| 42–up | E | F | G | H | I | J | J | | | | |

**Room width 10 (9½–10½)**

| Room length, ft | | | | | | | | | | | |
|---|---|---|---|---|---|---|---|---|---|---|---|
| 10–14 | G | H | I | J | J | | | | | | |
| 14–20 | G | H | I | J | J | J | | | | | |
| 20–30 | F | G | H | I | J | J | | | | | |
| 30–42 | F | G | G | H | I | J | J | | | | |
| 42–60 | E | F | G | H | I | J | J | | | | |
| 60–up | E | F | F | H | H | I | J | | | | |

**Room width 12 (11–12½)**

| Room length, ft | | | | | | | | | | | |
|---|---|---|---|---|---|---|---|---|---|---|---|
| 11–14 | G | H | I | I | J | J | | | | | |
| 14–20 | F | G | H | I | J | J | | | | | |
| 20–30 | F | G | G | H | I | J | J | | | | |
| 30–42 | E | F | G | H | I | J | J | | | | |
| 42–60 | E | F | F | G | H | I | J | | | | |
| 60–up | E | E | F | G | H | I | J | | | | |

**Room width 14 (13–15½)**

| Room length, ft | | | | | | | | | | | |
|---|---|---|---|---|---|---|---|---|---|---|---|
| 13–20 | F | G | H | H | I | J | J | | | | |
| 20–30 | E | F | G | H | I | J | J | | | | |
| 30–42 | E | F | F | G | H | I | J | J | | | |
| 42–60 | E | E | F | F | H | I | J | J | J | | |
| 60–90 | D | E | E | F | G | H | J | J | J | | |
| 90–up | D | E | E | F | F | G | I | J | J | | |

**Room width 17 (16–18½)**

| Room length, ft | | | | | | | | | | | |
|---|---|---|---|---|---|---|---|---|---|---|---|
| 16–20 | E | F | G | H | I | J | J | | | | |
| 20–30 | E | F | F | G | H | I | J | | | | |
| 30–42 | D | E | F | G | H | H | J | J | J | | |
| 42–60 | D | E | E | F | G | G | I | J | J | J | |
| 60–110 | D | E | E | F | G | G | I | J | J | J | |
| 110–up | C | D | E | E | F | G | H | I | J | J | |

**Room width 20 (19–21½)**

| Room length, ft | | | | | | | | | | | |
|---|---|---|---|---|---|---|---|---|---|---|---|
| 19–30 | D | E | F | G | H | I | J | J | | | |
| 30–42 | D | E | E | F | G | H | I | J | J | | |
| 42–60 | D | D | E | E | F | G | I | J | J | J | |
| 60–90 | C | D | E | E | F | G | H | J | J | J | |
| 90–140 | C | D | D | E | F | F | H | I | J | J | J |
| 140–up | C | D | D | E | F | F | H | H | I | J | J |

**Room width 24 (22–26)**

| Room length, ft | | | | | | | | | | | |
|---|---|---|---|---|---|---|---|---|---|---|---|
| 22–30 | D | E | E | F | G | H | I | J | J | | |
| 30–42 | C | D | E | F | G | G | I | J | J | | |
| 42–60 | C | D | D | E | F | G | H | I | J | J | |
| 60–90 | C | D | D | E | F | F | H | I | J | J | J |
| 90–140 | C | C | D | E | E | F | G | H | I | J | J |
| 140–up | C | C | D | E | E | F | G | H | I | I | J |

## TABLE 9-1. (Continued)

| | | Ceiling Height—Feet | | | | | | | | | | |
|---|---|---|---|---|---|---|---|---|---|---|---|---|
| Semi-indirect and indirect lighting | | 9 to 9½ | 10 to 11½ | 12 to 13½ | 14 to 16½ | 17 to 20 | 21 to 24 | 25 to 30 | 31 to 36 | 37 to 50 | | |
| | | Mounting Height Above Floor—Feet | | | | | | | | | | |
| Direct, semi-direct, general diffuse, and direct-indirect lighting | | 7 to 7½ | 8 to 8½ | 9 to 9½ | 10 to 11½ | 12 to 13½ | 14 to 16½ | 17 to 20 | 21 to 24 | 25 to 30 | 31 to 36 | 37 to 50 |
| Room width, ft | Room length, ft | Room Index | | | | | | | | | | |
| 30 (27–33) | 27–42 | C | D | D | E | F | G | H | I | J | J | |
| | 42–60 | C | C | D | D | F | F | H | H | I | J | |
| | 60–90 | B | C | C | D | E | F | G | H | I | J | J |
| | 90–140 | B | C | C | D | E | E | F | G | H | I | J |
| | 140–180 | B | C | C | D | E | E | F | G | H | I | J |
| | 180–up | B | C | C | D | E | E | F | G | H | I | J |
| 36 (34–39) | 34–42 | B | C | D | E | F | F | H | I | I | J | |
| | 42–60 | B | C | C | D | E | F | G | H | I | J | J |
| | 60–90 | A | C | C | C | E | E | F | H | H | J | J |
| | 90–140 | A | B | C | C | D | E | F | G | H | I | J |
| | 140–200 | A | B | C | C | D | E | F | F | G | H | I |
| | 200–up | A | B | C | C | D | E | F | F | G | H | I |
| 42 (40–45) | 40–60 | A | B | C | C | E | F | G | H | I | I | J |
| | 60–90 | A | B | B | C | D | E | F | G | H | I | J |
| | 90–140 | A | B | B | C | D | D | E | F | G | H | J |
| | 140–200 | A | A | B | C | D | D | E | F | G | H | I |
| | 200–up | A | A | B | C | D | D | E | F | F | G | I |
| 50 (46–55) | 46–60 | A | A | B | C | D | E | F | G | H | I | J |
| | 60–90 | A | A | B | C | C | D | F | F | G | H | J |
| | 90–140 | A | A | A | C | C | D | E | F | F | G | I |
| | 140–200 | A | A | A | C | C | D | E | E | F | G | I |
| | 200–up | A | A | A | C | C | D | E | E | F | G | H |
| 60 (56–67) | 56–90 | A | A | A | B | C | D | E | F | G | H | I |
| | 90–140 | A | A | A | B | C | C | D | E | F | G | H |
| | 140–200 | A | A | A | B | C | C | D | E | E | F | H |
| | 200–up | A | A | A | B | C | C | D | E | E | F | H |
| 75 (68–90) | 68–90 | A | A | A | A | B | C | D | E | F | G | I |
| | 90–140 | A | A | A | A | B | C | D | E | F | F | H |
| | 140–200 | A | A | A | A | B | B | C | D | E | F | G |
| | 200–up | A | A | A | A | B | B | C | D | E | F | G |
| 90 or more | 90–140 | A | A | A | A | A | B | C | D | E | F | G |
| | 140–200 | A | A | A | A | A | B | C | D | E | F | G |
| | 200–up | A | A | A | A | A | B | C | C | D | E | F |

### Designation of Room Index

| Letter | Number | Letter | Number |
|---|---|---|---|
| J | 0.6 | E | 2.0 |
| I | 0.8 | D | 2.5 |
| H | 1.0 | C | 3.0 |
| G | 1.25 | B | 4.0 |
| F | 1.50 | A | 5.0 |

For indirect and semi-indirect light distributions,

$$RI = \frac{3LW}{2H_c(L + W)}$$  (9-2)

where          $H_c$ = height of ceiling above work plane.

Values of room index for most of the interiors encountered in lighting practice have been computed and placed in tabular form (Table 9-1).  Instead of number values, letter designations have been used.  A work plane $2\frac{1}{2}$ ft above the floor has been assumed. These assumptions introduce error when precise values are desired, but for rough work the tables are satisfactory.

Experimental data discloses that there is no significant change in light utilization for rooms having an index greater than 5.0.

Rooms of dimensions greater than those included in Table 9-1 can be reduced to equivalent smaller rooms within the scope of the table.  Divide each of the principle dimensions by a number which brings them to values included in the table.  For example, consider a factory 250 by 600 ft with ceiling 45 ft above the work plane. Divide the length, width, and height above work plane by 5.  This then gives us a room of the same proportions, but 50 by 120 by 9 ft. The tables give heights above the floor, so the distance from floor to work plane must be added to the distance from work plane to light source before entering the table.  If the work plane is 3 ft above the floor, the equivalent room for tabular use is 50 by 120 by 12 ft.

### 9.2. Effect of Light Distribution from Luminaires

Flux which goes first to the ceiling must be reflected at least once before it reaches a horizontal work plane.  Flux which is directed horizontally may be reflected many times before reaching the work plane.  Flux which is directed downward will suffer less interference if it is concentrated in a narrow cone than if it is broadly distributed.

Therefore, the flux distribution from any luminaire is divided into three components; direct, indirect, and horizontal.  The direct flux is in turn subdivided into six classes.  By experiment, the percentage of each of these flux components which is utilized in a room of given index and various surface reflectances has been determined and put in tabular form (Table 9-2). The subdivisions of the direct flux, known as flux ratios, are shown in Table 9-3. The relationships in the tables are linear so that interpolation can be made for values of room index falling between those listed.

## 9.3. Analyzing the Distribution Curve

The solid line in Fig. 9-3 represents the actual candlepower distribution of a typical general diffuse luminaire. The tabulated

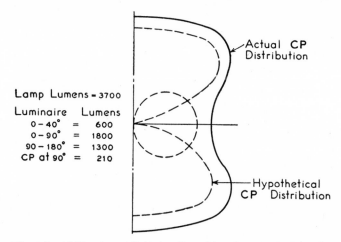

Lamp Lumens = 3700

| Luminaire | Lumens |
|---|---|
| 0 – 40° | = 600 |
| 0 – 90° | = 1800 |
| 90 – 180° | = 1300 |
| CP at 90° | = 210 |

Fig. 9-3.  Utilization of light is affected by three basic light flux distributions.

values give the flux in the various zones. The dotted lines represent the separation into three hypothetical luminaires having direct, indirect, and horizontal flux distributions. The horizontal distribution is computed first. This is assumed to be toroidal. The maximum candlepower of the torus is taken as the 90° candlepower of the luminaire. In Chapter 2 it was shown that the flux in a toroidal distribution is

$$F = \pi^2 I_N$$

Inasmuch as the candlepower at 90° is 210,

$$F = \pi^2 \times 120, \qquad F = 10 \times 210, \qquad F = 2100 \text{ lm}$$

## TABLE 9-2

### Zonal Constants ($K_z$) for Direct, Indirect, and Horizontal Flux*

**Ceiling reflectance 80%**

| Room index | Indirect 50% | Indirect 30% | Indirect 10% | Horiz 50% | Horiz 30% | Horiz 10% | Dir50 B | Dir50 M | Dir50 N | Dir50 VN | Dir50 C | Dir50 F | Dir30 B | Dir30 M | Dir30 N | Dir30 VN | Dir30 C | Dir30 F | Dir10 B | Dir10 M | Dir10 N | Dir10 VN | Dir10 C | Dir10 F |
|---|---|---|---|---|---|---|---|---|---|---|---|---|---|---|---|---|---|---|---|---|---|---|---|---|
| A 5.0 | .60 | .56 | .52 | .67 | .60 | .54 | .92 | .93 | .94 | .95 | .95 | .95 | .87 | .89 | .90 | .91 | .92 | .93 | .85 | .87 | .88 | .90 | .91 | .92 |
| B 4.0 | .57 | .53 | .49 | .64 | .57 | .50 | .89 | .91 | .92 | .93 | .93 | .94 | .85 | .87 | .88 | .89 | .90 | .91 | .82 | .84 | .86 | .88 | .89 | .90 |
| C 3.0 | .52 | .47 | .43 | .58 | .52 | .47 | .84 | .86 | .89 | .90 | .90 | .93 | .80 | .83 | .85 | .87 | .88 | .90 | .76 | .79 | .81 | .83 | .85 | .87 |
| D 2.5 | .49 | .43 | .39 | .54 | .46 | .43 | .81 | .84 | .86 | .88 | .90 | .91 | .77 | .80 | .82 | .84 | .86 | .88 | .72 | .76 | .79 | .82 | .85 | .86 |
| E 2.0 | .45 | .39 | .35 | .49 | .41 | .39 | .76 | .79 | .81 | .83 | .85 | .86 | .71 | .75 | .78 | .81 | .84 | .86 | .66 | .71 | .73 | .78 | .80 | .84 |
| F 1.5 | .39 | .33 | .29 | .42 | .35 | .35 | .70 | .73 | .76 | .79 | .81 | .83 | .64 | .68 | .72 | .75 | .79 | .81 | .59 | .64 | .68 | .72 | .76 | .79 |
| G 1.25 | .36 | .30 | .26 | .38 | .31 | .25 | .66 | .69 | .72 | .75 | .77 | .79 | .60 | .64 | .68 | .72 | .75 | .78 | .55 | .60 | .65 | .70 | .74 | .77 |
| H 1.0 | .31 | .26 | .23 | .33 | .26 | .21 | .61 | .64 | .67 | .70 | .72 | .74 | .55 | .59 | .63 | .67 | .70 | .73 | .50 | .55 | .60 | .65 | .69 | .72 |
| I 0.8 | .27 | .22 | .19 | .29 | .22 | .17 | .55 | .58 | .61 | .64 | .67 | .69 | .48 | .52 | .56 | .60 | .63 | .66 | .43 | .48 | .53 | .58 | .62 | .65 |
| J 0.6 | .21 | .16 | .14 | .22 | .16 | .12 | .44 | .47 | .50 | .53 | .56 | .58 | .36 | .40 | .44 | .48 | .51 | .54 | .30 | .35 | .40 | .45 | .49 | .52 |

**Ceiling reflectance 70%**

| Room index | Indirect 50% | Indirect 30% | Indirect 10% | Horiz 50% | Horiz 30% | Horiz 10% | Dir50 B | Dir50 M | Dir50 N | Dir50 VN | Dir50 C | Dir50 F | Dir30 B | Dir30 M | Dir30 N | Dir30 VN | Dir30 C | Dir30 F | Dir10 B | Dir10 M | Dir10 N | Dir10 VN | Dir10 C | Dir10 F |
|---|---|---|---|---|---|---|---|---|---|---|---|---|---|---|---|---|---|---|---|---|---|---|---|---|
| A 5.0 | .52 | .48 | .46 | .63 | .57 | .51 | .91 | .92 | .93 | .94 | .94 | .94 | .87 | .89 | .90 | .91 | .92 | .93 | .84 | .86 | .87 | .89 | .90 | .91 |
| B 4.0 | .50 | .46 | .43 | .60 | .53 | .47 | .88 | .90 | .91 | .92 | .93 | .93 | .85 | .87 | .88 | .89 | .90 | .91 | .82 | .84 | .86 | .88 | .89 | .90 |
| C 3.0 | .45 | .41 | .38 | .54 | .47 | .41 | .84 | .86 | .88 | .90 | .91 | .92 | .80 | .83 | .85 | .87 | .88 | .90 | .76 | .79 | .81 | .83 | .85 | .86 |
| D 2.5 | .42 | .38 | .35 | .50 | .43 | .38 | .81 | .84 | .86 | .88 | .90 | .91 | .77 | .80 | .82 | .84 | .86 | .88 | .72 | .76 | .79 | .82 | .84 | .86 |
| E 2.0 | .38 | .34 | .31 | .46 | .39 | .33 | .75 | .78 | .80 | .82 | .84 | .85 | .70 | .74 | .77 | .80 | .82 | .84 | .65 | .70 | .73 | .78 | .79 | .82 |
| F 1.5 | .34 | .30 | .26 | .40 | .33 | .27 | .69 | .72 | .75 | .78 | .80 | .82 | .63 | .67 | .71 | .74 | .77 | .79 | .58 | .63 | .67 | .71 | .73 | .78 |
| G 1.25 | .31 | .27 | .23 | .36 | .29 | .24 | .65 | .68 | .71 | .74 | .76 | .78 | .59 | .63 | .67 | .71 | .74 | .77 | .54 | .59 | .64 | .69 | .73 | .76 |
| H 1.0 | .27 | .23 | .20 | .31 | .24 | .20 | .60 | .63 | .66 | .69 | .71 | .73 | .54 | .58 | .62 | .66 | .69 | .72 | .49 | .54 | .59 | .64 | .68 | .71 |
| I 0.8 | .23 | .19 | .17 | .27 | .20 | .17 | .55 | .58 | .61 | .64 | .66 | .68 | .48 | .52 | .56 | .60 | .63 | .66 | .43 | .48 | .53 | .58 | .62 | .65 |
| J 0.6 | .19 | .15 | .13 | .21 | .15 | .13 | .44 | .47 | .50 | .53 | .55 | .57 | .36 | .40 | .44 | .48 | .51 | .54 | .30 | .35 | .40 | .45 | .49 | .52 |

**Ceiling reflectance 60%**

| Room index | Indirect 50% | Indirect 30% | Indirect 10% | Horiz 50% | Horiz 30% | Horiz 10% | Dir50 B | Dir50 M | Dir50 N | Dir50 VN | Dir50 C | Dir50 F | Dir30 B | Dir30 M | Dir30 N | Dir30 VN | Dir30 C | Dir30 F | Dir10 B | Dir10 M | Dir10 N | Dir10 VN | Dir10 C | Dir10 F |
|---|---|---|---|---|---|---|---|---|---|---|---|---|---|---|---|---|---|---|---|---|---|---|---|---|
| A 5.0 | .45 | .41 | .39 | .59 | .53 | .48 | .90 | .91 | .92 | .93 | .93 | .93 | .86 | .88 | .89 | .90 | .91 | .92 | .84 | .86 | .87 | .88 | .89 | .90 |
| B 4.0 | .43 | .39 | .37 | .56 | .50 | .45 | .87 | .89 | .90 | .91 | .91 | .92 | .84 | .86 | .87 | .88 | .89 | .90 | .81 | .83 | .86 | .87 | .86 | .89 |
| C 3.0 | .39 | .35 | .33 | .50 | .44 | .39 | .83 | .85 | .87 | .89 | .89 | .91 | .79 | .82 | .84 | .86 | .88 | .89 | .76 | .79 | .81 | .83 | .84 | .87 |
| D 2.5 | .37 | .33 | .30 | .46 | .40 | .35 | .80 | .83 | .85 | .87 | .88 | .89 | .77 | .80 | .82 | .84 | .86 | .87 | .72 | .76 | .79 | .82 | .84 | .86 |
| E 2.0 | .33 | .29 | .26 | .42 | .36 | .31 | .75 | .78 | .80 | .82 | .84 | .85 | .70 | .74 | .77 | .80 | .82 | .84 | .65 | .70 | .73 | .77 | .79 | .81 |
| F 1.5 | .29 | .25 | .22 | .37 | .31 | .26 | .68 | .71 | .74 | .77 | .79 | .81 | .63 | .67 | .71 | .74 | .77 | .79 | .58 | .63 | .67 | .71 | .73 | .78 |
| G 1.25 | .27 | .23 | .20 | .33 | .27 | .23 | .64 | .67 | .70 | .73 | .75 | .77 | .59 | .63 | .67 | .70 | .73 | .76 | .54 | .59 | .64 | .69 | .72 | .75 |
| H 1.0 | .23 | .19 | .17 | .29 | .23 | .19 | .60 | .63 | .66 | .69 | .71 | .73 | .54 | .58 | .62 | .66 | .69 | .72 | .49 | .54 | .59 | .64 | .68 | .71 |
| I 0.8 | .20 | .16 | .14 | .25 | .19 | .15 | .54 | .58 | .61 | .64 | .66 | .68 | .48 | .52 | .56 | .60 | .63 | .68 | .43 | .48 | .53 | .58 | .62 | .65 |
| J 0.6 | .16 | .13 | .11 | .20 | .14 | .10 | .44 | .47 | .50 | .53 | .55 | .57 | .36 | .40 | .44 | .48 | .51 | .57 | .30 | .35 | .40 | .45 | .49 | .52 |

**TABLE 9-2.  (Continued)**

| Ceiling reflectance | Room index | | Indirect — Horizontal (Wall reflectance) | | | Horizontal (Wall reflectance) | | | Direct component — Wall reflectance 50% | | | | | | Wall reflectance 30% | | | | | | Wall reflectance 10% | | | | | |
|---|---|---|---|---|---|---|---|---|---|---|---|---|---|---|---|---|---|---|---|---|---|---|---|---|---|---|
| | | | 50% | 30% | 10% | 50% | 30% | 10% | B | M | N | VN | C | F | B | M | N | VN | C | F | B | M | N | VN | C | F |
| Ceiling reflectance 50% | A | 5.0 | .38 | .35 | .33 | .55 | .49 | .45 | .89 | .90 | .91 | .92 | .92 | .92 | .85 | .87 | .88 | .89 | .90 | .90 | .83 | .85 | .86 | .87 | .88 | .89 |
| | B | 4.0 | .35 | .33 | .31 | .52 | .46 | .42 | .86 | .88 | .89 | .90 | .91 | .91 | .83 | .85 | .86 | .87 | .88 | .89 | .81 | .83 | .85 | .86 | .87 | .88 |
| | C | 3.0 | .32 | .29 | .27 | .47 | .41 | .36 | .82 | .84 | .86 | .88 | .89 | .90 | .78 | .81 | .83 | .85 | .87 | .88 | .76 | .79 | .81 | .83 | .84 | .85 |
| | D | 2.5 | .30 | .27 | .25 | .44 | .38 | .33 | .79 | .82 | .84 | .86 | .87 | .88 | .76 | .79 | .81 | .83 | .85 | .86 | .72 | .76 | .79 | .81 | .83 | .85 |
| | E | 2.0 | .28 | .24 | .22 | .40 | .34 | .29 | .74 | .77 | .79 | .81 | .83 | .84 | .69 | .73 | .76 | .79 | .81 | .83 | .65 | .70 | .73 | .76 | .79 | .81 |
| | F | 1.5 | .25 | .21 | .19 | .35 | .29 | .24 | .67 | .70 | .73 | .75 | .77 | .79 | .62 | .66 | .70 | .73 | .76 | .78 | .58 | .63 | .67 | .71 | .74 | .77 |
| | G | 1.25 | .23 | .19 | .17 | .31 | .25 | .21 | .64 | .67 | .70 | .73 | .75 | .77 | .59 | .63 | .67 | .70 | .73 | .75 | .54 | .59 | .64 | .68 | .71 | .74 |
| | H | 1.0 | .19 | .16 | .14 | .28 | .22 | .18 | .59 | .62 | .65 | .68 | .70 | .72 | .54 | .58 | .62 | .65 | .68 | .71 | .49 | .54 | .59 | .63 | .67 | .70 |
| | I | 0.8 | .17 | .14 | .12 | .24 | .18 | .14 | .54 | .57 | .60 | .63 | .65 | .67 | .47 | .51 | .55 | .59 | .62 | .65 | .42 | .47 | .52 | .57 | .61 | .64 |
| | J | 0.6 | .13 | .11 | .09 | .19 | .13 | .10 | .43 | .46 | .49 | .52 | .54 | .56 | .36 | .40 | .44 | .48 | .51 | .54 | .30 | .35 | .40 | .45 | .49 | .52 |
| Ceiling reflectance 30% | A | 5.0 | .22 | .21 | .19 | .46 | .42 | .40 | .88 | .89 | .90 | .91 | .91 | .91 | .86 | .87 | .88 | .88 | .89 | .89 | .84 | .85 | .86 | .86 | .87 | .88 |
| | B | 4.0 | .21 | .19 | .18 | .44 | .40 | .37 | .85 | .87 | .89 | .89 | .90 | .90 | .84 | .85 | .85 | .86 | .87 | .88 | .82 | .84 | .84 | .85 | .86 | .87 |
| | C | 3.0 | .19 | .17 | .16 | .40 | .36 | .32 | .81 | .83 | .85 | .86 | .87 | .87 | .80 | .82 | .84 | .85 | .85 | .86 | .77 | .78 | .80 | .81 | .83 | .84 |
| | D | 2.5 | .18 | .16 | .15 | .38 | .33 | .29 | .78 | .81 | .83 | .84 | .85 | .86 | .77 | .80 | .82 | .82 | .84 | .85 | .72 | .76 | .78 | .79 | .81 | .82 |
| | E | 2.0 | .16 | .14 | .13 | .34 | .29 | .25 | .73 | .76 | .78 | .81 | .83 | .84 | .68 | .72 | .75 | .78 | .80 | .82 | .65 | .70 | .73 | .76 | .78 | .80 |
| | F | 1.5 | .14 | .12 | .11 | .30 | .25 | .21 | .66 | .69 | .72 | .74 | .76 | .78 | .61 | .65 | .69 | .73 | .76 | .78 | .58 | .63 | .67 | .71 | .74 | .76 |
| | G | 1.25 | .13 | .11 | .10 | .27 | .22 | .18 | .62 | .65 | .68 | .71 | .74 | .76 | .57 | .61 | .65 | .69 | .72 | .75 | .54 | .59 | .64 | .68 | .71 | .73 |
| | H | 1.0 | .12 | .10 | .08 | .24 | .19 | .15 | .57 | .61 | .64 | .66 | .67 | .69 | .53 | .57 | .61 | .65 | .68 | .71 | .49 | .54 | .59 | .63 | .66 | .69 |
| | I | 0.8 | .10 | .08 | .07 | .21 | .16 | .13 | .54 | .57 | .60 | .61 | .62 | .63 | .47 | .51 | .55 | .59 | .62 | .65 | .42 | .47 | .52 | .56 | .59 | .62 |
| | J | 0.6 | .08 | .06 | .05 | .16 | .11 | .09 | .43 | .46 | .49 | .51 | .53 | .55 | .35 | .39 | .43 | .48 | .51 | .54 | .30 | .35 | .40 | .44 | .48 | .51 |

B = broad distribution = 35%–40%; M = medium = 40%–45%; N = narrow = 45%–50%; VN = very narrow = 50%–55%; C = concentrating = 55%–60%; F = focusing = 60%–up.
\* Based upon original work of Harrison and Anderson.

This 2,100 lm must be taken away from the total lumens output of the luminaire. One-half is assumed to be subtracted from the upper and lower hemispheres respectively. The hypothetical flux distribution is now

$$\text{direct zone} = 1{,}800 - \frac{2{,}100}{2} = 750 \text{ lm}$$

$$\text{indirect zone} = 1{,}300 - \frac{2{,}100}{2} = 250 \text{ lm}$$

$$\text{horizontal zone} = 2{,}100$$

The total lumens emitted by the luminaire have not been changed but simply redistributed.

### TABLE 9-3

**Classification of Direct Flux by Flux Ratios for Determining Coefficient of Utilization**

| Classification | Flux ratio, % |
|---|---|
| B: broad | 35–40 |
| M: medium | 40–45 |
| N: narrow | 45–50 |
| VN: very narrow | 50–55 |
| C: concentrating | 55–60 |
| F: focusing | over 60 |

$$\text{flux ratio} = \frac{\text{lumens } 0° \text{ to } 40° \text{ zone} - 0.65 \text{ (cp at } 90°)*}{\text{lumens } 0° \text{ to } 90° \text{ zone} - 5.0 \text{ (cp at } 90°)}$$

* If there is no horizontal candlepower emitted by the luminaire, the last term of both numerator and denominator simply drops out.

We now must find how many of the lumens in each of these three zones will reach the horizontal work plane in a given room. Let us assume a room with an index of 2, with ceiling of 80% reflectance and walls of 50% reflectance.

To enter Table 9-2 the direct flux distribution must be classified according to the degree of concentration. From Table 9-3 this is shown to be

$$\text{flux ratio} = \frac{500 - 0.65(210)}{1{,}800 - 5.0(210)} = \frac{364}{750}$$
$$= 48.5\% \text{ or } N \text{ (narrow)}$$

From Table 9-2 we find that 81% of the flux in the direct zone will reach the work plane. This amounts to $750 \times 0.81 = 606$ lm. Likewise we find that 45% of the flux in the indirect zone, or $250 \times 0.45 = 112.5$ lm, will reach the work plane.

Similarly, from Table 9-2 we find that 49% of the horizontal flux will reach the work plane, or $2,100 \times 0.49 = 1,030$ lm. From the three zones a total of 1,749 lm will reach the work plane. The lamp with which the luminaires was tested delivered 3,700 lm. The coefficient of utilization for this luminaire is therefore

$$C.U. = \frac{1,749}{3,700} = 0.472$$

When a luminaire emits little light below the horizontal, as is the case with a luminous indirect basin, the flux ratio formula may give values over 100%. This is obviously a physical impossibility and is due to the empirical nature of the formula. In such cases the flux ratio is therefore calculated with the last terms omitted. So little flux is being emitted in the downward zone that no appreciable error is committed.

When the horizontal candlepower is large, subtracting half the horizontal flux from the direct or indirect components may produce a negative value. The computations are made as usual, but the minus sign is carried through and additions made algebraically.

## 9.4. Determining Reflection Factors

The experiments from which the zonal constants were derived were conducted in rooms with a floor reflectance of 14%. Present practice is in the direction of lighter floors. With the usual light ceilings and walls, the effect on utilization is not marked. A floor of 40% reflectance, for example, increases the utilization 5%.

However, lighter floors and horizontal work surfaces contribute greatly to visual comfort because of the reduced brightness contrasts. They create the desirable impression of more light. They are highly recommended.

Reflectances of walls and ceilings have been rather broadly classified in the tables. The exact reflectance of a surface color can be obtained from the manufacturer, or by test. However, to aid the designer, Table 9-4 gives reflectances of common surface colors, grouped into the same classifications as the design tables. The reflection factor of an actual wall is not necessarily the same as the reflectance of the surface color. The chalkboard wall in a classroom may be painted a buff of 60% reflectance, but 20% of the wall is covered with slate of 10% reflectance. The effective reflectance

**TABLE 9-4**

**Reflection Factors of Common Room Surfaces and Colors**

| Reflectance, % | Material | Paints |
|---|---|---|
| 75 or more | White asbestos-finish Acoustic-Celotex | All whites, light ivory, cream |
| 40–75 | All white finish acoustical material | Light gray, light buff, light yellow, very light green |
| 40–60 | Unfinished acoustical materials. Light buff tile, natural finish maple, birch, mahogany, walnut | Light green, light blue, medium gray, salmon |
| 20–40 | Light, mottled floor coverings, light oak | Medium brown, green, blue, gray |
| 1 –20 | Dark walnut, oak, mahogany, majority of floor tiles | |

is therefore 50%, not 60%. Clear windows are considered to reflect not over 10% of the incident light. If the window is covered by a shade, then the reflectance of the shade must be taken into account.

The average reflectance of a room surface may be obtained by one of two simple methods. One way would be to weight the effect of each surface of different reflection factor. Assume a wall 8 by 15 ft with a chalkboard 4 by 10 ft. The wall is painted a buff of 60% reflectance and the clean chalkboard has a reflectance of 10%. The area of the chalkboard is one-third of the entire wall area. Therefore, add to the reflectance of the chalkboard twice the reflectance of the remaining wall surface. The result is 10% +

60% + 60% or 130%. Divide this by three, and the result is 43%.

The other way is to calculate what percentage of the total area is occupied by each area of different reflectance. Then multiply each of these percentages by the appropriate reflection factor and add the products. In the above example the given chalkboard occupies $33\frac{1}{3}$% of the total wall area, the remaining surface occupies $66\frac{2}{3}$%. Multiply $33\frac{1}{3}$% by 10% and $66\frac{2}{3}$% by 60%, add the products, and the result is 43+%.

Ceilings are usually homogeneous surfaces. If a ceiling is painted with 80% reflectance white, then for design purposes the entire ceiling is assumed to be of 80% reflectance. Perforated acoustical tile is an exception. The surface between holes may have an 80% reflectance, but the average reflectance of the ceiling may range from 64% to 73%, depending upon the number and size of perforations.

*Ceiling reflectance and utilization coefficient:* It will be noted that the maximum ceiling reflectances given in Tables 9-2 and 9-5 are 80% and 75% respectively. Flat white paints today approach 90% reflectance. The effect of ceiling reflectance upon coefficients of utilization is rather marked. It is possible to apply a correction factor to both the zonal constants of Table 9-2, and the simplified coefficients of Table 9-5. Actually the correction will depend upon room index and wall and floor reflectance as well as ceiling reflectance. However, within the limits of usual practice a generalized correction is possible.

Referring to Table 9-2, it has been found that the direct component is relatively unaffected by ceiling reflectance. The indirect component varies approximately in direct proportion to the change in ceiling reflectance. Thus a ceiling reflectance of 85% represents a 6.25% increase over an 80% reflectance ceiling. The indirect zonal constant can then be increased by 6.25%.

The horizontal component may be increased by one-fourth of the percentage increase in ceiling reflectance.

Therefore, when calculating precise coefficients of utilization for ceiling reflectances in excess of those given in the tables, appropriate corrections can be applied.

Generalized coefficients as found in Table 9-5 can be corrected by the following constants:

| Luminaire classification | Increase tabular coefficient by: |
|---|---|
| Direct<br>Semi-direct | 0% |
| General-diffuse | $\dfrac{\%\ \text{difference in ceiling reflectances}}{1.7}$ |
| Direct-indirect | $\dfrac{\%\ \text{difference in ceiling reflectances}}{2.0}$ |
| Semi-indirect | $\dfrac{\%\ \text{difference in ceiling reflectances}}{1.5}$ |
| Indirect | $\dfrac{\%\ \text{difference in ceiling reflectances}}{1.1}$ |

### 9.5. Simplified Coefficients

The coefficients of utilization for many standardized types of luminaires have been computed and placed in tabular form. Table 9-5 is an example. In addition many manufacturers compute the coefficients of utilization for their specific luminaires. The computations are made in the manner described in the preceding paragraphs.

In the initial stages of lighting design a specific luminaire may not have been decided upon. Rather, a general type of light distribution is investigated. Perhaps several types of distribution will be investigated. Much time is saved by using the generalized data in Table 9-5. After the general details have been worked out and a specific luminaire selected, the design can be refined by using coefficients of utilization as supplied by the manufacturer. The designer can also compute the coefficient with the aid of a candlepower distribution curve.

As an example, consider the lighting of a warehouse where direct lighting is satisfactory. The area is 50 by 80 ft with cross beams for mounting luminaires 15 ft above the floor. Walls and ceilings are dark and may be assumed of 30% reflectance.

From Table 9-1 the room index is found to be $D$. In Table 9-5, luminaire No. 1 is satisfactory. The coefficient of utilization is found to be 0.61.

Note that this coefficient is valid for a luminaire of 79% efficiency. If the designer finally selects a luminaire with an efficiency

# TABLE 9-5

| LUMINAIRE | Ceiling | 75% | | | 50% | | | 30% | |
|---|---|---|---|---|---|---|---|---|---|
| | Walls | 50% | 30% | 10% | 50% | 30% | 10% | 30% | 10% |
| | Room Index | COEFFICIENT OF UTILIZATION | | | | | | | |
| **1** Direct - RLM Dome Reflector (MF G-.75 M-.65 P-.55 ↓79) | J | .37 | .31 | .27 | .36 | .31 | .27 | .31 | .27 |
| | I | .45 | .41 | .38 | .45 | .40 | .37 | .40 | .37 |
| | H | .49 | .45 | .42 | .49 | .45 | .42 | .45 | .42 |
| | G | .53 | .49 | .46 | .53 | .49 | .46 | .48 | .46 |
| | F | .56 | .53 | .49 | .55 | .52 | .49 | .51 | .49 |
| | E | .61 | .58 | .55 | .60 | .57 | .55 | .56 | .55 |
| | D | .66 | .63 | .60 | .64 | .62 | .60 | .61 | .60 |
| | C | .67 | .65 | .62 | .66 | .64 | .62 | .63 | .61 |
| | B | .71 | .68 | .66 | .69 | .67 | .65 | .66 | .64 |
| | A | .72 | .70 | .67 | .71 | .68 | .67 | .67 | .66 |
| **2** Direct - RLM Deep Bowl Reflector (MF G-.75 M-.65 P-.55 ↓70) | J | .35 | .31 | .28 | .34 | .31 | .28 | .30 | .28 |
| | I | .43 | .39 | .37 | .42 | .39 | .37 | .39 | .37 |
| | H | .46 | .44 | .42 | .46 | .44 | .42 | .43 | .42 |
| | G | .50 | .47 | .45 | .49 | .47 | .45 | .46 | .45 |
| | F | .53 | .50 | .47 | .51 | .49 | .47 | .49 | .47 |
| | E | .56 | .54 | .52 | .56 | .54 | .51 | .53 | .51 |
| | D | .61 | .58 | .56 | .59 | .57 | .56 | .56 | .56 |
| | C | .62 | .60 | .57 | .61 | .58 | .57 | .58 | .56 |
| | B | .64 | .62 | .61 | .63 | .61 | .60 | .60 | .59 |
| | A | .65 | .63 | .61 | .64 | .62 | .61 | .61 | .60 |
| **3** Direct - Aluminum Hi-Bay Reflector - Concentrating (MF G-.75 M-.60 P-.40 ↓75) | J | .43 | .40 | .39 | .42 | .40 | .39 | .40 | .38 |
| | I | .51 | .50 | .49 | .50 | .49 | .48 | .49 | .46 |
| | H | .55 | .54 | .53 | .54 | .53 | .52 | .53 | .52 |
| | G | .59 | .58 | .57 | .58 | .56 | .55 | .56 | .55 |
| | F | .61 | .60 | .58 | .59 | .58 | .58 | .58 | .57 |
| | E | .64 | .63 | .62 | .63 | .62 | .61 | .61 | .60 |
| | D | .68 | .65 | .64 | .66 | .65 | .64 | .64 | .63 |
| | C | .69 | .67 | .65 | .67 | .66 | .64 | .64 | .64 |
| | B | .70 | .68 | .66 | .68 | .67 | .66 | .66 | .65 |
| | A | .71 | .70 | .67 | .69 | .67 | .67 | .67 | .66 |
| **4** Direct - Aluminum Hi-Bay Reflector Medium Spread (MF G-.75 M-.65 P-.50 ↓75) | J | .40 | .36 | .34 | .39 | .36 | .34 | .36 | .33 |
| | I | .48 | .45 | .43 | .47 | .44 | .43 | .44 | .42 |
| | H | .52 | .50 | .48 | .51 | .49 | .47 | .49 | .47 |
| | G | .55 | .53 | .52 | .55 | .52 | .51 | .52 | .51 |
| | F | .58 | .56 | .53 | .56 | .55 | .53 | .55 | .53 |
| | E | .62 | .60 | .58 | .61 | .59 | .57 | .58 | .57 |
| | D | .66 | .63 | .61 | .64 | .62 | .61 | .62 | .61 |
| | C | .67 | .65 | .62 | .65 | .64 | .62 | .63 | .62 |
| | B | .69 | .67 | .66 | .67 | .65 | .64 | .65 | .64 |
| | A | .70 | .68 | .67 | .69 | .67 | .65 | .66 | .64 |
| **5** Direct - Concentrating - or Medium Heavy Duty Type (MF G-.80 M-.72 P-.65 ↓70) | J | .40 | .38 | .36 | .39 | .38 | .36 | .38 | .36 |
| | I | .48 | .46 | .45 | .47 | .46 | .45 | .45 | .43 |
| | H | .52 | .51 | .50 | .51 | .50 | .49 | .50 | .48 |
| | G | .55 | .54 | .53 | .54 | .53 | .52 | .53 | .51 |
| | F | .57 | .56 | .55 | .56 | .55 | .54 | .55 | .53 |
| | E | .60 | .59 | .58 | .59 | .58 | .57 | .57 | .56 |
| | D | .64 | .61 | .60 | .62 | .60 | .59 | .60 | .59 |
| | C | .64 | .63 | .61 | .63 | .62 | .60 | .60 | .60 |
| | B | .65 | .64 | .63 | .64 | .63 | .62 | .62 | .61 |
| | A | .66 | .65 | .64 | .64 | .63 | .62 | .62 | .62 |
| **6** Direct - Wide Spread Heavy Duty Type (MF G-.80 M-.72 P-.65 ↓70) | J | .37 | .34 | .31 | .36 | .34 | .31 | .34 | .31 |
| | I | .45 | .42 | .41 | .44 | .41 | .40 | .41 | .39 |
| | H | .48 | .46 | .45 | .49 | .45 | .44 | .45 | .44 |
| | G | .52 | .50 | .48 | .51 | .49 | .48 | .49 | .48 |
| | F | .55 | .52 | .51 | .50 | .51 | .50 | .51 | .50 |
| | E | .57 | .56 | .55 | .57 | .55 | .53 | .55 | .53 |
| | D | .62 | .59 | .57 | .60 | .58 | .57 | .57 | .57 |
| | C | .63 | .62 | .58 | .62 | .59 | .58 | .59 | .57 |
| | B | .64 | .62 | .61 | .63 | .61 | .60 | .60 | .59 |
| | A | .66 | .64 | .62 | .64 | .62 | .61 | .62 | .60 |

155

TABLE 9-5.   (Continued)

| LUMINAIRE | Ceiling | 75% | | | 50% | | | 30% | |
|---|---|---|---|---|---|---|---|---|---|
| | Walls | 50% | 30% | 10% | 50% | 30% | 10% | 30% | 10% |
| | Room Index | COEFFICIENT OF UTILIZATION | | | | | | | |
| **7** Direct - RLM Glassteel Diffuser<br>MF G-.70 ↑5 M-.60 ↓58 P-.45 | J | .27 | .23 | .20 | .26 | .23 | .20 | .22 | .20 |
| | I | .34 | .30 | .28 | .33 | .29 | .27 | .29 | .27 |
| | H | .37 | .34 | .31 | .36 | .33 | .31 | .32 | .30 |
| | G | .40 | .37 | .34 | .39 | .36 | .34 | .35 | .33 |
| | F | .42 | .39 | .37 | .40 | .38 | .36 | .37 | .36 |
| | E | .46 | .43 | .41 | .45 | .42 | .40 | .41 | .40 |
| | D | .49 | .47 | .44 | .48 | .46 | .44 | .44 | .43 |
| | C | .51 | .49 | .46 | .49 | .47 | .46 | .46 | .44 |
| | B | .53 | .51 | .49 | .51 | .49 | .48 | .48 | .47 |
| | A | .54 | .53 | .51 | .53 | .51 | .49 | .49 | .48 |
| **8** Direct - RLM Silvered Bowl Diffuser<br>MF G-.60 ↑0 M-.50 ↓67 P-.40 | J | .41 | .39 | .37 | .40 | .39 | .37 | .39 | .36 |
| | I | .49 | .47 | .46 | .48 | .46 | .46 | .46 | .44 |
| | H | .52 | .51 | .51 | .51 | .51 | .50 | .51 | .49 |
| | G | .56 | .55 | .54 | .55 | .54 | .53 | .54 | .52 |
| | F | .59 | .57 | .56 | .56 | .56 | .55 | .56 | .54 |
| | E | .61 | .60 | .59 | .60 | .59 | .58 | .59 | .57 |
| | D | .65 | .62 | .61 | .63 | .61 | .61 | .61 | .60 |
| | C | .66 | .64 | .62 | .64 | .63 | .61 | .61 | .61 |
| | B | .66 | .65 | .64 | .65 | .64 | .63 | .63 | .62 |
| | A | .67 | .66 | .65 | .66 | .64 | .64 | .64 | .63 |
| **9** Direct - Wide Spread - Vapor Tight<br>MF G-.75 ↑0 M-.65 ↓65 P-.55 | J | .31 | .26 | .23 | .30 | .26 | .23 | .26 | .23 |
| | I | .38 | .34 | .31 | .37 | .33 | .31 | .33 | .31 |
| | H | .41 | .38 | .34 | .41 | .38 | .34 | .37 | .34 |
| | G | .45 | .41 | .39 | .44 | .41 | .39 | .40 | .39 |
| | F | .47 | .44 | .41 | .46 | .43 | .41 | .43 | .41 |
| | E | .51 | .48 | .46 | .50 | .48 | .46 | .47 | .46 |
| | D | .55 | .52 | .50 | .54 | .52 | .50 | .51 | .50 |
| | C | .56 | .54 | .52 | .55 | .53 | .52 | .52 | .51 |
| | B | .59 | .57 | .55 | .58 | .56 | .54 | .55 | .54 |
| | A | .60 | .58 | .56 | .59 | .57 | .56 | .56 | .55 |
| **10** Direct - Enclosed Lens Plate - Distributing Type<br>MF G-.70 ↑0 M-.60 ↓53 P-.50 | J | .25 | .22 | .20 | .24 | .22 | .20 | .22 | .20 |
| | I | .31 | .28 | .26 | .29 | .28 | .26 | .28 | .26 |
| | H | .34 | .31 | .29 | .32 | .31 | .29 | .30 | .28 |
| | G | .36 | .33 | .32 | .34 | .33 | .31 | .32 | .30 |
| | F | .38 | .35 | .34 | .36 | .34 | .33 | .34 | .32 |
| | E | .40 | .39 | .38 | .39 | .37 | .36 | .37 | .35 |
| | D | .43 | .41 | .40 | .42 | .40 | .39 | .39 | .38 |
| | C | .45 | .43 | .42 | .44 | .41 | .40 | .40 | .40 |
| | B | .48 | .45 | .44 | .47 | .43 | .42 | .42 | .41 |
| | A | .50 | .47 | .46 | .48 | .46 | .45 | .45 | .44 |
| **11** Direct 2 - 40 watt lamps<br>MF G-.65 ↑0 M-.55 ↓79 P-.45 | J | .38 | .32 | .28 | .37 | .32 | .28 | .31 | .28 |
| | I | .47 | .42 | .39 | .46 | .41 | .38 | .40 | .37 |
| | H | .51 | .47 | .44 | .50 | .47 | .43 | .46 | .43 |
| | G | .55 | .51 | .48 | .54 | .51 | .47 | .50 | .47 |
| | F | .58 | .54 | .51 | .57 | .53 | .51 | .52 | .50 |
| | E | .63 | .60 | .57 | .62 | .59 | .56 | .58 | .55 |
| | D | .68 | .64 | .61 | .66 | .64 | .61 | .63 | .60 |
| | C | .70 | .67 | .63 | .68 | .65 | .64 | .64 | .62 |
| | B | .73 | .70 | .68 | .71 | .68 | .67 | .67 | .66 |
| | A | .74 | .72 | .70 | .72 | .70 | .68 | .69 | .67 |
| **12** Direct 3 - 40 watt lamps<br>MF G-.65 ↑0 M-.55 ↓72 P-.45 | J | .34 | .29 | .25 | .33 | .29 | .25 | .28 | .25 |
| | I | .42 | .38 | .35 | .41 | .37 | .34 | .37 | .34 |
| | H | .46 | .42 | .39 | .44 | .42 | .39 | .41 | .39 |
| | G | .50 | .46 | .43 | .48 | .45 | .41 | .44 | .41 |
| | F | .53 | .49 | .46 | .51 | .47 | .44 | .47 | .44 |
| | E | .57 | .54 | .51 | .56 | .52 | .50 | .52 | .50 |
| | D | .61 | .58 | .55 | .59 | .56 | .54 | .56 | .54 |
| | C | .63 | .60 | .57 | .61 | .58 | .56 | .58 | .56 |
| | B | .66 | .64 | .61 | .64 | .60 | .59 | .60 | .59 |
| | A | .67 | .65 | .62 | .66 | .62 | .61 | .62 | .60 |

TABLE 9-5. (Continued)

| LUMINAIRE | Room Index | Ceiling 75% Walls 50% | 30% | 10% | Ceiling 50% Walls 50% | 30% | 10% | Ceiling 30% Walls 30% | 10% |
|---|---|---|---|---|---|---|---|---|---|
| **13** — MF G-.60 M-.50 P-.45 ↑0 ↓71 — Direct 2 - 100 watt lamps | J | .35 | .30 | .26 | .35 | .30 | .26 | .30 | .24 |
| | I | .44 | .39 | .36 | .43 | .38 | .35 | .38 | .34 |
| | H | .48 | .44 | .41 | .46 | .43 | .40 | .42 | .39 |
| | G | .51 | .48 | .43 | .50 | .47 | .43 | .47 | .42 |
| | F | .54 | .51 | .48 | .53 | .49 | .46 | .49 | .45 |
| | E | .59 | .56 | .53 | .58 | .54 | .52 | .54 | .51 |
| | D | .63 | .60 | .57 | .61 | .58 | .56 | .58 | .55 |
| | C | .65 | .62 | .59 | .63 | .60 | .58 | .60 | .57 |
| | B | .68 | .65 | .63 | .66 | .62 | .61 | .62 | .60 |
| | A | .69 | .67 | .65 | .68 | .64 | .63 | .64 | .62 |
| **14** — MF G-.65 M-.55 P-.45 ↑0 ↓64 — Direct - With Louvers 2 - 40 watt lamps | J | .33 | .28 | .26 | .32 | .28 | .26 | .28 | .26 |
| | I | .39 | .36 | .34 | .39 | .35 | .34 | .35 | .34 |
| | H | .43 | .40 | .38 | .42 | .40 | .38 | .39 | .38 |
| | G | .46 | .43 | .41 | .45 | .43 | .41 | .42 | .41 |
| | F | .48 | .46 | .43 | .47 | .45 | .43 | .45 | .43 |
| | E | .52 | .50 | | .51 | .49 | .47 | .48 | .47 |
| | D | .55 | .53 | .51 | .53 | .52 | .51 | .52 | .51 |
| | C | .57 | .55 | .52 | .56 | .53 | .52 | .53 | .52 |
| | B | .59 | .57 | .56 | .57 | .56 | .55 | .55 | .54 |
| | A | .60 | .58 | .56 | .59 | .57 | .56 | .56 | .55 |
| **15** — MF G-.70 M-.65 P-.55 ↑0 ↓60 — Direct - Vapor and Dust Tight 2 or 3 - 40 watt lamps | J | .29 | .26 | .23 | .28 | .25 | .23 | .25 | .23 |
| | I | .35 | .32 | .31 | .35 | .32 | .30 | .32 | .30 |
| | H | .38 | .36 | 34 | .38 | .36 | .34 | .35 | .34 |
| | G | .41 | .39 | 37 | .41 | 39 | .37 | .38 | .37 |
| | F | .44 | .41 | .39 | .42 | .41 | .39 | .40 | .39 |
| | E | .46 | .45 | 42 | .46 | 44 | .42 | .44 | .42 |
| | D | .50 | .48 | .46 | 49 | .47 | .46 | .46 | 46 |
| | C | .51 | .49 | 47 | .50 | .48 | .47 | 48 | 46 |
| | B | .53 | 51 | 50 | .52 | .50 | .49 | .49 | .49 |
| | A | .54 | .52 | 50 | 53 | 51 | .50 | .50 | .49 |
| **16** — MF G-.70 M-.60 P-.50 ↑0 ↓80 — Direct - 3 Kw Reflector 1 - 3000 watt mercury lamp | J | .38 | .32 | .28 | .37 | .32 | .28 | .31 | .28 |
| | I | .47 | .42 | .39 | .46 | .41 | .38 | 41 | .38 |
| | H | .51 | .47 | .43 | .50 | .47 | .43 | .46 | .43 |
| | G | .55 | .51 | .47 | .54 | .51 | .47 | .49 | .47 |
| | F | .58 | .54 | .51 | .56 | .53 | .51 | .52 | .51 |
| | E | .63 | .59 | .5 | .62 | .59 | .56 | .58 | .56 |
| | D | .67 | .64 | 61 | 66 | .63 | .61 | 63 | .61 |
| | C | .69 | .67 | .64 | .67 | .65 | .63 | .64 | .63 |
| | B | .72 | .70 | .67 | .71 | .68 | .67 | .67 | .66 |
| | A | .74 | .71 | 69 | .73 | .70 | .68 | .69 | .67 |
| **17** — MF G-.70 M-.60 P-.55 ↑0 ↓72 — Direct - Troffer Open Type | J | .40 | .37 | .35 | .39 | .37 | .35 | .37 | .35 |
| | I | .48 | .46 | .45 | .47 | .45 | .44 | .44 | .43 |
| | H | .52 | .50 | .50 | .51 | .49 | .48 | .48 | .48 |
| | G | .55 | .54 | .53 | .54 | .53 | .51 | .51 | .50 |
| | F | .58 | .56 | .54 | .55 | .54 | .53 | .53 | .52 |
| | E | .60 | .59 | .5 | .59 | .58 | .56 | .57 | .55 |
| | D | .65 | .62 | 60 | .62 | .61 | .59 | .59 | .58 |
| | C | .66 | .64 | .61 | .64 | .62 | .61 | .61 | .60 |
| | B | .67 | .65 | .64 | .65 | .63 | .62 | .62 | .61 |
| | A | .68 | .66 | .63 | .66 | .65 | .63 | .64 | .62 |
| **18** — MF G-.70 M-.60 P-.55 ↑0 ↓65 — Direct - Troffer with Louvers | J | .32 | .28 | .25 | .32 | .28 | .25 | .28 | .25 |
| | I | .40 | .36 | .34 | .39 | .35 | .33 | .35 | .33 |
| | H | .43 | .39 | .37 | .42 | .39 | .37 | .39 | .36 |
| | G | .46 | .43 | .41 | .45 | .43 | .41 | .43 | .40 |
| | F | .48 | .45 | .43 | .47 | .45 | .43 | .45 | .42 |
| | E | .52 | .50 | .48 | 51 | .49 | .47 | .49 | .46 |
| | D | .56 | .54 | 52 | 5 | .53 | .51 | .53 | .50 |
| | C | .57 | .55 | .53 | .56 | .54 | .52 | .54 | .51 |
| | B | .60 | .58 | .56 | .59 | .57 | .55 | .56 | .54 |
| | A | .61 | .59 | .57 | .60 | .58 | .57 | .57 | .56 |

### TABLE 9-5. (Continued)

| LUMINAIRE | Ceiling | 75% | | | 50% | | | 30% | |
|---|---|---|---|---|---|---|---|---|---|
| | Walls | 50% | 30% | 10% | 50% | 30% | 10% | 30% | 10% |
| | Room Index | COEFFICIENT OF UTILIZATION | | | | | | | |

**19 — Direct - Troffer with Louvers** (MF G-.70 | 0, M-.60 | 60, P-.55)

| Room Index | 75% 50% | 75% 30% | 75% 10% | 50% 50% | 50% 30% | 50% 10% | 30% 30% | 30% 10% |
|---|---|---|---|---|---|---|---|---|
| J | .30 | .26 | .23 | .29 | .26 | .23 | .26 | .23 |
| I | .37 | .33 | .31 | .36 | .32 | .30 | .32 | .30 |
| H | .40 | .36 | .34 | .39 | .36 | .34 | .36 | .33 |
| G | .42 | .40 | .38 | .41 | .40 | .38 | .40 | .37 |
| F | .44 | .41 | .40 | .43 | .41 | .40 | .41 | .39 |
| E | .48 | .46 | .41 | .47 | .45 | .43 | .45 | .42 |
| D | .52 | .50 | .48 | .51 | .49 | .47 | .49 | .46 |
| C | .53 | .51 | .49 | .52 | .50 | .48 | .50 | .47 |
| B | .55 | .53 | .52 | .54 | .53 | .51 | .52 | .50 |
| A | .56 | .54 | .53 | .55 | .54 | .53 | .53 | .52 |

**20 — Direct - Troffer with Ribbed Glass Cover** (MF G-.70 | 0, M-.60 | 55, P-.50)

| Room Index | 75% 50% | 75% 30% | 75% 10% | 50% 50% | 50% 30% | 50% 10% | 30% 30% | 30% 10% |
|---|---|---|---|---|---|---|---|---|
| J | .28 | .24 | .22 | .27 | .24 | .22 | .24 | .22 |
| I | .34 | .31 | .29 | .34 | .30 | .29 | .30 | .29 |
| H | .37 | .34 | .33 | .36 | .34 | .32 | .33 | .32 |
| G | .39 | .37 | .36 | .38 | .37 | .35 | .42 | .41 |
| F | .42 | .39 | .37 | .40 | .38 | .37 | .38 | .37 |
| E | .44 | .43 | .40 | .43 | .42 | .40 | .41 | .40 |
| D | .47 | .45 | .43 | .45 | .45 | .43 | .44 | .43 |
| C | .49 | .47 | .45 | .47 | .46 | .45 | .45 | .44 |
| B | .50 | .48 | .47 | .49 | .47 | .46 | .46 | .45 |
| A | .51 | .50 | .48 | .50 | .48 | .47 | .47 | .46 |

**21 — Direct - With Louvers 4 - 40 watt lamps** (MF G-.70 | 0, M-.60 | 60, P-.55)

| Room Index | 75% 50% | 75% 30% | 75% 10% | 50% 50% | 50% 30% | 50% 10% | 30% 30% | 30% 10% |
|---|---|---|---|---|---|---|---|---|
| J | .29 | .26 | .23 | .28 | .26 | .23 | .25 | .23 |
| I | .35 | .32 | .31 | .35 | .32 | .30 | .35 | .30 |
| H | .38 | .36 | .34 | .38 | .36 | .34 | .35 | .34 |
| G | .41 | .39 | .37 | .41 | .39 | .37 | .38 | .37 |
| F | .44 | .41 | .39 | .42 | .41 | .39 | .40 | .39 |
| E | .46 | .45 | .42 | .46 | .44 | .42 | .44 | .42 |
| D | .50 | .48 | .46 | .49 | .47 | .46 | .46 | .46 |
| C | .51 | .49 | .47 | .50 | .48 | .47 | .48 | .46 |
| B | .53 | .51 | .50 | .52 | .50 | .49 | .49 | .49 |
| A | .54 | .52 | .50 | .53 | .51 | .50 | .50 | .49 |

**22 — Direct Bare Lamp with White Reflecting Surface** (MF G-.75 | 8, M-.65 | 77, P-.55)

| Room Index | 75% 50% | 75% 30% | 75% 10% | 50% 50% | 50% 30% | 50% 10% | 30% 30% | 30% 10% |
|---|---|---|---|---|---|---|---|---|
| J | .32 | .27 | .23 | .32 | .26 | .23 | .25 | .23 |
| I | .40 | .35 | .31 | .39 | .34 | .30 | .34 | .30 |
| H | .44 | .39 | .36 | .43 | .39 | .35 | .36 | .35 |
| G | .48 | .43 | .40 | .50 | .46 | .42 | .41 | .39 |
| F | .52 | .47 | .43 | .55 | .51 | .47 | .45 | .42 |
| E | .57 | .52 | .48 | .59 | .55 | .51 | .50 | .46 |
| D | .62 | .56 | .52 | .62 | .57 | .54 | .54 | .51 |
| C | .65 | .59 | .54 | .65 | .61 | .58 | .56 | .53 |
| B | .69 | .63 | .59 | .65 | .61 | .58 | .60 | .58 |
| A | .71 | .66 | .62 | .67 | .63 | .60 | .61 | .60 |

**23 — Semi-direct Glass Enclosed 1 - 40 watt lamp** (MF G-.75 | 18, M-.65 | 53, P-.55)

| Room Index | 75% 50% | 75% 30% | 75% 10% | 50% 50% | 50% 30% | 50% 10% | 30% 30% | 30% 10% |
|---|---|---|---|---|---|---|---|---|
| J | .23 | .19 | .17 | .23 | .18 | .16 | .17 | .16 |
| I | .29 | .25 | .22 | .28 | .24 | .21 | .22 | .21 |
| H | .32 | .28 | .25 | .31 | .28 | .25 | .26 | .24 |
| G | .36 | .32 | .29 | .34 | .30 | .27 | .29 | .26 |
| F | .40 | .35 | .31 | .37 | .33 | .30 | .31 | .29 |
| E | .43 | .38 | .35 | .41 | .37 | .34 | .35 | .32 |
| D | .47 | .42 | .39 | .44 | .40 | .37 | .38 | .36 |
| C | .49 | .45 | .41 | .46 | .42 | .39 | .40 | .38 |
| B | .52 | .48 | .45 | .49 | .45 | .43 | .43 | .41 |
| A | .54 | .51 | .47 | .51 | .47 | .45 | .44 | .43 |

**24 — Semi-direct - Glass Enclosed 2 - 40 watt lamps** (MF G-.75 | 9, M-.65 | 55, P-.55)

| Room Index | 75% 50% | 75% 30% | 75% 10% | 50% 50% | 50% 30% | 50% 10% | 30% 30% | 30% 10% |
|---|---|---|---|---|---|---|---|---|
| J | .24 | .20 | .19 | .23 | .20 | .17 | .19 | .17 |
| I | .30 | .26 | .23 | .29 | .25 | .23 | .25 | .23 |
| H | .33 | .29 | .27 | .32 | .29 | .26 | .28 | .26 |
| G | .36 | .32 | .30 | .34 | .32 | .29 | .30 | .29 |
| F | .39 | .35 | .32 | .37 | .34 | .31 | .33 | .31 |
| E | .42 | .39 | .35 | .41 | .38 | .35 | .36 | .34 |
| D | .45 | .42 | .39 | .44 | .41 | .38 | .40 | .38 |
| C | .47 | .44 | .41 | .45 | .42 | .40 | .41 | .39 |
| B | .50 | .47 | .44 | .48 | .45 | .43 | .44 | .42 |
| A | .52 | .49 | .46 | .50 | .47 | .45 | .45 | .44 |

TABLE 9-5. (Continued)

| LUMINAIRE | Ceiling | 75% | | | 50% | | | 30% | |
|---|---|---|---|---|---|---|---|---|---|
| | Walls | 50% | 30% | 10% | 50% | 30% | 10% | 30% | 10% |
| | Room Index | COEFFICIENT OF UTILIZATION | | | | | | | |

**25** — MF G-.75 ↑8, M-.65, P-.55 ↓50 — Semi-direct Glass Enclosed 3 - 40 watt lamps

| Room Index | 50% | 30% | 10% | 50% | 30% | 10% | 30% | 10% |
|---|---|---|---|---|---|---|---|---|
| J | .21 | 17 | .14 | .20 | .16 | .14 | .16 | .14 |
| I | .26 | .22 | .20 | .25 | .21 | .19 | .21 | .19 |
| H | .29 | .25 | .23 | .28 | .25 | .22 | .24 | .22 |
| G | .32 | .28 | .25 | .30 | .27 | .25 | .26 | .24 |
| F | .34 | .30 | .27 | .38 | .30 | .27 | .29 | .27 |
| E | .38 | .34 | .31 | .36 | .33 | .31 | .32 | .30 |
| D | .41 | .37 | .34 | .39 | .36 | .34 | .35 | .33 |
| C | .42 | .39 | .36 | .41 | .38 | .36 | .37 | .35 |
| B | .45 | .42 | .39 | .42 | .40 | .39 | .39 | .38 |
| A | .47 | .44 | .41 | .45 | .42 | .40 | .41 | .39 |

**26** — MF G-.75 ↑25, M-.65, P-.55 ↓60 — Semi-direct Exposed Lamps

| Room Index | 50% | 30% | 10% | 50% | 30% | 10% | 30% | 10% |
|---|---|---|---|---|---|---|---|---|
| J | .27 | .25 | .19 | .26 | .23 | .19 | .20 | .18 |
| I | .35 | .29 | .26 | .33 | .28 | .25 | .27 | .24 |
| H | .38 | .34 | .30 | .36 | .32 | .29 | .30 | .28 |
| G | .43 | .38 | .34 | .40 | .36 | .32 | .33 | .31 |
| F | .46 | .41 | .37 | .43 | .39 | .35 | .37 | .33 |
| E | .50 | .46 | .42 | .47 | .43 | .40 | .40 | .38 |
| D | .55 | .50 | .46 | .51 | .47 | .44 | .44 | .42 |
| C | .58 | .53 | .49 | .53 | .49 | .46 | .46 | .44 |
| B | .62 | .57 | .53 | .57 | .53 | .51 | .50 | .48 |
| A | .64 | .60 | .56 | .59 | .55 | .52 | .51 | .49 |

**27** — MF G-.75 ↑39, M-.70, P-.65 ↓45 — General Diffuse - Totally Enclosed

| Room Index | 50% | 30% | 10% | 50% | 30% | 10% | 30% | 10% |
|---|---|---|---|---|---|---|---|---|
| J | .24 | .19 | .16 | .22 | .18 | .15 | .16 | .14 |
| I | .29 | .25 | .22 | .27 | .23 | .20 | .21 | .19 |
| H | .33 | .28 | .26 | .30 | .26 | .24 | .24 | .21 |
| G | .37 | .32 | .29 | .33 | .29 | .26 | .26 | .24 |
| F | .40 | .36 | .31 | .36 | .32 | .29 | .29 | .26 |
| E | .45 | .40 | .36 | .40 | .36 | .33 | .32 | .29 |
| D | .48 | .43 | .39 | .43 | .39 | .36 | .34 | .33 |
| C | .51 | .46 | .42 | .45 | .41 | .38 | .37 | .34 |
| B | .55 | .50 | .47 | .49 | .45 | .42 | .40 | .38 |
| A | .57 | .53 | .49 | .51 | .47 | .44 | .41 | .40 |

**28** — MF G-.70 ↑47, M-.60, P-.50 ↓36 — Direct - Indirect 2 - 40 watt lamps Suspension Type

| Room Index | 50% | 30% | 10% | 50% | 30% | 10% | 30% | 10% |
|---|---|---|---|---|---|---|---|---|
| J | .26 | .21 | .18 | .22 | .19 | .16 | .16 | .15 |
| I | .31 | .26 | .24 | .27 | .24 | .22 | .21 | .19 |
| H | .34 | .30 | .28 | .30 | .27 | .25 | .24 | .22 |
| G | .38 | .34 | .31 | .34 | .30 | .28 | .26 | .25 |
| F | .41 | .37 | .33 | .36 | .33 | .30 | .28 | .27 |
| E | .49 | .45 | .38 | .40 | .36 | .34 | .31 | .30 |
| D | .51 | .48 | .42 | .42 | .41 | .37 | .34 | .33 |
| C | .51 | 48 | .44 | .44 | .44 | .39 | .36 | .34 |
| B | .55 | .51 | .49 | .47 | .45 | .43 | .38 | .37 |
| A | .57 | .53 | .51 | .48 | .46 | .44 | .40 | .38 |

**29** — MF G-.70 ↑18, M-.60, P-.50 ↓49 — Semi - direct 2 - 40 watt lamps Ceiling Type

| Room Index | 50% | 30% | 10% | 50% | 30% | 10% | 30% | 10% |
|---|---|---|---|---|---|---|---|---|
| J | .24 | .20 | .17 | .23 | .19 | .16 | .18 | .16 |
| I | .30 | .26 | .23 | .28 | .24 | .22 | .24 | .21 |
| H | .33 | .29 | .27 | .31 | .28 | .26 | .27 | .25 |
| G | .36 | .32 | .29 | .34 | .31 | .28 | .29 | .27 |
| F | .39 | .35 | .32 | .36 | .33 | .31 | .31 | .30 |
| E | .42 | .39 | .36 | .40 | .37 | .35 | .35 | .33 |
| D | .46 | .43 | .40 | .43 | .40 | .38 | .38 | .37 |
| C | .48 | .45 | .42 | .44 | .42 | .40 | .40 | .38 |
| B | .51 | .48 | .45 | .47 | .45 | .43 | .42 | .41 |
| A | .52 | .50 | .47 | .49 | .46 | .45 | .43 | .42 |

**30** — MF G-.65 ↑46, M-.55, P-.50 ↓33 — Direct Indirect with Ribbed Glass Bottom 4 - 40 watt lamps

| Room Index | 50% | 30% | 10% | 50% | 30% | 10% | 30% | 10% |
|---|---|---|---|---|---|---|---|---|
| J | .27 | .24 | .22 | .24 | .22 | .21 | .21 | .19 |
| I | .33 | .30 | .29 | .29 | .27 | .26 | .25 | .23 |
| H | .36 | .34 | .32 | .32 | .30 | .29 | .28 | .26 |
| G | .39 | .37 | .35 | .36 | .33 | .32 | .30 | .28 |
| F | .43 | .40 | .37 | .38 | .35 | .34 | .31 | .30 |
| E | .46 | .43 | .41 | .41 | .38 | .37 | .34 | .32 |
| D | .50 | .46 | .44 | .43 | .41 | .39 | .36 | .35 |
| C | .52 | .49 | .46 | .45 | .43 | .41 | .37 | .36 |
| B | .55 | .52 | .50 | .47 | .45 | .44 | .38 | .37 |
| A | .56 | .54 | .52 | .49 | .47 | .45 | .40 | .38 |

TABLE 9-5. (Continued)

| LUMINAIRE | Ceiling | 75% | | | 50% | | | 30% | |
|---|---|---|---|---|---|---|---|---|---|
| | Walls | 50% | 30% | 10% | 50% | 30% | 10% | 30% | 10% |
| | Room Index | COEFFICIENT OF UTILIZATION | | | | | | | |
| **31** MF G-.65 M-.55 P-.50 ↑14 ↓45 — 4-40 watt lamps — Semi-direct With Ribbed Glass Bottom - Ceiling Type | J | .25 | .21 | .19 | .22 | .20 | .19 | .18 | .17 |
| | I | .30 | .28 | .27 | .27 | .25 | .24 | .22 | .21 |
| | H | .33 | .31 | .30 | .29 | .27 | .26 | .25 | .24 |
| | G | .36 | .34 | .32 | .31 | .30 | .28 | .26 | .26 |
| | F | .38 | .36 | | | .31 | .30 | .28 | .27 |
| | E | .40 | .39 | | .35 | .34 | .32 | .31 | .29 |
| | D | .43 | .41 | | | .36 | .34 | .32 | .31 |
| | C | .45 | .43 | .40 | | .37 | .36 | .33 | .32 |
| | B | .47 | .44 | .43 | .40 | .38 | .37 | .34 | .33 |
| | A | .48 | .46 | .44 | .41 | .39 | .38 | .35 | .34 |
| **32** MF G-.70 M-.65 P-.60 ↑45 ↓34 — Direct - Indirect with Louvers - Suspension Type — 4-40 watt lamps | J | .26 | .23 | .20 | .23 | .21 | .19 | .19 | .17 |
| | I | .31 | .28 | .27 | .28 | .26 | .24 | .23 | .20 |
| | H | .35 | .32 | .30 | .31 | .28 | .27 | .26 | .24 |
| | G | .38 | .35 | .33 | .34 | .31 | .30 | .28 | .27 |
| | F | .41 | .38 | | | .34 | .32 | .30 | .28 |
| | E | .44 | .42 | | .29 | .37 | .35 | .32 | .31 |
| | D | .48 | .45 | .42 | | .39 | .38 | .34 | .33 |
| | C | .50 | .49 | .44 | .46 | .41 | .39 | .35 | .34 |
| | B | .53 | .50 | .48 | .46 | .43 | .42 | .37 | .36 |
| | A | .54 | .52 | .50 | .47 | .45 | .43 | .39 | .37 |
| **33** MF G-.70 M-.65 P-.60 ↑15 ↓45 — 4-40 watt lamps — Semi-direct with Louvers - Ceiling Type | J | .24 | .21 | .19 | .21 | .19 | .18 | .19 | .17 |
| | I | .30 | .27 | .25 | .26 | .24 | .23 | .23 | .21 |
| | H | .32 | .30 | .28 | .29 | .27 | .25 | .25 | .24 |
| | G | .35 | .33 | | | .29 | .28 | .27 | .26 |
| | F | .38 | .35 | | | .31 | .29 | .29 | .27 |
| | E | .40 | .38 | | | .35 | .32 | .31 | .29 |
| | D | .43 | .40 | .39 | | .36 | .34 | .32 | .32 |
| | C | 45 | .42 | | .39 | .37 | .35 | .33 | .32 |
| | B | .47 | .45 | .43 | .4 | .39 | .38 | .34 | .34 |
| | A | .48 | .46 | .44 | .43 | .40 | .38 | .35 | .34 |
| **34** MF G-.70 M-.65 P-.60 ↑66 ↓20 — Semi-indirect - Totally Enclosed | J | .20 | .16 | .13 | .16 | .13 | .11 | .10 | .09 |
| | I | .24 | .20 | .18 | .20 | .17 | .15 | .13 | .12 |
| | H | .28 | .24 | .21 | .23 | .19 | .17 | .15 | .13 |
| | G | .31 | .27 | .24 | .26 | .22 | .20 | .17 | .15 |
| | F | .34 | .30 | .27 | .29 | .24 | .22 | .19 | .17 |
| | E | .38 | .34 | .31 | .31 | .27 | .25 | .21 | .19 |
| | D | .42 | .38 | .35 | .34 | .30 | .28 | .23 | .22 |
| | C | .45 | .41 | .37 | .36 | .32 | 30 | .25 | .23 |
| | B | .49 | .45 | .42 | .39 | .36 | .34 | .27 | .25 |
| | A | .51 | .47 | .44 | .41 | .38 | .36 | .28 | .27 |
| **35** MF G-.60 M-.50 P-.40 ↑70 ↓11 — Semi-indirect — 2-40 watt lamps | J | .18 | .14 | .12 | 14 | 11 | .09 | .08 | .07 |
| | I | .22 | .19 | .17 | 17 | 15 | .13 | .10 | .09 |
| | H | .26 | .22 | .19 | .20 | 17 | .15 | .12 | .10 |
| | G | .29 | .25 | .22 | .22 | .19 | .17 | .14 | .12 |
| | F | .32 | .28 | .25 | 27 | .24 | .21 | .15 | .14 |
| | E | .35 | .32 | .29 | .27 | .24 | .21 | .17 | .15 |
| | D | .39 | .35 | .32 | .29 | .26 | .24 | .19 | .18 |
| | C | .42 | .38 | .35 | .31 | .28 | .27 | .20 | .19 |
| | B | .46 | .42 | .39 | .34 | .31 | .29 | .22 | .21 |
| | A | .48 | .44 | .42 | .36 | .33 | .31 | .23 | .22 |
| **36** MF G-.70 M-.60 P-.50 ↑79 ↓3 — Indirect Glass | J | .16 | .13 | .11 | .12 | 10 | .08 | .06 | .05 |
| | I | .20 | .16 | 15 | .15 | 13 | .11 | .08 | .07 |
| | H | .23 | .20 | .17 | .17 | 14 | .13 | .10 | .08 |
| | G | .26 | .23 | .20 | .20 | 17 | .15 | .11 | .10 |
| | F | .29 | .26 | 22 | 22 | .19 | .17 | .12 | .11 |
| | E | .32 | .29 | .26 | .24 | .21 | .19 | .13 | .12 |
| | D | .36 | .32 | .30 | .26 | .24 | .22 | .15 | .14 |
| | C | .38 | .35 | .32 | .28 | .25 | .24 | .16 | .15 |
| | B | .42 | .39 | .36 | .30 | .29 | .27 | .18 | .17 |
| | A | .44 | .41 | .39 | .33 | .30 | .29 | .19 | .18 |

## TABLE 9-5. (Concluded)

| LUMINAIRE | Ceiling | 75% | | | 50% | | | 30% | |
|---|---|---|---|---|---|---|---|---|---|
| | Walls | 50% | 30% | 10% | 50% | 30% | 10% | 30% | 10% |
| | Room Index | COEFFICIENT OF UTILIZATION | | | | | | | |

**37** — MF G-.65, M-.60, P-.55 — 85 up, 0 down — Silvered Bowl Indirect

| Room Index | 50% | 30% | 10% | 50% | 30% | 10% | 30% | 10% |
|---|---|---|---|---|---|---|---|---|
| J | .17 | .14 | .12 | .13 | .11 | .09 | .07 | .06 |
| I | .21 | .17 | .16 | .16 | .14 | .12 | .09 | .08 |
| H | .24 | .21 | .18 | .18 | .15 | .14 | .11 | .09 |
| G | .27 | .24 | .21 | .21 | .18 | .16 | .12 | .11 |
| F | .30 | .27 | .23 | .23 | .20 | .18 | .13 | .12 |
| E | .33 | .30 | .27 | .25 | .22 | .20 | .14 | .13 |
| D | .37 | .33 | .31 | .27 | .25 | .23 | .16 | .15 |
| C | .39 | .36 | .33 | .29 | .26 | .25 | .17 | .16 |
| B | .43 | .40 | .37 | .31 | .30 | .28 | .19 | .18 |
| A | .45 | .42 | .40 | .34 | .31 | .30 | .20 | .19 |

**38** — MF G-.60, M-.50, P-.40 — 80 up, 0 down — Indirect

| Room Index | 50% | 30% | 10% | 50% | 30% | 10% | 30% | 10% |
|---|---|---|---|---|---|---|---|---|
| J | .15 | .11 | .10 | .09 | .08 | .06 | .04 | .03 |
| I | .19 | .15 | .13 | .12 | .10 | .09 | .06 | .04 |
| H | .22 | .18 | .16 | .14 | .12 | .10 | .07 | .05 |
| G | .26 | .22 | .19 | .17 | .14 | .13 | .08 | .07 |
| F | .28 | .24 | .21 | .19 | .16 | .14 | .09 | .08 |
| E | .32 | .28 | .25 | .21 | .18 | .17 | .11 | .10 |
| D | .35 | .31 | .29 | .23 | .21 | .19 | .12 | .11 |
| C | .38 | .34 | .31 | .25 | .22 | .21 | .13 | .12 |
| B | .42 | .39 | .36 | .27 | .25 | .24 | .15 | .14 |
| A | .43 | .41 | .38 | .29 | .27 | .25 | .16 | .15 |

### SYMBOLS
MF—Maintenance Factor
G—Good Maintenance Factor
M—Medium Maintenance Factor
P—Poor Maintenance Factor

### LAMP EFFICIENCIES USED IN DETERMINING MAINTENANCE FACTORS BASED ON 70% LIFE

| | | |
|---|---|---|
| 40W | Fluorescent | .76 |
| 100W | Fluorescent | .72 |
| | Incandescent | .85 |
| | Mercury | .84 |

### DISTRIBUTION
Curves represent shape and not quantity of light. Fluorescent curves are taken normal to lamp axis.

↑ 48 Percent Up
↓ 36 Percent Down

48 + 36 = 84% Luminaire Efficiency

other than 79%, the coefficient must be modified.  A simple ratio of efficiencies is all that is necessary.  Supposing the selected luminaire has an efficiency of 74%, then the true coefficient is

$$\tfrac{74}{79} \times 0.61 = 0.57$$

This ratio of efficiencies is valid only for totally direct or totally indirect light distributions.  For other light distributions the luminaire is considered as two separate and distinct luminaires.  One luminaire will contain all of the upward flux, the other all of the downward flux.  The coefficient of utilization will be computed for each.  The two coefficients will then be combined arithmetically to give the coefficient for the complete luminaire.

A little thought discloses the reason for this procedure.  A semi-indirect luminaire may have 60% upward and 40% downward flux; or 89% upward flux and 11% downward flux, within the limits of the definition of a semi-indirect luminaire.  A study of Table 9-2 shows that the zonal constant $K_z$ for indirect flux is lower than the constant $K_z$ for direct flux in the same room.  Therefore, the two luminaires might have the same efficiency but quite different coefficients of utilization.

The following example will illustrate the method to be followed.  Assume a room 20 by 30 ft with a 12-ft ceiling.  The walls will be of 30% reflectance, and the ceiling 75% reflectance.  The luminaire will be of the semi-indirect type similar to No. 35 in Table 9-5.  However, the lamp flux distribution will be 21% downward and 60% upward.  The efficiency is the same as for No. 35, but the coefficient of utilization will not be the same.

Consider first the indirect component.  We have to find the coefficient of utilization for an indirect luminaire having an efficiency of 60%.  From Table 9-1 the room index is $F$.  In Table 9-5, luminaire No. 38 is totally indirect and has a widespread distribution similar to the indirect distribution of our luminaire No. 35.  The coefficient of utilization is 0.24 when the luminaire efficiency is 80%.  Our theoretical luminaire has an efficiency of 60%.  We therefore modify the coefficient of 0.24, by the ratio of 60/80, the result being

$$\tfrac{60}{80} \times 0.24 = 0.18$$

Consider now the direct component.  The room index for direct lighting is different from that for indirect lighting. The luminaire is of the suspension type so we can assume that the light source will be 2 ft below the ceiling, or 10 ft above the floor. From Table 9-1, the room index is found to be $G$. A study of Table 9-5 shows that there are a number of totally direct distributions which can be used, such as No. 11, No. 12, No. 13, No. 15, and so forth. Select No. 11. The coefficient is 0.51 for an efficiency of 79%. Our theoretical luminaire has an efficiency of 21% so the ratio of 21/79 is applied to the coefficient, to yield a corrected coefficient of 0.135.

The coefficients for the indirect and direct components are added to yield a combined coefficient of utilization of 0.315. If we had accepted the tabular value for luminaire No. 35, the coefficient would have been 0.28.

The values obtained from Table 9-5 are quite accurate if the methods outlined here are followed. The values of room index taken from Table 9-1 are recommended for use only in preliminary computations. If the room index is computed according to eqs. (9-1) and (9-2), accurate interpolation can be made from Table 9-5. The same procedure should be followed when using specific luminaire data as supplied by the manufacturers.

## PROBLEMS

*Note:* Candlepower distribution curves referred to in these problems are those to be found in Chapter 8.

**1.** Calculate precisely the coefficient of utilization for the luminaires shown in Fig. 8-9. The room is 22 by 30 ft with a 12-ft ceiling. Luminaires are suspended 2 ft below the ceiling. Work plane is 2.5 ft above the floor. Ceiling reflectance is 75%; sidewall reflectance is 30%.

**2.** Compute precisely the coefficient of utilization for the luminaire shown in Fig. 8-13. The room is 40 by 50 ft with a 14-ft ceiling. Luminaire is suspended 2 ft below the ceiling. Work plane is 3 ft above the floor. Ceiling and sidewall reflectances are 30%.

**3.** Calculate precisely the coefficient of utilization for the luminaire shown in Fig. 8-8. The room is 38 by 54 ft with a 12-ft ceiling. Luminaire is suspended 1 ft below the ceiling. Work plane is 2.5 ft above the floor. Ceiling reflectance is 75%; sidewall reflectance is 50%.

**4.** Compute precisely the coefficients of utilization for the luminaires shown in Figs. 8-10 and 8-11. The room is 50 by 80 ft with 20-ft ceiling.

Luminaires will be suspended 2 ft below the ceiling.   Work plane is 3 ft above the floor.   Ceiling and sidewall reflectances are 30%.

**5.** (a)  Using Tables 9-1 and 9-5, calculate the coefficient of utilization for the luminaires shown in Fig. 8-12.   The room is 28 by 46 ft with a 12-ft ceiling.   The hanger-mounted luminaire is suspended 2 ft below the ceiling.   Ceiling reflectance is 75%; sidewall reflectance is 50%.

(b)  Rework part (a) above by computing the room index and then selecting the coefficient of utilization from Table 9-5.

**6.** (a)  Using Tables 9-1 and 9-5, calculate the coefficient of utilization for the luminaire shown in Fig. 8-1.   The room is 32 by 56 ft with a 13-ft ceiling.   Ceiling reflectance is 75%; wall reflectance 50%.

(b)  Rework part (a) above by computing the room index and then selecting the coefficient of utilization from Table 9-5.

**7.** A luminaire is tested with a lamp emitting 9,950 lm.   Flux in the 0° to 90° zone is 2,200 lm and in the 90° to 180° zone is 4,100 lm.   Using Tables 9-1 and 9-5, determine the coefficient of utilization in a room 18 by 24 ft with an 11-ft ceiling.   Suspend luminaire 2 ft below ceiling.   Walls are 30% reflectance, ceiling 50%.   Flux distribution approaches cosine law.

## REFERENCES

Harrison, W., and Anderson, E. A., "Coefficients of Utilization," *Trans. Illum. Eng. Soc.*, Vol. 15, page 97, 1920.

Harrison, W., and Anderson, E. A., "Illumination Efficiencies as Determined in an Experimental Room," *Trans. Illum. Eng. Soc.*, Vol. 11, page 67, 1916.

*Lighting Handbook.*   New York: Illuminating Engineering Society, 1947.

Smith, J. M., and Ickis, L. S., "Reflection Factors of Acoustical Materials," *Trans. Illum. Eng. Soc.*, Vol. 33, page 373, 1938.

# 10

# PRINCIPLES OF LIGHTING DESIGN

The calculations for the determination of the lumens incident upon a surface, or for source lumens and candlepower, are the same for any lighting application.   Such calculations are therefore included in this one chapter.   In succeeding chapters the discussion will emphasize the lighting methods for various interiors without repeating in each instance the identical calculations.

## 10.1. The Point-by-Point Method

The point-by-point method was one of the earliest developed. It is applicable only to those situations where the source of light may be considered as a point.   In engineering and photometry a source is considered as a point when its maximum dimension is less than one fifth the distance from source to plane of measurement.

If a source is acting as a point, the fundamental relationship

$$E = \frac{I}{d^2}$$

will apply, as discussed in Chapter 2.   The illumination $E$ is on a plane normal to the light ray.   For any other plane Lambert's law of illumination will apply.   This law states that the quantity of light per unit area is proportional to the cosine of the angle of deviation from the normal.

In Fig. 10-1 assume that the surface represented by the line $AB$ is 1 sq ft in area and is receiving 1 lm of light from source $S$. This surface subtends a certain solid angle.   The illumination upon it is 1 ft-c.

The line $A'B'$ represents a surface which subtends the same solid angle and receives 1 lm of light.   This surface is greater in

165

area than the surface $AB$ and hence does not have an illumination of 1 ft-c. The area of $A'B'$ is, in fact, equal to the area of a surface represented by the line $XY$. The area of $XY$ is equal to the area of $AB$ divided by the cosine of $\theta$. But the angle $\theta_1 = \theta_2 = \theta$, hence area $A'B'$ is greater than $AB$ by the inverse of the cosine of $\theta_2$. This is the same as stating that the illumination on $A'B'$ is equal to the illumination on $AB$ multiplied by the cosine of $\theta_2$. Thus Lambert's law has been satisfied.

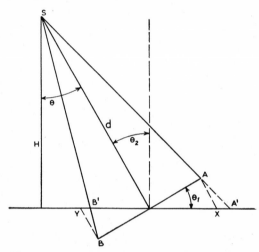

Fig. 10-1. Lambert's law of illumination. Illumination is affected by angle of incident light.

The illumination $E$ may be calculated for any point on a plane if the candlepower $I$ directed to the point, the distance $d$, and the angle $\theta_2$ are known. If the plane is rotated toward the horizontal, the formula is

$$E_{\mathrm{H}} = \frac{I \cos \theta_2}{d^2} \qquad (10\text{-}1)$$

If the plane is rotated toward the vertical the formula is

$$E_{\mathrm{V}} = \frac{I \sin \theta_2}{d^2} \qquad (10\text{-}2)$$

The candlepower or intensity $I$ is determined from a candlepower distribution curve. The angle $\theta_2$ appears directly on such a curve, as the angle $\theta$.

The majority of lighting calculations involving the point-by-point method are for light sources suspended a known distance above a plane. Matters are simplified if the distance $d$ is stated in terms of height $H$ above the plane. Then

$$d = \frac{H}{\cos \theta}$$

By substitution,     $$E_\text{H} = \frac{I \cos^3 \theta}{H^2} \qquad (10\text{-}3)$$

and     $$E_\text{V} = \frac{I \cos^2 \theta \sin \theta}{H^2} \qquad (10\text{-}4)$$

Values of $\sin \theta$, $\cos \theta$, $\cos^2\theta$, $\cos^3\theta$, and $\tan \theta$ are given in Table 10-1.

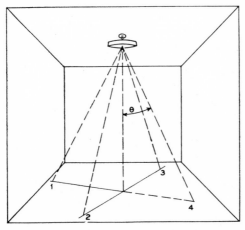

Fig. 10-2.   Point-by-point calculations.

The point-by-point method of calculation is widely used in computing the illumination from sources and luminaires having a direct light distribution. The spotlighting of statues and merchandise, the accent lighting of store counters, local lighting at machines and "downlighting" in auditoriums and theatres are cases in point. The computations are simple but tedious. In Fig. 10-2 there is represented a luminaire suspended 15 ft above the floor. The illumination at a number of points is desired. Select point 4 as an example. Determine the angle $\theta$ and, from the candle-

## TABLE 10-1

### Various Trigonometric Functions Used in Lighting Design

| $\theta°$ | $\sin \theta$ | $\cos \theta$ | $\cos^2 \theta$ | $\cos^3 \theta$ | $\tan \theta$ | $\theta°$ | $\sin \theta$ | $\cos \theta$ | $\cos^2 \theta$ | $\cos^3 \theta$ | $\tan \theta$ |
|---|---|---|---|---|---|---|---|---|---|---|---|
| 0 | 0.0 | 1.000 | 1.000 | 1.000 | 0.0 | 46 | 0.719 | 0.695 | 0.483 | 0.335 | 1.035 |
| 1 | .0175 | 1.000 | 1.000 | 1.000 | .0174 | 47 | .731 | .682 | .465 | .317 | 1.072 |
| 2 | .0349 | 0.999 | 0.999 | 0.998 | .0349 | 48 | .743 | .669 | .448 | .300 | 1.110 |
| 3 | .0523 | .999 | .997 | .996 | .0524 | 49 | .755 | .656 | .430 | .282 | 1.150 |
| 4 | .0698 | .998 | .995 | .993 | .0699 | 50 | .766 | .643 | .413 | .266 | 1.191 |
| 5 | .0872 | .996 | .992 | .989 | .0874 | 51 | .777 | .629 | .396 | .249 | 1.234 |
| 6 | .105 | .995 | .989 | .984 | .1051 | 52 | .788 | .616 | .379 | .233 | 1.279 |
| 7 | .122 | .993 | .985 | .978 | .1227 | 53 | .799 | .602 | .362 | .218 | 1.327 |
| 8 | .139 | .990 | .981 | .971 | .1405 | 54 | .809 | .588 | .345 | .203 | 1.376 |
| 9 | .156 | .988 | .976 | .964 | .1583 | 55 | .819 | .574 | .329 | .189 | 1.428 |
| 10 | .174 | .985 | .970 | .955 | .1763 | 56 | .829 | .559 | .313 | .175 | 1.482 |
| 11 | .191 | .982 | .964 | .946 | .1943 | 57 | .839 | .545 | .297 | .162 | 1.539 |
| 12 | .208 | .978 | .957 | .936 | .2125 | 58 | .848 | .530 | .281 | .149 | 1.600 |
| 13 | .225 | .974 | .949 | .925 | .2308 | 59 | .857 | .515 | .265 | .137 | 1.664 |
| 14 | .242 | .970 | .941 | .913 | .2493 | 60 | .866 | .500 | .250 | .125 | 1.732 |
| 15 | .259 | .966 | .933 | .901 | .2679 | 61 | .875 | .485 | .235 | .114 | 1.804 |
| 16 | .276 | .961 | .924 | .888 | .2867 | 62 | .883 | .470 | .220 | .103 | 1.880 |
| 17 | .292 | .956 | .915 | .875 | .3057 | 63 | .891 | .454 | .206 | .0936 | 1.962 |
| 18 | .309 | .951 | .905 | .860 | .3249 | 64 | .899 | .438 | .192 | .0842 | 2.050 |
| 19 | .326 | .946 | .894 | .845 | .3443 | 65 | .906 | .423 | .179 | .0755 | 2.144 |
| 20 | .342 | .940 | .883 | .830 | .3639 | 66 | .914 | .407 | .165 | .0673 | 2.246 |
| 21 | .358 | .934 | .872 | .814 | .3838 | 67 | .921 | .391 | .153 | .0597 | 2.355 |
| 22 | .375 | .927 | .860 | .797 | .4040 | 68 | .927 | .375 | .140 | .0526 | 2.475 |
| 23 | .391 | .921 | .847 | .780 | .4244 | 69 | .934 | .358 | .128 | .0460 | 2.605 |
| 24 | .407 | .914 | .835 | .762 | .4452 | 70 | .940 | .342 | .117 | .0400 | 2.747 |
| 25 | .423 | .906 | .821 | .744 | .4663 | 71 | .946 | .326 | .106 | .0347 | 2.904 |
| 26 | .438 | .899 | .808 | .726 | .4877 | 72 | .951 | .309 | .0955 | .0295 | 3.077 |
| 27 | .454 | .891 | .794 | .707 | .5095 | 73 | .956 | .292 | .0855 | .0250 | 3.270 |
| 28 | .470 | .883 | .780 | .688 | .5317 | 74 | .961 | .276 | .0762 | .0211 | 3.487 |
| 29 | .485 | .875 | .765 | .669 | .5543 | 75 | .966 | .259 | .0670 | .0173 | 3.732 |
| 30 | .500 | .866 | .750 | .650 | .5773 | 76 | .970 | .242 | .0585 | .0142 | 4.010 |
| 31 | .515 | .857 | .735 | .630 | .6008 | 77 | .974 | .225 | .0506 | .0114 | 4.331 |
| 32 | .530 | .848 | .719 | .610 | .6248 | 78 | .978 | .208 | .0432 | .0090 | 4.704 |
| 33 | .545 | .839 | .703 | .590 | .6494 | 79 | .982 | .191 | .0364 | .0070 | 5.144 |
| 34 | .559 | .829 | .687 | .570 | .6745 | 80 | .985 | .174 | .0302 | .0052 | 5.671 |
| 35 | .574 | .819 | .671 | .550 | .7002 | 81 | .988 | .156 | .0245 | .0038 | 6.313 |
| 36 | .588 | .809 | .655 | .530 | .7265 | 82 | .990 | .139 | .0194 | .0027 | 7.115 |
| 37 | .602 | .799 | .638 | .509 | .7535 | 83 | .993 | .122 | .0149 | .0018 | 8.144 |
| 38 | .616 | .788 | .621 | .489 | .7812 | 84 | .995 | .105 | .0109 | .0011 | 9.514 |
| 39 | .629 | .777 | .604 | .469 | .8097 | 85 | .996 | .0872 | .0076 | .0007 | 11.430 |
| 40 | .643 | .766 | .587 | .450 | .8391 | 86 | .9976 | .0698 | .0048 | .0003 | 14.300 |
| 41 | .656 | .755 | .570 | .430 | .8692 | 87 | .9986 | .0523 | .0027 | .0001 | 19.080 |
| 42 | .669 | .743 | .552 | .410 | .9004 | 88 | .9993 | .0349 | .0012 | .0000 | 28.630 |
| 43 | .682 | .731 | .535 | .391 | .9325 | 89 | .9998 | .0175 | .0003 | .0000 | 57.280 |
| 44 | .695 | .719 | .517 | .372 | .9656 | 90 | 1.0000 | 0.0000 | .0000 | .0000 | Infinite |
| 45 | .707 | .707 | .500 | .354 | 1.0000 | | | | | | |

power distribution curve of the luminaire, ascertain the intensity at that angle. By substitution in Eq. (10-3) the illumination at that point is calculated. If there are a number of luminaires in the space, many of them or all of them will contribute light flux to that point. The illumination is calculated for each contributory luminaire and added together to provide the total.

Isofootcandle curves can be prepared, or are sometimes available, for specific equipment located at various distances from the

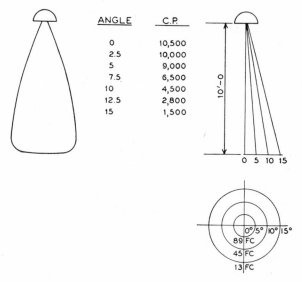

| ANGLE | C.P. |
|-------|--------|
| 0 | 10,500 |
| 2.5 | 10,000 |
| 5 | 9,000 |
| 7.5 | 6,500 |
| 10 | 4,500 |
| 12.5 | 2,800 |
| 15 | 1,500 |

Fig. 10-3. Isofootcandle curves prepared from candlepower distribution curve.

work plane. Their use may save time when extensive calculations are involved. Fig. 10-3 is an example of isofootcandle curves for a direct luminaire located 10 ft above the work plane. The candlepower at various angles is determined from a candlepower distribution curve. The illumination $E$ (in footcandles) is calculated for the various angles. The results are plotted to scale in a series of rings representing points of equal footcandles. This plot can then be laid upon a plan of the interior drawn to the same scale and the results transferred as desired. When the distribution of candlepower is not symmetrical about the source, the isofootcandle curves are obviously not circles. Many computations are then required to plot a usable curve.

In Chapter 6 it was pointed out that the almost universal practice is to design incandescent lamp luminaires to accommodate more than one size of lamp. Provision is made to place the light center at the design point by means of an adjustable socket. When this is done the shape of the candlepower distribution curve is practically the same throughout the range of lamp sizes. Therefore the candlepower at any angle can be considered as proportional to the size of the lamp. Let us assume the designer wishes the candlepower values for a given luminaire equipped with a 750-watt filament lamp. He has available a candlepower distribution curve of the same style of luminaire but tested with a 300-watt lamp. The simple ratio:

$$\frac{\text{lumens of 750-watt lamp}}{\text{lumens of 300-watt lamp}}$$

is applied to the candlepower values.

## 10.2. Linear and Non-Point Sources

When individual light sources of relatively large dimension are placed fairly close to the work point the inverse square law does not apply. This is particularly true of fluorescent lamps and large diffusing types of filament luminaires. Many luminaire manufacturers supply data on the footcandle performance of their equipment under such conditions.

An indication of the illumination to be obtained from a single porcelain-enameled reflector is shown in Table 10-2. Generalized empirical data for several fluorescent reflectors joined together, end-to-end, is given in Table 10-3.

When the lamp and reflector are known, the footcandles to be obtained are found as follows:

$$\text{ft-c} = C \times \text{lamp lumens per foot}$$

When the design level of footcandles is known and the single lamp lumens per foot are required,

$$\text{lamp lumens per foot} = \frac{\text{ft-c desired}}{C}$$

The constants for horizontal and vertical footcandles are selected from Table 10-3.

Suppose the designer wishes to know how many footcandles will be obtained from a row of 2-lamp, porcelain-enameled fluorescent luminaires mounted 4 feet above a bench. The $C_H$ factor is 0.106. If the luminaire is equipped with 4-ft lamps producing 2,300 lumens each, the lumens per foot of a single lamp are 575.

### TABLE 10-2

**Footcandles from Single Fluorescent Direct Luminaire (Two lamps)**

| Height of lamps above work, ft | Footcandles | | | | | |
| --- | --- | --- | --- | --- | --- | --- |
| | Distance from center of unit, ft | | | | | |
| | 0 | 2 | 4 | 6 | 8 | 10 |
| 4 | 60 | 35 | 14 | 5 | 2 | 1.0 |
| 6 | 25 | 12.5 | | 7.5 | 4.5 | 2 |
| 8 | 14 | 13 | | 9.5 | 4 | 3 |
| 10 | 8 | 7 | | 5 | 4 | 3 |

There are two lamps in each reflector so the total lumens per foot are 1,150. Then the footcandles on the bench top will be

$$\text{ft-c} = 0.106 \times 1,150 = 122$$

A more common situation is that in which the desirable footcandles for a certain task are specified. The designer then must provide the necessary lighting equipment. As an example, consider the problem of bench assembly requiring 50 ft-c. To avoid reflected glare the light source will be mounted over the edge of the bench with the work point 1 ft away from the center line of the reflectors. Height of reflectors above bench will be 3 ft. An inspection of Table 10-3 shows that a polished aluminum reflector of narrow light distribution provides more illumination for this condition than a diffuse reflector with broad distribution. The value of $C_H$ is 0.161.

**TABLE 10-3**

**Illumination Constants (*C*) for a Single Row of Fluorescent Direct Luminaires***

| Distance from lamp center to plane of measurement, ft | Horizontal constants | | | | | | | |
|---|---|---|---|---|---|---|---|---|
| | Diffuse reflector | | | | Specular reflector | | | |
| | Distance from center line, ft | | | | Distance from center line, ft | | | |
| | 0 | 1 | 2 | 3 | 0 | 1 | 2 | 3 |
| 1 | .438 | .127 | .008 | .001 | .753 | .079 | | |
| 2 | .223 | .150 | .061 | .017 | .330 | .165 | .035 | .006 |
| 3 | .145 | .120 | .077 | .041 | .212 | .161 | .066 | .022 |
| 4 | .106 | .095 | .072 | .048 | .153 | .131 | .086 | .038 |

| Distance from lamp center to plane of measurement, ft | Vertical constants | | | | | | | | | |
|---|---|---|---|---|---|---|---|---|---|---|
| | Diffuse reflector | | | | | Specular reflector | | | | |
| | Distance from center line, in. | | | | | Distance from center line, in. | | | | |
| | 3 | 6 | 9 | 12 | 18 | 3 | 6 | 9 | 12 | 18 |
| 1 | .185 | .159 | .175 | .165 | .129 | .121 | .125 | .135 | .096 | .080 |
| 2 | .011 | .028 | .044 | .057 | .068 | .028 | .056 | .077 | .086 | .090 |
| 3 | .004 | .010 | .017 | .023 | .032 | .010 | .028 | .036 | .044 | .059 |
| 4 | .002 | .005 | .008 | .012 | .018 | .006 | .013 | .020 | .031 | .037 |

* These constants hold to within about 2 ft from the end of the continuous strip. At that point the illumination begins to decrease rapidly. Data derived from General Electric Co., *Bulletin LD-2*, February 1950.

The lumens per foot of reflector are

$$\text{lumens per foot} = \frac{50}{0.161} = 310$$

Inspection of the various tables of lamp characteristics in Chapter 3 discloses that the 100-ma iron-cathode lamp produces 270 lm per ft, and the 200-ma standard cool white (4,500°) Slimline lamp produces 380 lm per ft. Because the nature of the bench work is likely to change, a wise choice would be to provide more, rather than less, footcandles. A single Slimline lamp luminaire would then be selected.

## 10.3. Rectangular Luminous Areas

Rectangular and square panels of diffusing materials, or complete ceilings of such materials, with light sources concealed above, are extensively used in modern lighting practice. The brightness of these panels must be known in order to calculate the illumination on the work plane. Visual comfort also hinges upon certain limiting brightness values.

**TABLE 10-4**

**Ratios of Brightness in Footlamberts to Illumination in Footcandles for Rectangular Luminous Panels**

(Plane parallel to panel.   Ratios of $B/E$)

| $\alpha$ = vertical angle | $\theta$ = horizontal angle | | | | | | | | | | | | | | | | | |
|---|---|---|---|---|---|---|---|---|---|---|---|---|---|---|---|---|---|---|
| | 5 | 10 | 15 | 20 | 25 | 30 | 35 | 40 | 45 | 50 | 55 | 60 | 65 | 70 | 75 | 80 | 85 | 90 |
| 5 | 415 | 209 | 141 | 108 | 88 | 75 | 67 | 60 | 56 | 53 | 50 | 49 | 48 | 47 | 46 | 46 | 46 | 46 |
| 10 | 209 | 105 | 71 | 54 | 44 | 38 | 34 | 30 | 28 | 27 | 25 | 24 | 24 | 23 | 23 | 23 | 23 | 23 |
| 15 | 141 | 71 | 48 | 37 | 30 | 26 | 23 | 20 | 19 | 18 | 17 | 16 | 16 | 16 | 16 | 16 | 15 | 15 |
| 20 | 108 | 54 | 37 | 28 | 25 | 19 | 17 | 16 | 14 | 14 | 13 | 12 | 12 | 12 | 12 | 12 | 12 | 12 |
| 25 | 88 | 44 | 30 | 25 | 19 | 16 | 14 | 13 | 12 | 11 | 10 | 10 | 10 | 10 | 10 | 10 | 9 | 9 |
| 30 | 75 | 38 | 26 | 19 | 16 | 14 | 13 | 11 | 10 | 9 | 9 | 9 | 8 | 8 | 8 | 8 | 8 | 8 |
| 35 | 67 | 34 | 23 | 17 | 14 | 13 | 11 | 10 | 9 | 8 | 8 | 8 | 7 | 7 | 7 | 7 | 7 | 7 |
| 40 | 60 | 30 | 20 | 16 | 13 | 11 | 10 | 9 | 8 | 7 | 7 | 7 | 7 | 6 | 6 | 6 | 6 | 6 |
| 45 | 56 | 28 | 19 | 14 | 12 | 10 | 9 | 8 | 7 | 7 | 6 | 6 | 6 | 5.8 | 5.7 | 5.7 | 5.7 | 5.7 |
| 50 | 53 | 27 | 18 | 14 | 11 | 9 | 8 | 7 | 7 | 6 | 6 | 5.7 | 5.5 | 5.4 | 5.3 | 5.2 | 5.2 | 5.2 |
| 55 | 50 | 25 | 17 | 13 | 10 | 9 | 8 | 7 | 6 | 6 | 5.6 | 5.3 | 5.1 | 5.0 | 5.0 | 4.9 | 4.9 | 4.9 |
| 60 | 49 | 24 | 16 | 12 | 10 | 9 | 8 | 7 | 6 | 5.7 | 5.3 | 5.0 | 4.9 | 4.7 | 4.7 | 4.6 | 4.6 | 4.6 |
| 65 | 48 | 24 | 16 | 12 | 10 | 8 | 7 | 7 | 6 | 5.5 | 5.1 | 4.9 | 4.7 | 4.6 | 4.5 | 4.4 | 4.4 | 4.4 |
| 70 | 47 | 23 | 16 | 12 | 10 | 8 | 7 | 6 | 5.8 | 5.4 | 5.0 | 4.7 | 4.6 | 4.4 | 4.3 | 4.3 | 4.2 | 4.2 |
| 75 | 46 | 23 | 16 | 12 | 10 | 8 | 7 | 6 | 5.7 | 5.3 | 5.0 | 4.7 | 4.5 | 4.3 | 4.2 | 4.2 | 4.2 | 4.2 |
| 80 | 46 | 23 | 16 | 12 | 10 | 8 | 7 | 6 | 5.7 | 5.2 | 4.9 | 4.6 | 4.4 | 4.2 | 4.2 | 4.2 | 4.2 | 4.2 |
| 85 | 46 | 23 | 15 | 12 | 9 | 8 | 7 | 6 | 5.7 | 5.2 | 4.9 | 4.6 | 4.4 | 4.2 | 4.2 | 4.2 | 4.0 | 4.0 |
| 90 | 46 | 23 | 15 | 12 | 9 | 8 | 7 | 6 | 5.7 | 5.2 | 4.9 | 4.6 | 4.4 | 4.3 | 4.2 | 4.1 | 4.0 | 4.0 |

The mathematical relationships between the brightness of the panel and the illumination on planes, both parallel and at right angles to the panel, are well developed in other texts, notably those of Moon[1] and Boast.[2] If the dimensions of the luminous panels are stated in terms of the angles subtended at the point where the illumination is desired, data can be derived which is easily utilized by the designer. Tables 10-4 and 10-5 have been prepared on this basis. The derivation is based upon locating the point at which the illumination is desired, directly under one corner of the luminous

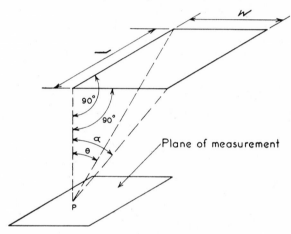

Fig. 10-4.    Illumination from surface source.

area (See Fig. 10-4). In practice such a situation rarely exists, so both real and fictitious luminous areas are set up and calculations made accordingly.

As an example, consider a glass-bottom trough 1 ft wide and 4 ft long, suspended 4 ft above a work bench (Fig. 10-5). The brightness of the glass is assumed to be 1,000 ft-L. Calculate the illumination at a point on the bench directly beneath the center of the luminaire.

The rectangular source is divided into four smaller rectangles so that the point $P$ lies directly under the common corner. Cal-

[1] Moon, Parry, *Scientific Basis of Illuminating Engineering.* New York: McGraw-Hill Book Co., Inc., 1937.

[2] Boast, W. B., *Illumination Engineering.* New York: McGraw-Hill Book Co., Inc., 1942.

## TABLE 10-5

### Ratio of Brightness in Footlamberts to Illumination in Footcandles for Rectangular Luminous Panels

(Plane perpendicular to panel.  Ratio of $B/E$)

$\theta$ = horizontal angle

| $\alpha$ = vertical angle | 5 | 10 | 15 | 20 | 25 | 30 | 35 | 40 | 45 | 50 | 55 | 60 | 65 | 70 | 75 | 80 | 85 | 90 |
|---|---|---|---|---|---|---|---|---|---|---|---|---|---|---|---|---|---|---|
| 5 | 9,080 | 4,765 | 3,226 | 2,420 | 2,000 | 1,728 | 1,538 | 1,430 | 1,284 | 1,206 | 1,150 | 1,110 | 1,088 | 1,075 | 1,065 | 1,054 | | |
| 10 | 2,380 | 1,206 | 813 | 622 | 507 | 435 | 385 | 348 | 324 | 304 | 290 | 289 | 273 | 268 | 265 | 263 | | |
| 15 | 1,076 | 542 | 366 | 279 | 230 | 195 | 172 | 156 | 145 | 136 | 130 | 125 | 121 | 120 | 118 | 117 | | |
| 20 | 607 | 311 | 210 | 159 | 130 | 111 | 98 | 89 | 82 | 77 | 73 | 71 | 69 | 67 | 67 | 66.7 | | |
| 25 | 403 | 203 | 137 | 104 | 85 | 73 | 64 | 58 | 53 | 50 | 48 | 46 | 45 | 44 | 43 | 43 | | |
| 30 | 288 | 145 | 98 | 74 | 60 | 52 | 45 | 41 | 38 | 35 | 33 | 32 | 31 | 30 | 30 | 30 | | |
| 35 | 219 | 111 | 74 | 56 | 46 | 39 | 34 | 30 | 28 | 26 | 25 | 24 | 23 | 23 | 22 | 22 | | |
| 40 | 174 | 88 | 59 | 45 | 36 | 31 | 27 | 24 | 22 | 21 | 19 | 18.5 | 18 | 17.5 | 17 | 17 | | |
| 45 | 144 | 72 | 49 | 37 | 30 | 25 | 22 | 20 | 18 | 17 | 16 | 15 | 14.4 | 14 | 13.8 | 13.7 | | |
| 50 | 123 | 62 | 41 | 31 | 25 | 21 | 19 | 17 | 15 | 14 | 13 | 12 | 12 | 11.5 | 11.4 | 11.2 | | |
| 55 | 107 | 54 | 36 | 27 | 22 | 19 | 16 | 14 | 13 | 12 | 11 | 10.5 | 10 | 9.8 | 9.5 | 9.4 | | |
| 60 | 96 | 48 | 32 | 24 | 20 | 16 | 14 | 13 | 11 | 10 | 10 | 9 | 8.6 | 8.4 | 8.2 | 8 | | |
| 65 | 88 | 44 | 29 | 22 | 18 | 15 | 13 | 11 | 10 | 9 | 8.5 | 8 | 7.6 | 7.3 | 7.1 | 7 | | |
| 70 | 81 | 41 | 27 | 20 | 17 | 14 | 12 | 11 | 10 | 9 | 8 | 7.2 | 6.8 | 6.5 | 6.3 | 6.1 | | |
| 75 | 77 | 39 | 26 | 19 | 16 | 13 | 11 | 10 | 9 | 9 | 7.2 | 6.7 | 6.3 | 5.9 | 5.7 | 5.5 | | |
| 80 | 74 | 37 | 25 | 19 | 15 | 12 | 11 | 10 | 9 | 8 | 7 | 6.3 | 5.9 | 5.5 | 5.2 | 5 | | |
| 85 | 72 | 36 | | | | | | 9 | 8 | | | | | | | | | |
| 90 | 72 | 36 | | | | | | | | | | | | | | | | |

culate or determine graphically the values of the two angles $\alpha$ and $\theta$. These are

$$\alpha = 7° \quad \text{and} \quad \theta = 27°$$

By interpolation from Table 10-4, the ratio of

$$\frac{B}{E} = 67.8$$

Therefore, $\quad E = \dfrac{B}{67.8} = \dfrac{1000}{67.8} = 14.75 \text{ ft-c}$

This illumination is derived from only one-quarter of the luminous panel, or area $ABCD$. The total illumination at point $P$ is therefore 59 ft-c.

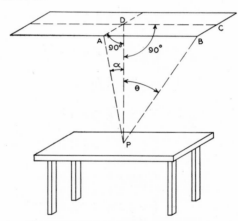

Fig. 10-5. A surface source may have to be subdivided into a number of sources before a solution can be had.

If the point at which the illumination is desired does not lie under the luminous panel, fictitious areas can be set up so that the point lies properly under one corner. By subtraction, the illumination from the real panel can be found. As an example, consider the situation shown in Fig. 10-6. The real luminous area is $ABCD$. The point at which the illumination is desired lies to one side. The fictitious area $HADK$ is added to the real area. Then the illumination from area $HADK$ is subtracted from the illumination provided by area $HBCK$. The result is the illumination from the real luminous area $ABCD$.

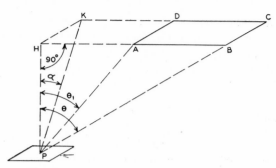

Fig. 10-6. Fictitious areas can be added to surface sources in order to establish the basic mathematical relationships.

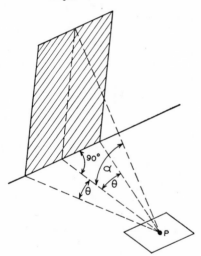

Fig. 10-7. When the luminous source is at right angles to the illuminated plane, choose the proper angles with care.

These illustrations have dealt with the illumination on a plane parallel to the luminous area. When the plane is at right angles to the luminous area the procedure is exactly the same but the ratios of $B/E$ are taken from Table 10-5. Care must be taken to enter the table with the right values of the angles $\theta$ and $\alpha$. These are easy to visualize if the luminous panel and the point of measurement are set up as in Fig. 10-7. Even though the real panel is in the ceiling and the point of measurement is on the sidewall, the relationship is the same as if the panel were in the sidewall and the point of measurement on the floor.

The angle $\theta$ is then described as the horizontal angle, and $\alpha$ as the vertical angle.

### 10.4. Circular Luminous Areas

Circular luminous areas, located in symmetrical patterns on the ceiling, are often used to provide moderate levels of illumination.

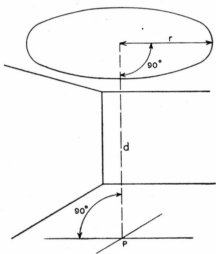

Fig. 10-8. Illumination from circular luminous area.

The effect is decorative and spectacular, rather than utilitarian. However, they are useful lighting elements. The brightness of the element, in relation to the illumination produced, is the principal design consideration.

The mathematics are adequately covered in the texts previously mentioned. The basic relationship, Fig. 10-8, is expressed by

$$E = B \left( \frac{r^2}{r^2 + d^2} \right)$$

where $E$ = illumination on plane parallel to source,
$B$ = brightness of luminous area in footlamberts.

The ratio $B/E$ for panels usually found in practice is given in Table 10-6.

**TABLE 10-6**

**Ratio of $B/E$ for Circular Diffusing Panels of Various Diameters on Plane of Illumination Parallel to Panel**

| Diameter of panel, ft | Distance from center of panel to plane of illumination, ft | $B/E$ |
|:---:|:---:|:---:|
| 2 | 5 | 25 |
| 4 | 5 | 7.1 |
| 6 | 5 | 3.8 |
| 2 | 6 | 37 |
| 4 | 6 | 10 |
| 6 | 6 | 5 |
| 2 | 7 | 50 |
| 4 | 7 | 12.5 |
| 6 | 7 | 6.2 |
| 2 | 8 | 67 |
| 4 | 8 | 16.5 |
| 6 | 8 | 8.3 |

If the circular disk is not uniform in brightness, but consists, for example, of a center disk of lower brightness surrounded by a ring of higher brightness, each area can be treated separately. Determine the ratio of $B/E$ for the entire area. Calculate the value of $E$, using the higher value of $B$. Then determine the ratio of $B/E$ for the center area. Calculate the value of $E$, using the higher brightness. The difference between the two values of $E$ will represent the illumination contribution from the outer ring.

Now determine the ratio of $B/E$ for the center area, using the lower value of brightness. Compute the value of $E$. This value, added to the one determined above, will give the total illumination provided by the circular disk.

It will have been observed that calculations of illumination by the point-by-point method or from luminous panels do not take into account the effect of light reflected from ceiling, walls, and floor. For spotlighting, floodlighting, or strictly localized lighting this omission introduces no significant error.  When the entire space is lighted it is obvious that light will be reflected back and forth from the surrounding surfaces and tend to increase the illumination on the work plane beyond the calculated value.  Fortunately, this is an error in the right direction.  Methods of evaluating the effect of these inter-reflections are now being developed and will be in general use after a period of laboratory and field testing.

### 10.5. Flux-of-Light Method

The design of indirect, semi-indirect, or general diffuse types of lighting systems by using the point-by-point method of calculation would be extremely laborious.  A method was perfected in 1920 by Harrison and Anderson relating the total lumens generated by the light sources in a room to the footcandles obtained on a horizontal work plane.  It is extremely simple and easy to use, and is often referred to as the "lumen" method, or "flux-of-light" method.

The basic formula was given in Chapter 9 as

$$E = \frac{F_g \times \text{C.U.} \times \text{D.F.}}{A}$$

This can be rewritten as

$$F_g = \frac{E \times A}{\text{C.U.} \times \text{D.F.}}$$

$F_g$ = luminous flux generated by light sources,
C.U. = coefficient of utilization,
D.F. = depreciation factor,
$A$ = floor area of lighted space.

The coefficient of utilization is determined by the methods outlined in Chapter 9.  The depreciation factor is a factor of safety. By its use the engineer provides enough additional light flux to assure the design level of footcandles throughout the life of the lighting system.

**a. Depreciation factor.**  A widely used term for this is "maintenance factor."  This is a poor choice of words because maintenance implies the performance of certain operations to prevent deterioration.  A depreciation factor is applied to lighting calculations because of the physical impossibility of preventing deterioration.

The depreciation of a lighting system is due to four causes:

1. Loss of lumens due to aging of lamps in service.

2. Increasing absorption of lumens by dust, dirt, insects, and the like on luminaire and lamp surfaces.  Also, chemical changes in luminaire reflecting surfaces.

3. Increasing absorption of lumens by dust, dirt, and chemical changes in room reflecting surfaces.

4. Difference between socket voltage and lamp design voltage.

The loss of lumens due to hours of burning of lamps is determined by laboratory test.  Values were given in Chapter 3 for the various light sources.  The mean average of lumens has been arbitrarily taken as the lumens output at 70% of rated life for filament lamps and 40% of rated life for fluorescent lamps.  In general these represent a reduction of from 15% to 25% below initial values.

The effect of dust, oil, insects, and the like upon the absorption of lumens by the luminaire will vary widely depending upon atmospheric conditions.  The design of the luminaire also affects this greatly.  The chemical change caused by heat and aging is a variable.  Glass, for example, may be said to undergo no change.  Plastics have variable resistance to change in reflectance characteristics.  Metal surfaces either slowly oxidize or are attacked by acids or alkalis in the air.

The loss of reflectivity of room surfaces depends upon the nature of the surface and the atmospheric conditions.  If the lighting system is indirect or semi-indirect, the loss of reflectance in ceiling and walls seriously affects the performance of the system.  If the lighting is predominantly direct, the reflectance of walls and ceiling is of less importance.  The effect of dirt can be periodically reduced by cleaning and painting.

The loss of lumens in the light source is inevitable, but prompt renewal of burned-out lamps or replacement of very old and blackened lamps is desirable.  Chemical changes in luminaire reflecting surfaces can only be offset by renewal or refinishing.  The voltage at the socket rarely agrees with the lamp design voltage.  It is generally lower.  Since a 1% decrease in voltage results in approximately a 3% decrease in light output, another substantial loss of light is introduced.

It is therefore a physical impossibility and beyond the realm of reason to maintain a lighting system at its initial or maximum value. Good housekeeping and a planned program of maintenance can slow down the rate of depreciation, but never eliminate it. Therefore a depreciation factor must be introduced into lighting calculations.

### TABLE 10-7

**Depreciation Factors for Luminaires (Dust and Dirt Only)**

[For Total Depreciation Multiply by Mean Lamp Lumens Given Below

(Table 10-7a)]

| Atmosphere | Direct | | | | Semi-direct | | General diffuse | | Indirect | |
| --- | --- | --- | --- | --- | --- | --- | --- | --- | --- | --- |
| | Fil. | Flu. | Flu. Troffers | Bare Flu. | Fil. | Flu. | Fil. | Flu. | Fil. | Flu. |
| Clean | 83% | 76% | 82% | 88% | 85% | 82% | 84% | 82% | 78% | 70% |
| Average | 72% | 65% | 70% | 76% | 80% | 70% | 78% | 70% | 67% | 60% |
| Dirty | 60% | 53% | 65% | 65% | 65% | 60% | 72% | 60% | 56% | 47% |

### TABLE 10-7a

**Mean Lumens of Light Sources**

| Watts | Filament lamps, % | Silver bowl filament lamps, % | Fluorescent lamps, % |
| --- | --- | --- | --- |
| Up to 100 | 94 | 88 | Tungsten cathode 82 |
| 100 to 200 | 90 | 80 | Iron cathode 88 |
| 300 to 500 | 88 | 76 | |
| 750 to 1000 | 87 | 74 | |
| 1500 | 77 | | |

Common practice is to include a range of depreciation factors in tables of coefficients of utilization. Many luminaire manufacturers suggest values for their products. Generalized data is given in Table 10-7. The designer should exercise considerable judgment in the selection. A low depreciation factor results in an increase in the required amount of generated lumens. This is obtained by more or larger luminaires and lamps. A high depreciation factor results in a lesser required amount of generated lumens. This appears to save money, but the end result will be lowered visibility of visual tasks as the system ages. As an example of choice of a depreciation factor refer to luminaire No. 36 in Table 9-5. Three values are given; 50%, 60%, and 70%. If the atmospheric conditions are reasonably clean it is safe to assume the middle value of 60%. If the area were air-conditioned, with filtered air and no opened windows, the 70% value could be used. Of the 40% loss in the middle value 17% is inevitable loss of lamp lumens during burning (Fig. 3-5). This leaves 23 percentage points to account for dust on the luminaire and lamp, and dust and deterioration of the walls and ceilings. With indirect lighting this is a very reasonable factor of safety. If the air were dirty and smoky a 33 percentage point factor would not be unreasonable. Viewed in this light a depreciation factor of 40% appears as a common sense precaution.

**b. Calculation of generated lumens.** Assume an office 30 by 60 ft with a 75% reflectance ceiling and 50% reflectance walls, to be lighted to an average level of 25 ft-c. Select luminaire No. 36 (Table 9-5) utilizing filament lamps. For purposes of illustration, values of room index and coefficient of utilization will be taken from standard tables.

The room index (Table 9-1) is $D$ and the coefficient of utilization (Table 9-5) is 0.36. Assume a depreciation factor of 0.60. Then

$$F_g = \frac{25(30 \times 60)}{0.36 \times 0.60} = 208,000 \text{ lm}$$

**c. Arrangement of luminaires.** The number of luminaires and light sources necessary to introduce these lumens into the room will depend upon a number of factors. The light flux should be reasonably distributed over the work plane and walls and ceiling. In general a ratio of maximum to minimum footcandles of 1.25/1 is desirable. Obviously there is a relationship between the candlepower distribution of the luminaire, its distance from work plane and ceiling, and the spacing between luminaires. These interrelated variables are included in the spacing-mounting height values (Table 10-8). Structural features such as columns, beams, pipes, ducts, sprinkler heads, and the like may influence the spacing. However, the values in Table 10-8 should be considered as maximum. Closer spacings and smaller lamps always produce more uniform illumination and better brightness ratios.

**TABLE 10-8**

**Spacing of Outlets and Mounting Height of Luminaires for Uniform Illumination**

| Mounting height above work plane, ft | Concentrating (approx. 30° beam spread) | Semi-concentrating (approx. 90° beam spread) | Direct, semi-direct, and general diffusing | Semi-indirect or indirect |
|---|---|---|---|---|
| | Max. spacing, ft | Max. spacing, ft | Max. spacing, ft | Max. spacing, ft |
| 5.5 | 2.5 | 5.5 | 8 | 9 |
| 6.5 | 3 | 6 | 10 | 10.5 |
| 7.5 | 4 | 7 | 11 | 12.5 |
| 8.5 | 4.5 | 8 | 12.5 | 13.5 |
| 9.5 | 5 | 9 | 14 | 15 |
| 10.5 | 5.5 | 10 | 16 | 17 |
| 11.5 | 6 | 11 | 17 | 19 |
| 12.5 | 6.5 | 12 | 18.5 | 20 |
| 13.5 | 7 | 13 | 20 | 22 |
| 16.5 | 8 | 15.5 | 23 | 24 |
| 17.5 | 9 | 17.5 | 26 | 28 |

*Note:* Distance of luminaires from walls to be 1/3 of maximum spacing between luminaires if desks or other work areas are near walls. Otherwise 1/2 the maximum spacing is satisfactory.

Suspension distance of luminaires below ceiling is subject to many variables. A general rule is to suspend them not more than 1/6 of the distance between floor and ceiling. For mounting height greater than given in the table apply the same spacing-mounting height ratios as indicated in the Table.

**d. Filament lamp size.** A plan of the ceiling is laid out and the luminaire locations indicated (Fig. 10-9). For the present example, 15 luminaires meet the spacing-mounting height requirements. Then the lamp lumens for each luminaire are

$$\text{lamp lumens} = \frac{208,000}{15} = 13,850$$

According to Table 3-3, the nearest standard filament lamp produces 15,500 lm at 750 watts. This should then be the size of lamp selected. However, the 15 lamps will produce more than the 208,000 lm required for 25 ft-c in service. The predicted foot-candles will be

$$\frac{15,500}{13,850} \times 25 = 28$$

A 10% variation above or below the design footcandles is quite permissible. If the nearest standard lamp changes the predicted

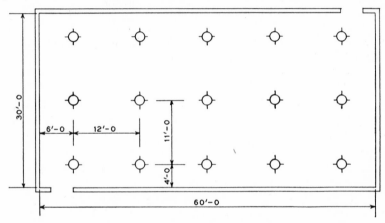

Fig. 10-9.   Typical layout of luminaires.   This is known as a reflected ceiling plan.

footcandles much beyond this value, the number of lamps and luminaires should be changed. In any case do not exceed the spacing-mounting height ratio.

e. Fluorescent lighting system. When the choice of a fluorescent luminaire is made, the size of lamp for that luminaire must also be determined. The fluorescent lamp and ballast are designed as a unit and there is no interchangeability as with filament lamps. The lamp color must also be selected because of the variation in lumens output. The generated lumens, divided by the output of the fluorescent lamp, indicate the number of lamps necessary to provide the design footcandles.

Referring to our example, let it be assumed that the 40-watt, 48-in., 3,500° white fluorescent lamp has been selected. According

to Table 3-6 this has an output of 2,450 lm.   Indirect lighting is
desired.   From Table 9-5 it will be noted that available indirect
fluorescent luminaires (No. 35) incorporate two lamps only.   The
coefficient of utilization is 0.39.   The middle depreciation factor is
0.50.   The generated lumens will be

$$F_g = \frac{25(30 \times 60)}{0.39 \times 0.50} = 230,500 \text{ lm}$$

The number of fluorescent lamps required to generate these lumens
will be

$$\text{number of fluorescent lamps} = \frac{230,500}{2,450} = 94$$

If a 4-lamp luminaire were available, the correct coefficient of
utilization would be ascertained and used in the formula.

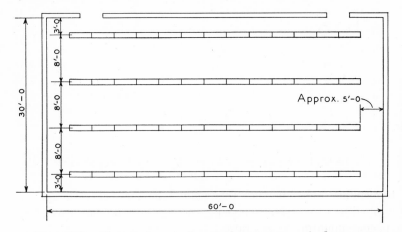

Fig.  10-10.  Typical  layout  for  continuous  rows  of  fluorescent
luminaires.

For this example assume the 2-lamp luminaire as selected.   The
number of luminaires required will be 47.   These must be fitted
into the office in a logical plan.   Each luminaire will be somewhat
over 48 in. long, the exact dimension to be ascertained from the
manufacturer's data.   Four rows of 12 luminaires each will be
arranged as shown in Fig. 10-10.   The spacing between rows is
less than the maximum indicated in Table 10-4, and the ends of
each row are also within required distances of the wall.

Many fluorescent lighting designs, such as the example above, require continuous rows of luminaires. It is often more economical to add a few luminaires in order to achieve this, because they can be wired from one to the other, thus eliminating many ceiling outlets.

## PROBLEMS

**1.** A show window is 13 ft long, 5 ft deep, and 7 ft from floor to ceiling. Two identical spotlights are placed respectively in the upper corners of the window next to the glass. They will light a small advertising panel placed 5 ft 6 in. from the floor and 3 ft back from the glass. The panel is midway from the ends of the window. What central beam candlepower must be provided in the spotlamp to obtain 160 ft-c on the face of the panel?

**2.** A 500-watt bare lamp of 800 mscp is mounted outdoors 8 ft above a table 15 ft in diameter. Find the level of illumination at a point on the table (1) directly under the lamp, (2) 5 ft away from (1), (3) on the outer edge of the table.

**3.** Assume that a work bench 20 ft long is illuminated by two 150-watt, 2,600-lm bare lamps, each placed 5 ft apart above the center line of the bench and 4 ft from the respective ends of the bench. Find (1) the illumination on the bench directly under one lamp, (2) the illumination on the bench midway between the lamps, (3) the illumination on the end of the bench.

**4.** Two sources of light of 16 and 48 cp respectively are placed 10 ft apart. Find (1) on a line running through the centers of these lamps the point, or points, of equal illumination, (2) the point or points of equal illumination on a line 4 ft below the above mentioned line.

**5.** A diffusing panel 4 by 6 ft with a brightness of 300 ft-L is placed 6 ft 5 in. above a desk. Calculate the illumination at a point on the desk directly under the center of the panel.

**6.** A diffusing panel 10 by 14 ft is centered in the ceiling of an exhibition gallery 20 by 24 ft with 12-ft ceiling. Panel brightness is 600 ft-L. Calculate the illumination on the sidewall at a point 5 ft above the floor and 8 ft from the end of the room.

**7.** A diffusing glass window 3 ft high and 8 ft long is set into a wall with the lower edge of the window 5 ft 6 in. above the floor. Calculate the horizontal footcandles at a point 8 ft from the center line of the window and 30 in. above the floor. Brightness of the window is 500 ft-L.

**8.** A plaster ceiling dome 6 ft in diameter is lighted by a cove to an average brightness of 200 ft-L. It is in effect a circular diffusing panel. How many footcandles are produced at a point 7 ft below the center of the dome?

**9.** A circular dome 4 ft in diameter is lighted by means of a silver bowl lamp suspended from the middle of the dome. Around the lamp is a diffusing glass disk 2 ft in diameter. This has a brightness of 125 ft-L. The remainder of the circular area has a brightness of 400 ft-L. How many footcandles are produced at a point 8 ft below the center of the disk?

**10.** How many and what size of filament lamps will be necessary to light a factory 80 by 140 ft using a direct type of luminaire such as No. 1 in Table 9-5? Luminaires will be mounted 14 ft above the floor. Reflectance of sidewalls and ceiling is 30%. Use a depreciation factor of 0.65. Twenty footcandles are desired. What will be the spacing between lamps?

**11.** How many fluorescent luminaires similar to No. 30, Table 9-5, will be needed to light a store 22 by 60 ft to a level of 40 ft-c? Ceiling height is 12 ft; reflectance of ceiling 75%; reflectance of sidewalls 30%; depreciation factor 0.55. Use 3,500°, 48-in., 40-watt fluorescent lamps.

## REFERENCES

General Electric Company, *Bulletin LD-2*, October 1948.

Harrison, W., and Anderson, E. A., "Coefficients of Utilization," *Trans. Illum. Eng. Soc.*, Vol. 15, page 97, March 1920.

*Lighting Handbook*. New York: Illuminating Engineering Society, 1947.

# 11

# VISION

---

The material so far presented in this text might be considered as the mechanical part of illuminating engineering. Light sources, luminaires, and the mathematics and procedures of design are the tools of the engineer. But these are in a sense only raw materials. By definition, light is "visually evaluated radiant energy." Actually light is the energizing force which makes vision possible.

The engineer must therefore apply light with due regard to the workings of the visual sense. The eye is but one part of the phenomenon of vision. It receives and transforms radiant energy. It is an optical device subject to well known laws. The transformed radiant energy is, however, transmitted to the brain, where vision occurs. This involves the central nervous system and is a subjective sensation.

The organization of knowledge concerning vision is extremely difficult. The purely optical aspects are subject to measurement. But what we see and how we see involve many complex psychological factors. The researcher must work with living organisms and construct his theories by questioning and deduction. What appears as lack of precision in lighting application is not always due to faulty technique but to the very nature of the end product, which is vision.

## 11.1. Definitions

Understanding of the material which follows will be facilitated by a description of some of the terms which are generally unfamiliar to engineers.

**a. Accommodation:** The muscular changes that allow the eyes to focus from near to distant objects.

**b. Adaptation:** A set of processes which occur after change of exposure to various brightnesses, whereby the eye is better able to receive the new stimulus.

**c. Size:** The size of objects for the purposes of visual analysis depends both upon the physical size of the object and its distance from the eye. Size is therefore measured in visual angle, usually in minutes or seconds.

**d. Acuity:** Visual acuity is the ability to discriminate fine detail. It is expressed as the reciprocal of the angle in minutes which the just discernible object subtends at the retina.

**e. Contrast sensitivity:** This is the ability to discriminate contrasts in brightness between adjacent surfaces.

## 11.2. Structure of the Eye

The eye (Fig. 11-1) may be considered as a sphere enclosed by a tough covering called the sclera. It is filled with a clear, jelly-like substance called the vitreous humor. Attached to the sclera are a number of muscles which provide lateral, vertical, and rotary movement of the eye for the purpose of fixing upon the object of vision.

Light is admitted to the eye only through the front, this clear portion being known as the cornea. Behind the cornea is a transparent fluid known as the aqueous humor. Next will be found a pigmented shutter called the iris. The iris opens and closes in response to light and also in the process of focusing objects upon the retina. The range of opening and closing is limited to between 2 and 8 mm. In terms of area of pupil opening this represents a range of 16 to 1. The iris thus serves as a partial regulator of the amount of light which is admitted to the eye. The total range of adaptation of the eye is approximately 1,000,000 to 1.

**a. Lens.** Immediately behind the iris is found the crystalline lens, a flexible optical instrument filled with a remarkably clear, colorless fluid. This lens automatically changes curvature to provide for the focusing of near or far distant objects upon the retina. When viewing objects beyond twenty feet from the eye the lens has the least curvature and places the least pull upon the adjusting ciliary muscles. This is called distant vision. It imposes the least strain upon the muscles of accommodation, and represents the easiest eye work. When viewing near objects the lens becomes more convex due to contraction of the ciliary muscles. Other eye muscles act to turn the eyeball inward. The whole process calls for muscle work, as a result of which close vision is fatiguing.

The lens exhibits all of the optical characteristics of a simple lens. It transmits an inverted image and has the errors of chromatic aberration and diffraction. In conjunction with the other transparent substances in the eye the lens serves to absorb certain

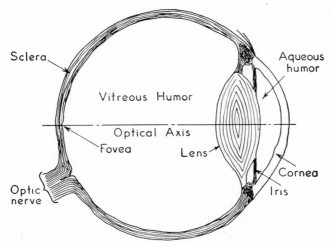

Fig. 11-1. A simplified cross section of the human eye.

radiation other than light. Ultra-violet is completely absorbed. Small quantities of infrared are absorbed but large quantities of infrared cannot be handled. If such radiation reaches the retina there is danger of damage or even complete destruction of the retinal cells.

**b. Retina.** The retina overlays almost all of the inner surface of the eyeball. Its function is to convert light energy into electrical impulses through photochemical action. The retina is composed of nerves with cells of modified ends. One type of cell end is blunt and is called a rod. The other type of cell end is conical and is called a cone. It is estimated that the normal retina contains 15,000,000 rods and 34,000 cones!

A small central area of the retina is called the fovea. It contains nothing but cones and subtends an area of from one to two degrees.

Objects are focused upon this area and most of our seeing and all discrimination of fine detail results from this action.   If the viewed object subtends an angle greater than the area of the fovea, all of it cannot be distinctly seen at one time.   The eye then makes rapid movements similar to the "scanning" of a television tube in order to bring all parts of the object into focus.   We are not conscious of these movements.   The phenomenon of persistence of vision provides for "memory" so that, in effect, the object is considered to be perceived in one instant.   It is obvious that an object will not be seen if, upon focusing, it subtends an area less than the area of one cone.   This absolute threshold, or the minimum sized object which can be seen, is about three-quarters of one minute of arc. However, two lines can be seen when displaced by as little as five seconds of arc.   This is only one of the many visual phenomena as yet unexplained.

The retinal area outside of the fovea is called the parafovea. Here the rods are located, interspersed with cones.   The cones decrease in number from the fovea outward, so that in the peripheral region of the retina there are none.   The rods perceive objects indistinctly, but are alert to brightness and motion.

c. Optic nerve.   It is known that several rods are connected together in one nerve path and it is suspected that each cone has its own nerve path to the brain.   All the nerve fibers together form the optic nerve.   There is, however, a partial interchange of energy between adjacent bundles of rods and cones.   Thus while each has very distinct functions, the entire retina does work as a unit. This has an important bearing upon the lighting of the entire field of view.

Rods and cones contain pigments which undergo change when exposed to light.   The cone pigment has not been identified, but the rod pigment is called rhodopsin or visual purple.   This bleaches under the action of light.   The photochemical process results in electrical impulses in the optic nerve.   These impulses are of constant amplitude but varying frequency.   A high brightness stimulation results in greater frequency of impulses than a lower brightness. These impulses travel through the optic nerve to the brain cortex where what we describe as "seeing" takes place.   Thus the eye as an optical device receives and transforms the light stimulus, while the central nervous system translates the resulting nerve stimulus and initiates the response to that stimulus. Vision constitutes one of the highest categories of human activity.

d. Response to light. The rods and cones vary in their characteristic response to light. The cones operate at brightness levels above 1/1,000 of a footlambert. If an object has a brightness less than this, it cannot be seen by the fovea. Since color is perceived only by the cones there is no color perception at low levels of brightness. This is the basis for the old saying, "In the dark all cats are gray." When the eye is receiving light at a level above 1/1,000 of a footlambert both the rods and the cones are operating. This condition is known as photopic vision. If the light is removed the cones become inoperative, and remain so. The rods, however, slowly increase in sensitivity for a period of about one hour. At the end of this time a condition known as dark adaptation is complete. This is the condition known as scotopic vision. The rods are then extremely sensitive to light, easily able to discern a brightness of 1/10,000 of a footlambert.

When the brightness changes within the range of cone vision the adaptation is very rapid. Upon entering a motion picture theatre, for example, the screen brightness is sufficient to maintain cone or foveal vision. One can see the picture without difficulty. The surrounding areas are not of sufficient brightness to maintain good cone vision or to enable the rods to operate satisfactorily until several minutes have passed. Therefore there is difficulty in finding seats or recognizing objects or persons upon first entering the theatre. After a time, however, visibility becomes quite good.

Upon exposure to light, adaptation is very rapid for both rods and cones. The rate is about sixty times greater than for dark adaptation. Upon leaving a motion picture theatre there is no conscious lag in the exercise of full vision. The change may be actually painful but the adaptation is so rapid that it appears to be instantaneous. This matter of adaptation is of real significance to the illuminating engineer in many fields of lighting application.

## 11.3. Visibility Curves

The retina is responsive to radiation between approximately 400 $\mu$ and 760 $\mu$, but not equally responsive to every wavelength within this range. What is known as a standard visibility curve is shown in Fig. 11-2. The full-line curve is for photopic vision. For the condition of scotopic vision (when the brightness is below 1/1,000 of a footlambert) only the rods are operative, and the visibility curve is as shown by the broken line. The curves are almost identical in shape, but the rod vision curve is displaced to the left. This shift is known as the Purkinje effect. Under low illumination,

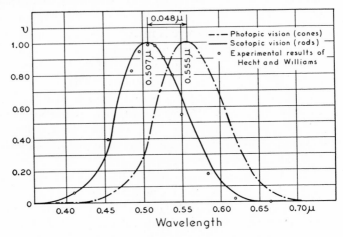

Fig. 11-2. The standard visibility curve for the human eye.

or rod vision, the eye becomes almost blind to red, but quite sensitive to blue. It is for this reason that deep-red glasses are worn to facilitate and maintain dark adaptation.

## 11.4. Field of Vision

The eye is recessed into a bony socket which provides not only mechanical protection, but a certain amount of shielding from light overhead. The nose offers some obstruction to side vision. Figure 11-3 shows the angular extent of the visual fields from each eye (monocular field) and the combined, or binocular, field. When the eye is fixed on some object it is obvious that a large area of the surroundings is also within view, even though the details are not sharply clear. Thus the brightness in the surroundings has an important bearing upon eye function. The circular zone subtending an angle of thirty degrees about the line of vision is of particular importance.

Figure 11-4 shows the loss of visibility due to direct glare in terms of wasted light.

When an object is viewed, it is focused upon the fovea. The fovea subtends an angle not over 2° in diameter. The object is viewed against a *background* which will almost certainly subtend the area of the fovea. The remainder of the large visual field is called the *surround*. The surround is divided into two portions

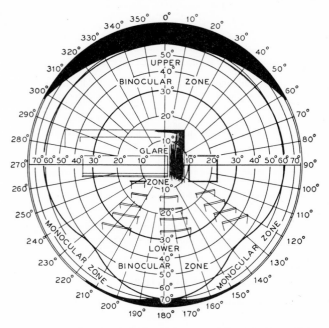

Fig. 11-3.   The visual field.   (*Courtesy of the Holophane Co.*)

for purposes of lighting design; the 30° zone or immediate surround, and the remainder or remote surround. In Table 11-1 will be found the angular size of various objects. Table 11-2 lists the relationship between physical and visual size for various printing types.

Differences in brightness between the object of regard and its background should be high. Differences in brightness between this background and the surround should be low. For good vision the brightness of the background should not be more than three times the brightness of the 30° or near surround. The brightness

## TABLE 11-1

### Angle Subtended at Eye by Various Surfaces

8½ by 11-in. sheet of paper:
at 14 in. from eye..................................... 40°
at 10 ft from eye..................................... 5°
4-in. clock face:
at 10 ft from eye..................................... 2°
End view of automobile:
300 ft from eye...................................... 1°
100 ft from eye...................................... 3°

| Angle | Diameters of areas included within certain angles at varying distances from the eye | | | | |
|---|---|---|---|---|---|
| | 14 in. | 24 in. | 48 in. | 10 ft | 20 ft |
| 0°–30° | 8 in. | 13 in. | 25 in. | 5 ft | 10 ft |
| 0°–60° | 16 in. | 28 in. | 55 in. | 11 ft | 22 ft |
| 0°–120° | 48 in. | 7 ft | 14 ft | 34 ft | 68 ft |
| 0°–170° | 26 ft | 46 ft | 92 ft | 228 ft | 456 ft |

## TABLE 11-2

### Relation of Visual and Physical Size at 14 Inches from the Eye

| Object | Visual size of critical detail in minutes | Physical size in inches |
|---|---|---|
| 6-point type | 1.7 | .007 |
| 8-point type | 3.9 | .016 |
| 10-point type | 6.4 | .026 |
| 14-point type | 7.8 | .032 |

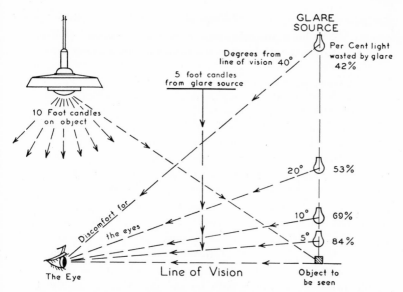

Fig. 11-4.   The effect of glare in the central visual field.   (*From data by Luckiesh and Moss.*)

of the background should not be greater than ten times the brightness of the remote surround.   If the surround, or any object in it, has a brightness greater than the background there is a reduction in visual efficiency.   As a practical matter there are almost always some brightnesses within the field of view in excess of object or

### TABLE 11-3

**Brightness Ratios**

*Ratio of visual task to immediate surround:
  Best condition.............................................   1 to 1
  Good condition..............................................   3 to 1
*Ratio of luminaire to background:
  Best condition.............................................   1 to 1
  Good condition..............................................   3 to 1
†Ratio of visual task to immediate surround.....................   3 to 1
Ratio of visual task to far surround............................  10 to 1
Ratio of visual task to brighter surfaces in far surround..........   1 to 10
Ratio between luminaire or window and surround................  20 to 1

---

\* Research values from *Trans. Illum. Eng. Soc.*, page 720, December 1944.
† From *I.E.S.—A.I.A. School Standard*, September 1948.

background brightness. The degree of skill in the lighting design determines in large measure how small the brightness differences will be. Table 11-3 lists some recommended brightness ratios.

## 11.5. Fundamental External Vision Factors

Having focused on an object, the eye sees it because it has size, brightness, and contrast with a background. The element of time must also be introduced because the visual process is not instantaneous. These four factors are interrelated in a complicated way, but for clarity each one will be discussed separately.

a. Size. It is quite obvious that of two objects of unequal size, the larger will subtend more retinal area than the smaller. If they are of the same brightness, the larger will introduce more light energy into the retina. It will therefore be easier to see. If the two objects are of unequal brightness this may not be true. The smaller object can have its brightness increased to the point where it will introduce as much light energy into the eye as the larger object. Both may then be equally visible.

Suppose both objects are black. To be seen they must appear against a lighter background. The pattern on the retina is then one of darkness surrounded by light. Again the larger object is easier to see. However, if the background of the smaller object be increased in brightness it may be made as visible as the large object against its lower brightness background.

b. Brightness. Light energy sets into motion the photochemical process in the retina. The greater the energy, within certain maximum values, of course, the better the eyes will perform. This energy consists of the total from object and background. We may have a light object against a darker background or a dark object against a lighter background. No matter what combination we have, that which introduces the greater light energy constitutes the better seeing environment.

c. Contrast. Contrast is a shortened term for brightness contrast. If an object has the same brightness and color as its background, it will be invisible no matter how much light is transmitted to the retina. To establish a pattern on the retina there must be a brightness difference between the elements of the pattern. If the printing on this page had exactly the same reflectivity as the paper, it would not be visible no matter how much light was directed to it or reflected by it. Inasmuch as the printing is a good black against a good white paper the contrast is high. It will be visible over a wide range of brightnesses.

The basic formula for the numerical determination of contrast is

$$C = \frac{B_1 - B_2}{B_1} \tag{11-1}$$

where $B_1$ = brightness of background,
$B_2$ = brightness of object.

d. Time. It takes time to see. There is a definite sequence of events which must occur. We must first become aware of the object and then use the muscles of accommodation to focus clearly on it. There is a mysterious "telegraphing" between the retinal stimulation and these active muscles of accommodation. Objects of low brightness require more time for accurate focusing than ones of higher brightness.

Then the light energy must be transformed into the electrical impulses which travel along the optic nerve to the brain. The brain must then sort out these impulses and achieve recognition. Of course, there is a definite upper limit to the speed of vision. It is subject, however, to considerable control through the manipulation of the factors of size, contrast, and brightness.

The element of time takes in not only the speed of seeing, but the duration of the exercise. For example, looking for a telephone number is a seeing task of some difficulty, but lasts only a short time. The person who reads galley proof for the telephone directory, however, is confronted with a difficult seeing task for a long period of time. It is obvious that favorable conditions of size, contrast, and brightness are not nearly so important for the casual search as they are for the continued examination.

This brief discussion should be sufficient to indicate the complexity of relationship between the external vision factors of size, brightness, contrast, and time. But it should be clear that brightness is a common denominator. Since brightness results from the application of light to surfaces, the illuminating engineer can influence greatly the visibility of objects and the whole mechanism of vision.

## 11.6. Lighting to Facilitate Vision

As a practical matter, lighting is one of the most controllable factors in the production of good visual conditions. Size and contrast are usually presented as fixed conditions. If the task is reading, the size of type and the character of the paper are fixed. In reading a given scale or vernier the size of the markings and the background are not changeable. Time, both with respect to speed and duration, is often inexorable. But something can usually be done about the lighting.

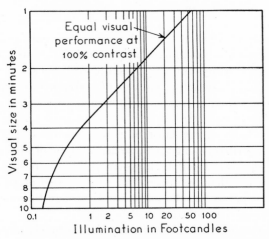

Fig. 11-5. Visibility improves as object brightness increases. (*From data by Weston.*)

**a. Brightness.** A study of Fig. 11-5 shows that a small object may be made equal in visibility to a larger object by increasing its brightness. It is quite obvious that any object can become easier to see if its brightness is increased.

**b. Contrast.** Contrast between an object and its background is inherently a property of the materials. The inked characters on this paper possess a fixed contrast. Illuminated to 20 ft-c they have a certain brightness and a certain stimulation value on the retina. If the reflection factor of the paper were to be reduced, the contrast would be reduced. If the incident illumination is increased, a point will be reached where the brightness of the paper is back to its previous value. The contrast is not equal to what it was before, and never can be. But continue to increase the illumination and the background brightness, and a point will be reached where the visual acuity is equal to its previous value (Fig. 11-6).

The reason is that as the total amount of light energy reaching the retina is increased, the sensitivity to contrast is increased. This simply means that lesser contrasts can be perceived with the same ease as higher contrasts if the total background brightness, hence

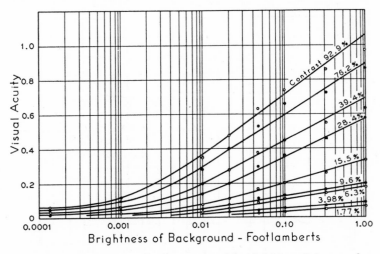

Fig. 11-6. Visual acuity increases as object brightness is increased. (From *Scientific Basis of Illuminating Engineering*, by Parry Moon, McGraw-Hill Book Co., Inc., New York.)

the total retinal stimulation, is increased. The same reasoning will apply if the reflection factor of the characters were changed, instead of that of the paper.

The increase of contrast sensitivity with increase in background brightness is shown in Fig. 11-7. Increasing the footcandles in any space will increase the brightness of the surfaces in that space. This in turn will increase the sensitivity of the eye to brightness differences. Consequently, to maintain visual comfort, brightness differences must be reduced as the general level of brightness is increased. Lighting installations which are planned solely from the standpoint of footcandles often cause dissatisfaction because of failure to recognize this. For example, one may look at a full moon against a dark night sky with no discomfort. The contrast between moon and sky is of the order of 5,000,000 to 1, but the background brightness is low, and the eye will accept large contrasts in brightness.

In a room lighted to 10 ft-c a bare lamp is not comfortable even if the contrast of bare lamp to general background is only 400 to 1. The adaptation level is higher than when out of doors on a moonlight night, and hence the eye is less tolerant of brightness difference.

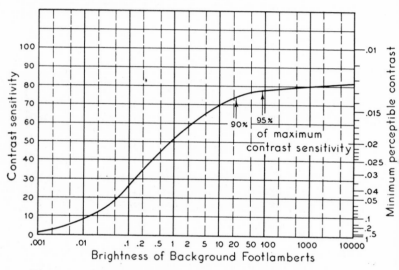

Fig. 11-7. Contrast sensitivity increases as background brightness is increased. (*From data by Moon and Spencer.*)

c. **Time.** As shown in Fig. 11-8, an object of given size and contrast with its background will be seen faster under increased levels of illumination. The abscissa could have been stated in footlamberts without changing the curves. It will be noted that the improvement is greater for larger objects and higher contrasts. Obviously the speed of seeing must approach a limit regardless of object size or contrast. Research indicates that improvement tends to level off beyond 100 ft-L.

d. **Surround brightness.** It has been previously stated that brightness ratios in the entire visual field should be kept within prescribed limits. The amount of light and the way it is dis-

tributed can accomplish only so much in this direction. Ultimately the reflection factors of surfaces will exert the greater effect.

It was pointed out in Chapter 9 that light surrounding surfaces
increase the utilization of light in any room. If the light flux is
properly distributed from correctly designed luminaires, the
achievement of proper brightness ratios in the room is not a difficult
matter. Figure 11-9 shows the general effect of surrounding bright-

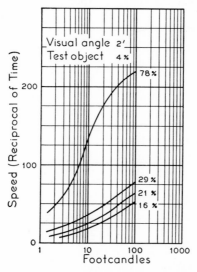

Fig. 11-8. Vision is speeded up
as object brightness is increased.
(From data by Ferree and Rand.)

ness ratios upon vision. It will be noted that maximum visual
efficiency occurs in the region where surrounding brightness is
not less than 1/10 that of the work. When the surrounding brightness exceeds that of the work, vision is poor.

This latter condition is often called glare. Glare is then
described as that condition in which brightness or contrast of
brightnesses interferes with vision. It is commonly divided into
two categories: (1) direct glare, when the offending brightness is
in the field of view, and (2) reflected glare, when the brightness is
reflected from the work in such a manner as to reduce contrast or
produce discomfort. From the standpoint of quantitative analysis,

both direct and reflected glare may be treated from the standpoint
of disability and discomfort.　The subject is too comprehensive
for treatment here.　In general, direct glare is controlled by keeping
the intrinsic brightness of luminaires below certain values.　Locating any unavoidable glare sources as far as possible from the visual
axis will also reduce the negative effects.

Reduction of reflected glare depends upon the limitation of
brightness within areas that are specularly reflected to the eyes

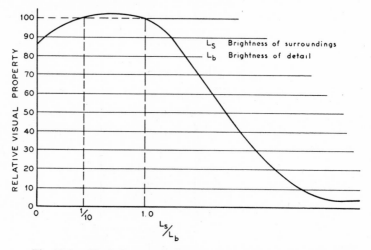

Fig. 11-9.　The influence of brightness ratios upon visual efficiency.
(From *Scientific Basis of Illuminating Engineering*, by Parry Moon,
McGraw-Hill Book Co., Inc., New York.)

from the work surfaces (Fig. 11-10).　Increasing the diffusely
reflected light from the work surfaces will also assist in maintaining
suitable contrasts.　Conditions can also be improved by providing
work surfaces with diffuse or mat finishes.　A shiny surface can
reflect bright images to the eye but a diffuse surface cannot.

The various published standards of lighting application usually
suggest brightness values for luminaires.　These values are based
upon assumptions which experience has shown to be valid.　In
general, the trend is to limit brightnesses in those angles which
contribute to direct glare and to pay scant attention to the brightnesses in those angles which contribute to reflected glare.　The
reason is found in the fact that the control of glare is expensive

either in direct cost or in loss of "efficiency."  Therefore, published values of brightness in application standards should be considered as maximum values, because, in general, they are much in excess of those which research indicates are desirable.

The attainment of proper brightness ratios and the reduction or elimination of glare, are often referred to as the quality factors

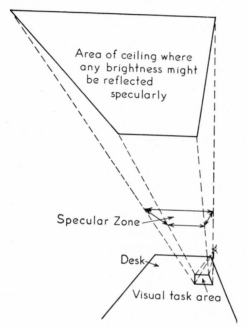

Fig. 11-10.  Reflected images have an important bearing upon visual comfort and visibility.

in lighting.  They are slighted in all too many instances because of poor equipment design, cost, or faulty application technique.

It is no problem today to put enough light into a space.  Low cost of electrical energy and high efficiency of light sources make possible the attainment of high footcandles (and hence of task brightness) well within the optimum ranges indicated by research. Provision of adequate footcandles requires very little skill.  It is in the realm of brightness control and distribution that the highest standards of illuminating engineering meet the test.

# PROBLEMS

**1.** Why does the lens of the eye change curvature as the point of fixation changes?

**2.** Name the two principal functions of the iris.

**3.** Of what significance are the visibility curves for scotopic and photopic vision?

**4.** Show by simple sketches the portions of a classroom 22 ft wide and 30 ft long, with a 12-ft ceiling, that are included in the binocular and monocular visual fields of a student seated at the middle of the rear wall with line of vision horizontal.

**5.** Why should luminaires be of low brightness and mounted near the ceiling of interior spaces?

**6.** A page of printed material, average reflection factor 65%, lies on a large desk of 10% reflection factor. The floor of the room has a reflection factor of 16%. Illumination on the desk top is 30 ft-c. What are the brightness ratios between paper and immediate surround? Between paper and far surround? What should be the reflection factor of the desk to achieve a brightness ratio of 3 to 1 between paper and desk?

**7.** The diffuse reflection factor of black ink letters is 5% and of newsprint, 66%. Under 20 ft-c of diffuse illumination what is the percentage of contrast between letters and paper?

**8.** The specular reflection factor of the above materials is 0.234% for the ink and 0.337% for the paper. If a light source of 1,700 ft-L brightness is imaged by the sheet of newspaper, the diffuse illumination remaining at 20 ft-c, what is the percentage of contrast?

# REFERENCES

Crouch, C. L., "The Relation Between Illumination and Vision," *Trans. Illum. Eng. Soc.*, Vol. 40, page 747, November 1945.

Hardy, LeGrand H., M.D., "The Eye as Affected by Illumination," *Trans. Illum. Eng. Soc.*, Vol. 29, page 364, May 1934.

Holophane Company, Inc., *Architects*, Vol. 7, no. 2, June 1946.

Luckiesh, M., and Moss, Frank, *Seeing*. Baltimore: Williams and Wilkins Co., 1931.

Moon, Parry, *Scientific Basis of Illuminating Engineering*. New York: McGraw-Hill Book Co., Inc., 1937.

# 12

# OFFICES AND SCHOOLS

The work performed in offices and schools is principally visual. Reading, typing, bookkeeping, drafting, sewing, and manual arts require the discrimination of fine detail and close concentration. Similarly, participation in indoor sports demands considerable physical activity coupled with seeing rapidly moving objects.

Lighting systems for these activities are designed on the over-all or general basis because the entire space is usable. Supplementary lighting is sometimes necessary for special tasks such as at blackboards, office machines, file cabinets, and fine bench or machine work. The prime function of the lighting is to make these visual tasks as easy to see as their characteristics require and the state of the lighting art will permit. Most of these tasks have a measurable limiting visibility.

It is now possible to provide lighting which will produce better than 90% over-all visual efficiency. The esthetic or appearance factor is a secondary consideration. However, good lighting can always be pleasant; good lighting is always comfortable.

## 12.1. Quantity of Light

The brightness of an object depends upon its reflection or transmission factor and the amount of light upon it. Footcandles have no direct meaning in terms of visibility. They must always be considered in partnership with the reflection or transmission characteristics of the object to be viewed.

The visual tasks in schools and offices cover a wide range of size and contrast. Theoretically each calls for a different brightness to attain a high degree of visibility. Since it is impossible to arrange for this, lighting practice aims at an over-all average of footcandles which suffices for the majority of visual tasks.

As previously pointed out, the prescription of footcandles is not precise. Recommended values move upward as advances in the art and improvement in lighting systems permit. In Table 12-1 are recommended values of footcandles for various spaces and tasks

### TABLE 12-1

**Recommended Footcandles for Schools and Offices**

| Type of use | Minimum horizontal footcandles in service* |
|---|---|
| Classrooms—on desks and chalkboards.......... | 15–30 |
| Study-halls, laboratories, art rooms............ | 15–30 |
| Sight-saving classrooms........................ | 50 |
| Bookkeeping, tabulation, auditing.............. | 50 |
| Drafting, typing, and sewing, rooms............ | 25–50 |
| General correspondence, private offices: Conference, file, and mail rooms.............. | 25 |
| Reception rooms, wash rooms, cafeterias: Locker rooms, auditoriums, stairways, corridors with lockers............................... | 10 |
| Open corridors, store rooms................... | 5 |

* These values represent a range selected from various authoritative sources such as:

*American Recommended Practice for School Lighting*, A.S.A. Standard A-23.1, 1948.
*Visual Comfort and Efficiency in School Buildings*, University of the State of New York, Division of School Buildings and Grounds.
*Lighting Schoolrooms*, Pamphlet No. 104, Federal Security Agency, U.S. Office of Education.
*Guide For Planning School Plants*, National Council of Schoolhouse Construction, 1946.

in schools and offices. These footcandle values represent combined daylighting and electric lighting. In many States there are minimum legal standards of footcandles for school areas.

## 12.2. Lighting Design

Design methods are as outlined in Chapter 10. The lumen method is used for general lighting and the point-by-point method for supplementary lighting. Examples of practice are given in Figs. 12-4 to 12-19.

The light source may be either filament or fluorescent. In general, the filament lamp is preferred when not over 30 footcandles are required. For higher levels of illumination the fluorescent

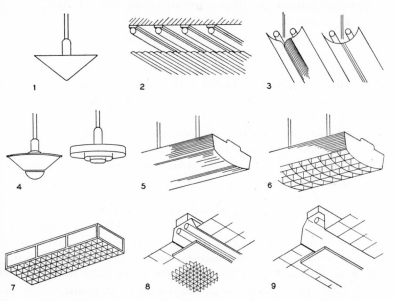

Fig. 12-1. Luminaire types used in classrooms and offices. Indirect—1,3,4. Semi-indirect—5. Direct-indirect—6,7. Direct troffers—8,9. The completely luminous ceiling, 2, is direct lighting but with all of the qualities of indirect lighting.

lamp is more satisfactory. The fluorescent lamp color which corresponds to the so-called 3,000°–3,500° Kelvin temperature range is suitable for classrooms. This is an efficient lamp and causes the least distortion in the color of familiar surfaces. For art rooms and laboratories the 4,500° Kelvin color provides a closer approach to the daylight color usually preferred in these areas. The silver-bowl filament lamp is an effective source because of favorable maintenance characteristics. It is used in indirect luminaires in classrooms, libraries, and laboratories, and in direct-type luminaires in shops and gymnasiums.

The types of lighting most suitable for offices, drafting rooms, classrooms and libraries, in order of quality are:

1. Luminous indirect.
2. Totally indirect.
3. Semi-indirect (brightness not to exceed 500 ft-L in the 0° to 45° zone).
4. Direct-indirect (45° shielding toward line of sight).
5. Glass-covered troffers on 3 to 4-ft centers (glass not to exceed 500 ft-L brightness in 0° to 45° zone).
6. Deep open-bottom troffer with single lamp (spacing not to exceed 5 ft and brightness not to exceed 1,200 ft-L in 0° to 45° zone).
7. Glass-covered troffers on conventional spacings (brightness not to exceed 100 ft-L in 0° to 45° zone).
8. Open-bottom or louvered troffers on conventional spacings with standard lamps.

For the lighting of shops and gymnasiums, direct systems are favored, as in factory buildings (Chapter 13). In shops, the luminaires are usually attached to the ceiling or suspended a short distance below. In gymnasiums the luminaires are attached to the ceiling, or recessed flush with it. To prevent damage from a direct hit by a ball, the luminaire is provided with a wire guard, louver, or shatter-proof lens.

## 12.3. Brightness Limits for Luminaires

The selection of a luminaire with definite brightnesses will aid the designer in achieving satisfactory brightness ratios in the room. For convenience, three portions of the luminaire are considered (Fig. 12-2):

a.   0° to 45° (reflected glare zone).
b.   45° to 60° (direct glare zone).
c.   60° to 90° (direct glare zone).

In Table 12-2 will be found some recommended brightness values for these zones. The designer has only to refer to the photometric data for any luminaire to determine whether it meets these requirements.

Strictly speaking, any brightness in the field of view bears a certain relationship to the brightness of the seeing task. As a practical matter, in any space, all identical luminaires will possess the same brightness once a selection has been made. The values given in Table 12-2 will apply for footcandle levels up to 50. If

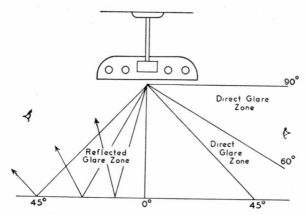

Fig. 12-2. Luminaire zones in which brightness should be regulated.

the design level is less than this the brightness limits are still satisfactory because of lowered contrast sensitivity. If the design level is above 50 the recommended values can only be exceeded by a small amount.

The classical experiments of Nutting showed that for a footcandle level of 10, no brightness in the visual field should exceed 250 ft-L. Further, he showed that the footcandle level must increase by 10 times before the limiting brightness can be doubled. In other words, in a room lighted to 100 ft-c the maximum brightness in the field of view should not exceed 500 ft-L.

The values in Table 12-2 should therefore be considered as maximum. Lower brightness limits will always lead to greater visual comfort. Note also *that as the total luminous area increases, the maximum brightness must decrease.* This is in accord with basic visual theory. For example, a luminaire suspended alone in a conventional office may have a brightness of 350 ft-L in the 45° to 90° zone. If this luminaire is joined to others like it to form a continuous row, the brightness in the direct viewing zone should not exceed 200 ft-L. When the entire ceiling is of luminous diffusing material with lamps above, the brightness should be less than 175 ft-L.

Unshielded lamps of any description are not permissible within the limits of good lighting practice in offices and schools. The

TABLE 12-2

**Brightness Limits for Luminaires for Offices and Schools***

| Zone | Footlamberts |
|------|--------------|
| 0°–45° | 500–1,000 |
| 45°–90° | 350 for single luminaire, 200 for continuous row of luminaires |
| 45°–60° | 450 |
| 60°–90° | 225 |
| Luminous ceiling | 175 |

* These values are based on a study of successful lighting installations, and recent work of Crouch and of Crouch and Fowler.

so-called low brightness fluorescent lamps have a brightness in the neighborhood of 1,000 ft-L. Other fluorescent lamps range from 1,600 to 2,000 ft-L in brightness. Filament lamps have enormously greater brightnesses.

The control of brightness in the 0° to 45° zone presents a difficult problem to the designer. In the first place it does not receive the attention it deserves. This portion of the luminaire is not so readily seen. It does not have much bearing upon immediate visual comfort. Luminaire designers like to push as much light as possible through this zone because of the favorable effect upon "footcandles." But this part of the luminaire is "seen by the work" and often reflected by the work toward the eye. This reflection is annoying and reduces the visibility of the seeing task.

Printing and pencil or ink marks have a surface sheen and act

## TABLE 12-3

### Reflection Factors of Papers and Inks*

| Type of paper | Diffuse reflection factor, % | | Specular reflection factor, % | |
|---|---|---|---|---|
| | Paper | Ink | Paper | Ink |
| Mat white paper | 77 | | | |
| Mat black paper | 4 | | | |
| Printed page of coated magazine paper | 65 | | | |
| Printed page of coated book paper | 65–68 | | | |
| Typewritten letter | 52–63 | | | |
| Carbon copy of typewritten letter | 52 | | | |
| 80# gloss paper | 78 | 2.85 | 0.418 | 0.543 |
| Newsprint | 66 | 4.7 | 0.337 | 0.234 |
| 16# sulphate bond | 63 | 4.15 | 0.265 | 0.22 |
| 25# rag paper | 72 | 3.54 | 0.204 | 0.26 |
| 70# offset paper | 73 | 4.4 | 0.143 | 0.189 |
| 20# Hammermill Bond | 71 | 4.0 | 0.143 | 0.202 |
| 50# semi-gloss | 73 | 4.0 | 0.235 | 0.437 |
| 24# 75% rag paper | 76 | 2.3 | 0.102 | 0.54 |
| Canary Sulphate | 65 | 3.88 | 0.265 | 0.255 |

* From studies conducted by the author.

like tiny mirrors.   They possess both specular and diffuse reflection characteristics (Table 12-3).   The same applies to most papers. When paper and printing reflect diffusely, the condition is known as "no glare."   The contrast under such circumstances is

$$C = \frac{B_{1D} - B_{2D}}{B_{1D}}$$

where $B_{1D}$ = brightness of background,
$B_{2D}$ = brightness of object.

EXAMPLE:

For black ink printing on white paper, the diffuse reflectance of ink may be assumed as 4%, and that of the paper as 73%.   Under 30 ft-c of illumination $B_{1D}$ is 22 ft-L, and $B_{2D}$ is 1.2 ft-L. The contrast is, then,

$$C = \frac{22 - 1.2}{22} = 94.5\%$$

Suppose now that a source of 1,600 ft-L is reflected from the work to the eye of an observer. The specular reflectance of the ink may be assumed as 0.19% and that of the paper 0.14%. The total brightness of ink and paper will be the sum of the specular and diffuse brightness. Contrast is, then,

$$C = \frac{(B_{1S} + B_{1D}) - (B_{2S} + B_{2D})}{(B_{1S} + B_{1D})} \qquad (12\text{-}1)$$

where $B_{1S}$ = specular brightness of background,
    $B_{1D}$ = diffuse brightness of background,
    $B_{2S}$ = specular brightness of object,
    $B_{2D}$ = diffuse brightness of object.

The specular brightness of the paper is .0014 × 1600 = 2.24 ft-L. The specular brightness of the ink is 3.04 ft-L. The contrast is, then,

$$C = \frac{(22 + 2.24) - (1.2 + 3.04)}{(22 + 2.24)} = 82.5\%$$

This reduction in contrast has about the same effect upon visibility as reducing the footcandles by 40% (Fig. 12-3).

As a practical matter it is impossible to eliminate some degree of specularly reflected image brightness. However, the lower the brightness of the source to be reflected, the less will be the reduction in visibility.

The value of 1,000 ft-L given in Table 12-2 for the 0° to 45° zone is a compromise between what is theoretically correct and a practical value. There are many luminaires available which have low brightness in the 0° to 45° zone. An engineer can always custom-design a luminaire to provide a brightness that is practically attainable and within the limits which research discloses is desirable. Many qualified illuminating engineers believe that no brightness in excess of 500 ft-L should be allowed in the 0° to 45° zone. In

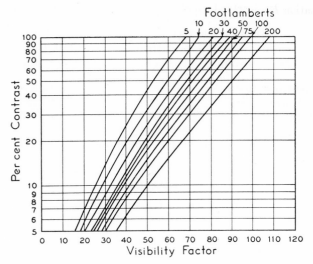

Fig. 12-3. The relationship between visibility factor, contrast, and brightness. (*From data by Darley and Ickis.*)

the 45° to 90° zone the limit should be in the neighborhood of 350 ft-L.

## 12.4. Brightness Ratios in the Visual Field

When the engineer has worked out a design for a certain number of footcandles, and specified a luminaire with the proper brightness values, there remains the specification of reflectances for surfaces in the room. The brightness ratios in the room can then be determined.

In Table 12-4 will be found the brightness ratios suggested for offices, drafting rooms, classrooms, libraries, or any space where close visual work is carried on. A method[1] is now being developed whereby the ratios and absolute values of brightness can be determined by a coordinated series of computations. Until it has been expanded and laboratory tested, the engineer must proceed as outlined in this chapter.

The printed page of a book has an average reflectance of 65%.

---

[1] "Interreflection method," based on the original work of Buckley, Hisano, Yamauti, Moon, and Spencer.

If the book is read while resting on a desk, the desk surface should have a reflectance of not less than 22%. This will produce the minimum ratio of 1 to 1/3 in brightness. The desk top constitutes the immediate surround. It should not have a reflectance greater than the task. A desirable range of work surface reflectance is 25% to 50%. The floor constitutes the far surround. Its reflectance should not be less than 1/10 of 65% or 6.5%. In classrooms the desk space often consists only of the arm of a chair. The floor then constitutes the immediate surround and its reflectance should be 1/3 that of the task.

### TABLE 12-4

**Brightness Ratios for Good Visual Conditions***

| | |
|---|---|
| Task to immediate surround (desk or floor).. | 1 to $\frac{1}{3}$ minimum |
| Task to far surround (floor beyond desk).... | 1 to $\frac{1}{10}$ minimum |
| Task to ceiling.......................... | 1 to 10 maximum |
| Task to walls........................... | 1 to $\frac{1}{5}$ minimum |
| Task to luminaire....................... | 1 to 50 maximum |
| Luminaire to ceiling..................... | 20 to 1 maximum |
| Window to wall......................... | 20 to 1 maximum |

* Based upon recommendations and studies listed in the references.

Floor surfaces of 25% reflectance are now available for offices and schools, and their use is highly desirable.

The sidewalls sometimes appear in the immediate surround and sometimes in the far surround. Their brightness will depend upon incident illumination and reflectance. Experience indicates that the light on sidewalls is approximately one-half that on horizontal surfaces if the lighting system falls within the listing on page 210. The reflectance of such surfaces should not be less than 40% that of the task if the ratios of Table 12-4 are to be maintained. Fortunately, reflectances of 30% to 70% are favored for side-walls.

The ceiling usually constitutes a portion of the far surround. The brightness with indirect lighting may turn out to be higher than that of the task. This departure from basic visual theory cannot be avoided. It is necessary in order to achieve other benefits of greater value. When the luminaire is recessed into the ceiling, as with troffers, the brightness ratio between the luminaire and adjacent ceiling is rarely within prescribed limits. The ceiling almost never exceeds 10 ft-L brightness. The luminaire should not exceed 200 ft-L brightness if the 1 to 20 ratio is to be maintained. However so many luminaires do that these lighting methods rate low in the quality scale.

Ceiling reflectances should be above 75% because of the influence on over-all light utilization and brightness ratios. Windows under some conditions present a very bright area. Because of the wide variation in the brightness that may occur, some method of shading should be provided. Through the use of shades, blinds, or jalousies the window areas can be reduced in brightness to a comfortable value. Walls, ceilings, and work surfaces should have dull finishes. Shiny, specular surfaces reflect bright images. These reflections lead to discomfort and loss of visibility. A fundamental of vision is that, for most school and office tasks, diffuse brightness alone is of use to the eye.

EXAMPLE:

An office is lighted to a level of 30 ft-c by a luminous indirect system of individual luminaires. Maximum luminaire brightness is 225 ft-L. Walls are 50% reflectance; ceiling 80% reflectance. Average ceiling brightness is 100 ft-L. Desk surface is 25% reflectance; floor 16%. The eye task is the reading of a printed page of 60% reflectance. Assume a wall illumination of 15 ft-c.

The brightnesses and the brightness ratios will be as follows:

| Brightness, ft-L | | Ratios | |
| --- | --- | --- | --- |
| Task | 18 | Task to desk | 1 to 1/2.4 |
| Desk | 7.5 | Task to floor | 1 to 1/3.75 |
| Floor | 4.8 | Task to wall | 1 to 1/2.4 |
| Walls | 7.5 | Task to ceiling | 1 to 5.6 |
| Ceiling | 100 | Task to luminaire | 1 to 12.5 |
| Luminaire | 225 | Luminaire to ceiling | 2.25 to 1 |

All values are well within the range of good practice.

Pertinent brightness values are often "written in" on photographs or perspective sketches of the installation. This is an effective way of presenting the brightness pattern to others or for purposes of record. Illustrations of such prints are found in Figs. 12-12, 12-18, and 12-19.

Fig. 12-4. An office lighted by a luminous ceiling of low and uniform brightness. Fluorescent lamps are located in the space above the translucent panels.

Fig. 12-5. A conventional method for lighting offices, using continuous rows of louvered fluorescent lamps. There is no brightness control in the reflected glare zone.

Fig. 12-6.   Fluorescent lamps are placed above large-scale cubical louvers in this public space.   Louvers control brightness in the direct glare zone.

Fig. 12-7.   Luminous indirect fluorescent luminaires provide excellent diffusion and brightness control in all zones for exacting eye work.

Fig. 12-8. Illumination on the sidewalls from sources around the dropped ceiling reduces brightness contrasts in this reading area.

Fig. 12-9. Glass-covered fluorescent light boxes of low brightness, and cove lighting in the public space provides good quality lighting for clerical tasks.

Fig. 12-10. (a) Silvered bowl lamps above an "egg-crate" ceiling provide the finest control of brightness in both direct and reflected zones.

Fig. 12-10. (b) Simple wiring and replacement of silvered bowl lamps through the "egg-crate" results in low cost and easy maintenance.

Fig. 12-11. Silvered bowl lamps provide high quality lighting in a classroom. High reflection factors for all surfaces including chalkboards improve brightness ratios and light utilization.

Fig. 12-12. Silvered bowl lamps in large luminaires provide good quality lighting for gymnasiums.

Fig. 12-13. Fluorescent lamps are located above diffusing glass panels between the beams. The brightness and brightness ratios are low, and light utilization is high. The imposed figures indicate brightness values in footlamberts.

Fig. 12-14. A single row of louvered fluorescent lamps produces good illumination on the vertical surfaces of the lockers. It also is in harmony with the long corridor.

Fig. 12-15. This combination gymnasium and auditorium has two lighting systems. Direct lighting from the continuous troughs is of high level for sports. Indirect lighting from coves is suitable for dancing and public gatherings.

Fig. 12-16. Utilitarian lighting of a gymnasium with industrial type fluorescent luminaires. Note the continuous wire mesh underneath the luminaires to protect against flying objects.

Fig. 12-17. The prismatic glass luminaires, equipped with incandescent lamps and wire guards, allow sufficient light to pass upward to the white, acoustically treated ceiling to produce a pleasing brightness contrast. Light walls add to the lighting effectiveness.

Fig. 12-18. Luminous indirect luminaires and filament lamps produce a pleasing and comfortable brightness balance. The various brightness values in footlamberts are indicated. (*Wakefield Brass Co. photograph.*)

Fig. 12-19. Luminous indirect fluorescent luminaires produce excellent brightness ratios in an office or classroom. The values indicated are in footlamberts. (*Wakefield Brass Co. photograph.*)

# PROBLEMS

**1.** An office is lighted by a system of direct-indirect luminaires. Brightness in the 0° to 45° zone is 1,600 ft-L. Average horizontal illumination is 40 ft-c. What is the percentage of contrast of a printed character on newsprint under the diffuse illumination alone? What is the contrast when the light source is imaged in the printing? Is this an acceptable condition?

**2.** A classroom is to be indirectly lighted to a level of 30 ft-c. Illumination on the vertical wall surfaces can be assumed as 15 ft-c. The average ceiling brightness can be assumed as 125 ft-L. The visual task will be the reading of a page of text of 68% reflection factor.

Specify the minimum reflectances of various room surfaces, and the brightness of the luminaire in the 60° to 90° zone to obtain the ratios indicated in Table 12-4.

**3.** An office is lighted to a level of 40 ft-c by means of louvered, flush ceiling troffers. Vertical illumination at the walls can be assumed as 15 ft-c. Ceiling has 75% reflectance, walls 50% reflectance, desks 25% reflectance, and floors 20% reflectance. The lamps will have a brightness of 1,200 ft-L; louvers in the 60° to 90° zone 400 ft-L; and ceiling between troffers, 8 ft-L.

The visual task will be considered the reading of a book printed in black ink on 75% rag, semi-gloss paper.

What will be the percentage of contrast at the task under the diffuse illumination and also where the lamps are imaged in the printing? What will be the brightness ratios in the room?

**4.** An office is 32 by 58 ft with 12-ft ceiling. Ceiling will have reflectance of 75%; walls 30%. Average horizontal illumination desired is approximately 25 ft-c.

Design four lighting systems utilizing (1) indirect silver-bowl lamp luminaires similar to No. 37 in Table 9-5, (2) luminous indirect fluorescent luminaires similar to No. 35 in Table 9-5, (3) louvered direct-indirect luminaires similar to No. 32 in Table 9-5, and (4) glass-covered flush-ceiling troffers utilizing two 40-watt fluorescent lamps, similar to No. 20 in Table 9-5.

Draw the reflected ceiling plan for each system.

**5.** A printed page of 50-lb semi-gloss paper is lighted to 25 ft-c. Calculate the percentage of contrast of ink against paper. If a source of 1,700 ft-L is reflected by the printing, and the diffuse illumination is increased to 100 ft-c, what will be the percentage of contrast? Calculate the relative visual efficiency under both conditions using the curves in Fig. 12-4.

# REFERENCES

Allen, C. J., and Holmes, R. E., "Studies in Gymnasium Lighting," *Trans. Illum. Eng. Soc.*, Vol. 44, page 278, May 1949.

*Architectural Forum* (School Issue), October 1949.

A. S. A. *Standard Practice for School Lighting*, 1948.

Committee report, "Brightness and Brightness Ratios," *Trans. Illum. Eng. Soc.*, Vol. 39, page 713, December 1944.

Crouch, C. L., "Brightness Limitations for Luminaires," *Trans. Illum. Eng. Soc.*, Vol. 40, page 427, July 1945.

Crouch, C. L., and Fowler, E. W., "Glare and Lighting Design," *Trans. Illum. Eng. Soc.*, Vol. 36, page 897, November 1941.

Darley, W. G., "An Analysis of Reflected Glare," *Trans. Illum. Eng. Soc.*, Vol. 43, page 85, January 1948.

———, "Applied Brightness Engineering," *ibid.*, Vol. 43, page 1159, December 1948.

Darley, W. G., and Ickis, L. S., "Lighting and Seeing in the Drafting Room," *Trans. Illum. Eng. Soc.*, Vol. 36, page 1462, December 1941.

*Guide for Planning School Plants* (*Tentative*), National Council on Schoolhouse Construction, 1946.

*I. E. S. Recommended Practice of Office Lighting*, 1942.

*Lighting Handbook*, Illuminating Engineering Society, 1947.

*Lighting Schoolrooms*, Pamphlet no. 104, Federal Security Agency, U. S. Office of Education.

Nutting, P. G., *Journal of Franklin Institute*, page 287, March 1917.

———, *Trans. Illum. Eng. Soc.*, Vol. 11, page 939, 1916.

———, *ibid.*, Vol. 15, page 529, 1920.

———, *Jour. Optical Society of America*, Vol. 4, 1919.

*Visual Comfort and Efficiency in School Buildings*, University of the State of New York, 1948.

# 13

# FACTORIES

---

The lighting of factory areas calls for the highest skill of the illuminating engineer. The visual tasks cover the widest range of forms, size, and contrast. Moving machinery and moving production lines call for speed and accuracy of seeing. Color enters into many of the design problems.

Many industrial buildings make little or no use of daylight. Large-scale production requires huge buildings and floor areas. Lighting systems must be efficient and practical as well as eminently suited to the visual tasks.

The Illuminating Engineering Society has made, and is making, studies of lighting for specific industrial processes in cooperation with the industries affected. The reports include studies of what the worker looks for and the kind of lighting needed to make seeing easier for specific tasks. In spite of appearances, there is little standardization in industrial lighting application. American industry is a dynamic institution. Lighting designs that are adequate today will be obsolete tomorrow because the processes they serve have changed.

Industrial lighting systems are in three forms:

    1. General.
    2. Localized general.
    3. Supplementary.

## 13.1. General Lighting

Even lighting for the entire production space is necessary for the following reasons:

1. A suitable visual environment and a pleasing atmosphere aids morale.

2. Movement of employees is made safer.
3. Handling and storage of materials is expedited.
4. Performance of many production jobs is improved.
5. All space is made visually usable.
6. Machine placement is independent of lighting arrangement.

The prediction of footcandles or the determination of generated lumens are as outlined in Chapter 10. The lumen method is extensively used. Its application should be tempered by the realization that it is based upon the constants of a room in which the work plane is relatively unobstructed.

In factory areas, machines are often large and high. Materials may be stored in strategic spots to heights of ten feet or more. These obstruct the light from distant luminaires. The footcandles at certain work points may be much less than the design value due to this obstruction. When the location and nature of obstructions are known, the footcandles at specific locations can be more accurately determined by means of the point-by-point method of calculation. The spacing-mounting height table for general lighting is given in Chapter 10. A supplementary table for industrial interiors is given in Table 13-1.

**TABLE 13-1**

**Relation between Luminaire Spacing and Light Distribution**

| Mounting above work plane | Ratio of spacing to mounting height | Zone in which luminaire lumens are emitted |
|---|---|---|
| Less than 16 ft | 1.5 to 1 | 0°–60° (wide spread) |
| 16 to 30 ft | 1.0 to 1 | 0°–40° (semi-concentrating or medium spread) |
| Over 30 ft | 0.5 to 1 | 0°–20° (concentrating) |

a. Footcandle values. Recommended footcandles for specific industrial operations are generally determined by empirical methods. The operation is studied from the viewpoint of what the worker has to see. Various lighting solutions are applied until the seeing tasks can be performed most satisfactorily. Many of the more simple operations can be done satisfactorily under the general interior lighting. Others require the special attention of supplementary lighting, localized general lighting, or both. As is to be expected, the footcandle levels for many industrial operations are considerably higher than those recommended for school and office operation. Table 13-2 includes some footcandle values that are representative of current practice. The extensive literature on the subject should be consulted for more detailed information.

TABLE 13-2

**Representative Footcandle Recommendations for Industrial Lighting***

| Type of lighting | Footcandles in service |
|---|---|
| General lighting: | |
| Rough bench and machine work | 20 |
| Fine bench and machine work | 20 plus supplementary |
| Average assembly | 20 |
| Airplane hangar repair department | 50 |
| Laundries | 20 |
| Meat packing | 20 |
| Textile weaving | 25–50 |
| Welding | 30 |
| Woodworking | 20–50 |
| Foundries | 15 |
| Canning factories | 20 |
| Supplementary lighting: | |
| Leather stitching | 50–75 |
| Radio chassis assembly | 200 |
| Radio chassis inspection | 75 |
| Tool making | 100 |
| Wax engraving | 40 |
| Photo-engraving masking | 100 |
| Fruit sorting | 50–85 |

*Based on the many publications of the Illuminating Engineering Society dealing with industrial lighting.

**b. Quality of lighting.** The majority of luminaires used for the lighting of factory space are of the direct type. Direct and reflected glare are always present to a degree. These negative qualities are reduced in effect by the following measures:

1. Locate luminaires as far as possible above the work plane.
2. Shield the light source by as deep an angle of cut-off as is

consistent with other factors in design. Shielding may also be accomplished by use of louvers and baffles.

3. Use low brightness sources, such as white-bowl or silvered-bowl filament lamps, or fluorescent lamps, if the working materials are shiny.

4. Paint the surroundings in as light colors as the circumstances will permit.

5. Paint machinery in light colors of egg-shell finish.

6. Never use less than two rows of luminaires in any space.

For most industrial processes the color of the light from various white or daylight fluorescent lamps or filament lamps has no effect upon the clearness or quickness of seeing. Certain industrial processes, however, require color matching or color discrimination. For such purposes a light of definite spectral composition is required. The specification is a matter of careful investigation and analysis. Usually such lighting is provided as supplementary to the general lighting or in limited areas.

Mercury-vapor lamps produce light that is deficient in red. The resulting illumination gives an unnatural appearance to people and familiar objects. In some industrial areas, such as foundries and steel mills, this is not considered objectionable. Better practice, however, is to mix the mercury light with light from tungsten-filament lamps. When this is done the technique of lighting design is somewhat altered from that previously outlined.

c. Designing for mercury lamps. There are a limited number of types and sizes of mercury lamps. The particular lamp to be used is selected *before* the design proceeds. Its lumen output is known. Therefore the generated lumens, as determined by the methods outlined in Chapter 10, when divided by this lumen output, will give us the number of lamps required to deliver the footcandles. If this number of lamps is not sufficient to satisfy the spacing-mounting height ratios, the number must be increased. It is seldom possible to choose another size of lamp or change the luminaire to achieve the originally specified level of footcandles.

The mercury lamp has a high brightness. Direct and reflected glare are difficult to control. The net result is that mercury lamps are best suited for the attainment of high levels of illumination in large areas where the mounting height is over 30 ft, and where the work surfaces are not highly specular.

In Chapter 3 it was pointed out that the mercury lamp, once extinguished, must cool for several minutes before it can be re-started. This characteristic may introduce some hazard if the lighting is provided solely by these lamps. An auxiliary system of filament lamps eliminates this danger, and also provides the yellow and red light rays for improved appearance of objects.

It has been found that a satisfactory color of light is provided by equal lumens from mercury and filament lamps. If the A-H1, 400-watt mercury lamp were selected (output—16,000 lm), it would be matched with a 750-watt filament lamp (output—15,600 lm). However, the conditions are often such that lamps of 500-watt to 1,500-watt in size are combined with the 400-watt mercury lamp in order to maintain a desired lighting level. The same size and shape of reflector is used for both mercury and filament lamps; only the sockets are different. The efficiency of the luminaire is not always the same with both lamps, due to the difference in size and shape of the two sources.

Two, and sometimes three, reflectors may be attached to a common bracket so that they may be supplied by a single electrical outlet. One reflector may be equipped with a filament lamp, the other with a mercury lamp. The filament and mercury lamps need not be adjacent. They may be on alternate outlets in any conventional spacing.

EXAMPLES:

1. A factory area 60 by 140 ft has a 35-ft ceiling. Walls are 10% reflectance, ceiling 30% reflectance. Thirty footcandles in service are required. How many 400-watt, A-H1 mercury lamps will be required, and on what spacings?

The mounting height of the luminaires is 30 ft above the work plane. From Table 13-1 a concentrating reflector is indicated, corresponding to unit No. 3, Table 9-5. The room index is from Eq. (9-1).

$$\text{RI} = \frac{140 \times 60}{30(140 + 60)} = \frac{8,400}{6,000} = 1.4$$

By interpolation in Table 9-5 the coefficient of utilization is 0.56. The generated lumens required to produce 30 ft-c will be

$$\text{G.L.} = \frac{\text{ft-c} \times \text{area}}{\text{C.U.} \times \text{depreciation factor}} = \frac{30(60 \times 140)}{0.56 \times 0.60} = 750,000$$

The 400-watt A-H1 mercury lamp produces 16,000 lm. Therefore 750,000/16,000 = 47 lamps required. Obviously only an even number of lamps will fit into the space.

A tentative layout is made (Fig. 13-1). From Table 13-1 we know that a spacing of 15 ft between units is desirable. Therefore, 4 rows of luminaires will be required to meet the cross-room spacing. Twelve luminaires in each row will satisfy the total number and give us a spacing of 15 by 12 ft. The design is satisfactory. Bear in mind that the efficiency

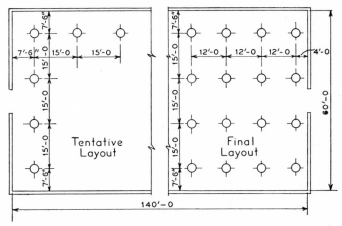

Fig. 13-1. Tentative and final layout of luminaires for general lighting. This type of drawing is called a "reflected ceiling plan."

of the luminaire was assumed to be the same as though a filament lamp were used in it. If the efficiency were otherwise, the coefficient derived from Table 9-5 would be modified by the ratio of efficiencies.

**2.** For the same factory area assume that a combination mercury and filament installation is desired. Starting on the basis of equal lumens from both sources, the nearest size of filament lamp is the 750-watt, producing 15,600 lm. Therefore 24 mercury lamps and 24 filament lamps at alternate outlets will still produce more than the required 750,000 lm. The design is satisfactory.

If the mercury luminaire did not have the same efficiency as the filament luminaire, carry through the design as before, on the basis of the filament luminaire efficiency. The filament lamps would contribute 374,400 lm, or 15 ft-c.

If the efficiency of the mercury luminaire were 65% instead of 75% as stated in Table 9-5, the coefficient of utilization would be

$$\tfrac{65}{75} \times 0.56 = 47.6\%$$

The footcandles produced by the mercury lamps would be 13 plus. The total footcandles delivered by the combination system would be 27 plus instead of 30 plus. This would still be satisfactory.

**d. Selection of luminaires.** As stated before, luminaires of the direct type are generally used. Some direct types emit a small proportion of light upward. This is useful in lighting the upper

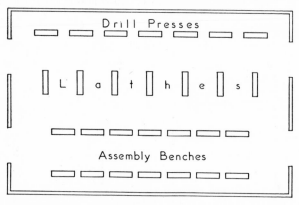

Fig. 13-2. Plan of luminaires for a localized general lighting system.

part of the area, thereby creating a more pleasant appearance and reducing the contrast between luminaire and ceiling.

Luminaires should be of sturdy construction. Prismatic glass, mirrored glass, aluminum, and porcelain-enamelled steel are recommended materials. Specular metal reflecting surfaces are not satisfactory. Either they are low in efficiency or suffer a slow but permanent depreciation.

Enclosing the luminaire to prevent accumulation of dust is a dubious expedient. The changes in internal temperature cause a "breathing" action which brings dust into the luminaire. It must be cleaned at intervals. The enclosure adds to the first cost and lowers the efficiency. This is not to say that vapor-proof and explosion-proof luminaires are not necessary under prescribed conditions. The indiscriminate use of so-called "dust tight" luminaires is not recommended. Experience has shown that properly designed open and ventilated luminaires may collect less dust than enclosed ones.

Localized general lighting (Fig. 13-2) resembles the conventional general symmetrical system except that the rows are spaced more

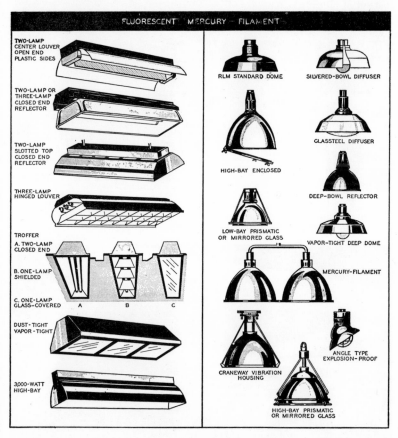

Fig. 13-3. Types of luminaires generally used for the lighting of industrial processes.

closely over rows of machines, counters, or benches. The "practical efficiency" of such a system is high. It frequently eliminates the need for local lighting.

Representative luminaires are shown in Fig. 13-3. Examples of industrial lighting are shown in Figs. 13-4 to 13-12.

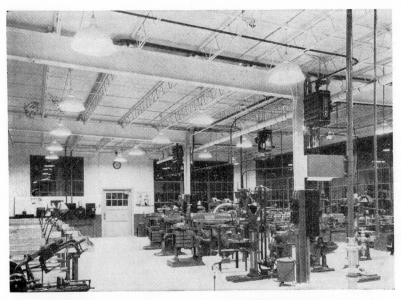

Fig. 13-4. Light walls and ceilings greatly improve the appearance of an industrial area. Silvered bowl lamps in metal reflectors reduce direct glare and specular reflections.

Fig. 13-5. When luminaires are located on "squares," shadows and specular images are greatly reduced. (*Westinghouse Electric & Manufacturing Co. photograph.*)

Fig. 13-6. Continuous rows of luminaires parallel to lines of machines build up the vertical illumination where needed. (*General Electric Co. photograph.*)

Fig. 13-7. An example of localized-general lighting. Light comes to the work from the left side to aid the normally right-handed worker. (*General Electric Co. photograph.*)

Fig. 13-8. The 3000-watt A-H9 mercury lamps 40 feet above the floor provide 70 footcandles in this press shop. (*Westinghouse Electric & Manufacturing Co. photograph.*)

Fig. 13-9. Incandescent and fluorescent lamps installed along the bottom of the main roof girders provide good over-all illumination. This neat arrangement of luminaires is maintained from the top of the crane. (*Westinghouse Electric & Manufacturing Co. photograph.*)

Fig. 13-10.  Mercury and incandescent lamps combined at the same location.  Light spilled from the top of the luminaires eliminates the cave-like appearance of dark ceilings.  (*General Electric Co. photograph.*)

Fig. 13-11. A large-area, low-brightness luminaire provides diffuse illumination over the entire machine. A well shielded spot lamp projects a high-intensity beam at the work point. General lighting in the shop produces a balanced brightness background. (*General Electric Co. photograph.*)

Fig. 13-12. 400-watt mercury and 1500-watt incandescent lamps at alternate outlets provide 35 footcandles. Luminaires are 50 feet above the floor. (*Westinghouse Electric & Manufacturing Co. photograph.*)

## 13.2. Supplementary Lighting

There is almost limitless challenge in the design of lighting to meet the specialized seeing tasks in industry. The engineer manipulates the surroundings and the light, in relation to the seeing task, to achieve a result. There are no standardized solutions. Each operation is analyzed from the viewpoint of what is to be seen, and how it can best be seen. The function of the lighting is to aid the visual functions to the greatest possible extent.

The solutions to a number of specialized applications are given in some detail. A study of them will disclose a variety of methods and devices utilized by the designers. The fundamental ideas can be used in other applications that may differ externally but possess the same underlying characteristics.

EXAMPLES:

1. **Flat-bed punch press (Fig. 13-13).** The operator has two visual problems: (a) to place the material properly in the press, (b) to observe

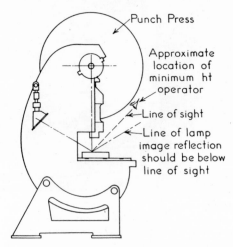

Fig. 13-13. The lighting of a punch press utilizes silhouette or shadow to good advantage.

small bits of metal remaining on the bed which might damage the next piece, or the die. Vision is largely by silhouette. The entire bed of the press should be illuminated. The light sources must be low in brightness

(a)

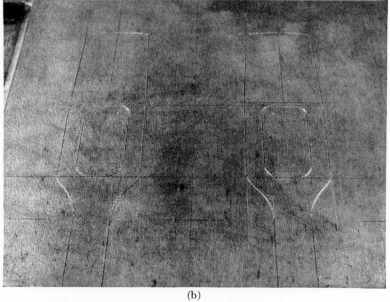

(b)

Fig. 13-14.   (a) Proper direction of light eliminates reflected glare and brings out fine detail.   (b) The fine lines of metal scribing are clearly visible against a non-glossy background.

245

(a)

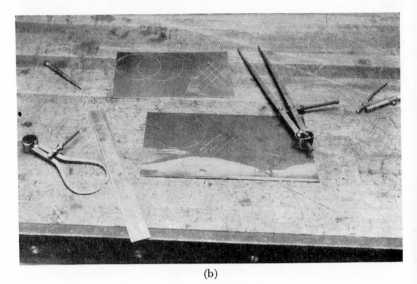

(b)

Fig. 13-15. (a) A large-area, low-brightness luminaire provides comfortable lighting for working with specular surfaces. (b) The scribed lines are diffuse in reflectance and appear either light or dark against the specular metal background.

246

in order that their reflection does not obscure the work points. With a one-man machine a light trough with diffusing cover can be placed properly at the rear. With a two-man machine, men on both sides, the sources are placed at the four corners of the press, on adjustable brackets. Each luminaire should have a diffusing cover of approximately 100 sq in. area.

**2. Scribing.** As a guide for the machining of metal parts or the fabrication of sheet metal, the outlines of the work are scratched or scribed on the metal surface.

If the metal surface is dark, the scratch can be made to appear bright and in sharp contrast with the background. If the surface is diffuse, it can be made to appear bright, while the scribed lines are dark.

The light is directed at an angle of 45° or greater from the vertical in order to eliminate direct reflection of the source to the eyes of the worker. The luminaire may be either a continuous reflector or one or more deeply shielded individual reflectors, all on adjustable brackets (Fig. 13-14).

When the metal surface is bright or shiny the scribed lines can only be seen as dark or light lines against the background. This is accomplished by having the metal sheet reflect a uniformly low brightness source (Fig. 13-15). The scribed lines interrupt the reflected image and appear either light or dark depending upon the operator's position. The diffusing source should have a brightness not to exceed 500 ft-L, if uncomfortable glare is to be avoided.

**3. Detection of minute flaws and cracks in metal (Fig. 13-16).** When the flaws are extremely small their detection is often a matter of per-

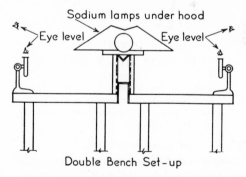

Fig. 13-16. Monochromatic yellow sodium light aids in seeing flaws that are near the visual threshold of size.

ceiving a shadow rather than details of the flaw. If the light is directed obliquely across the piece to be inspected, the flaw will show up as an interruption of the light pattern. The source should be low in brightness so that if its reflection is seen by the worker, there will be no consequent dazzle glare or discomfort.

Research has shown that monochromatic yellow light aids in the perception of objects that are near the absolute threshold of vision. The sodium lamp produces this kind of radiation. The diffused, low brightness of the lamp makes it well suited for this type of inspection.

**4. Inspection of ball bearings (Fig. 13-17).** The flaws to be detected are pits and scratches. The convex surface tends to localize the

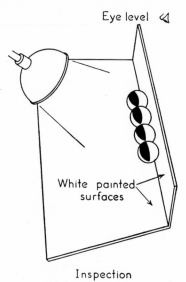

Eye level ◁

White painted surfaces

Inspection

Fig. 13-17. Diffuse light from the white background allows pits and scratches to be seen on the ball bearings. The reflections of the high-brightness sources are small and not annoying.

reflection of light sources into small bright patches which obscure the flaws. When a uniform and diffuse source of low brightness is supplied, the flaws will readily show as interruptions of the reflection. The reflection is low enough in brightness so that the flaws can easily be seen through it.

The method illustrated is to place the bearings in a white painted trough, illuminated by a diffused source. The bearings can be rolled around in the trough by the inspector so that all portions ultimately come into view.

**5. Lighting a hemispherical ball seat (Fig. 13-18).** The production problem is to coat the lower portion of the seat with a green stop-off lacquer without spilling the lacquer over onto the lip of the seat.

Objects are colored because they reflect certain wavelengths of light. If the color is not present in the light, or is very weak, the colored object will appear dark.

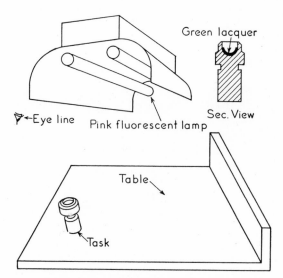

Fig. 13-18. The principle of selective reflections is utilized in the lighting for this inspection bench.

For seeing small color differences the color of the light used needs to be rich in the spectral region in which the material has maximum absorption. Some light of all colors is desirable, however. For this operation, therefore, the work bench was lighted with pink fluorescent lamps. There is little green light in these lamps, hence the green lacquer appears very dark. The lip of the seat is polished, and appears light, because it reflects the images of the fluorescent lamps. Any lacquer on the seat appears in good contrast with the background, and it is easily detected.

The pink light is pleasant and agreeable to the workers.

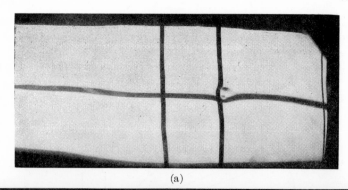

(a)

(b)

Fig. 13-19.   (a) When a sheet of glass is viewed against a diffusely lighted background on which a series of dark lines is traced, the imperfections distort the image of the lines and hence are discovered.   (b) Reflected images may also be utilized to discover imperfections in metal surfaces.   (*General Electric Co. photographs.*)

**6. Plate glass inspection (Fig. 13-19).**   The imperfections to be noted are whorls, waves, and scratches.   The glass is viewed against a large, diffusely lighted background, over which black lines are placed. These black lines appear wavy or are distorted by the imperfections in the glass.   Scratches and polishing marks appear as fine milky lines against the image of the black bands.

The brightness of the diffusing background must be low because it is constantly in the field of view of the inspectors.

**7. Wax engraving (Fig. 13-20).** This process is very delicate and exacting. Impressions on a plate of white wax are built up by hand so that a deep, sharp, copper electrotype can be obtained from the mold. The detail to be seen consists of shadow impressions. The sharper the

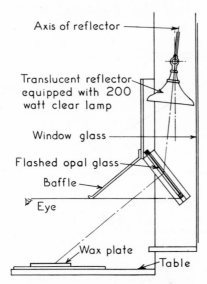

Axis of reflector

Translucent reflector equipped with 200 watt clear lamp

Window glass

Flashed opal glass

Baffle

Eye

Wax plate

Table

Fig. 13-20. The electric lighting and the daylighting come from the same direction to maintain constant conditions on this work bench for wax engraving.

shadow, the greater is the resulting visibility. This calls for light sweeping obliquely across the work. In order to clear the movements of the engraver this light can only come from the front. But the wax is shiny, consequently the light must be well diffused and of low brightness in order to avoid uncomfortable reflections.

Experience indicated that the quality of light from the north sky was considered ideal. On dark days or in the late afternoon, however, it was not strong enough.

The engineer's lighting scheme as illustrated did not alter the lighting quality when the electric lamps were turned on. The complete absence of direct light toward the eyes of the engraver made it even better than daylight.

**a. Size of source and reflected image.** In many of the preceding examples, the key feature of the lighting was the reflection of a light source in a specular work surface. The size of the source or the size of the image can be determined graphically.

When the surface is a plane, one dimension of the area (the width) can be found by the method shown in Fig. 13-21. The length of the reflected image is equal to the length of the source.

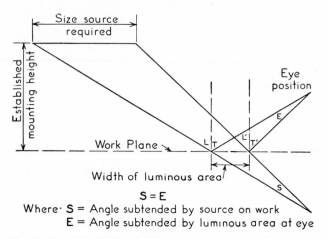

Fig. 13-21.   Relationship between size of light source and size of reflected image in a plane surface.

Obviously the source need not lie in a plane parallel to the plane of the work.

When the surface is convex, the construction shown in Fig. 13-22 is used. The reading of scales is a common eye task. When the scales are portable, the worker manipulates them until visibility is satisfactory. It will be surmised that the best visibility is obtained when the scale can reflect a relatively large, diffuse source of low brightness.

Many convex scales are fixed in position upon machines. The light source, when fluorescent, should, if possible, be positioned so that the tube axis is at right angles to the scale axis. As shown in Fig. 13-22, this will extend the reflected image over the greatest possible extent of the scale. Fifty degrees of arc seems to be the minimum satisfactory coverage.

**b. Brightness ratios.**  The geometry of the visual field and the brightness ratios within it are of prime concern to the engineer when designing industrial lighting.  The brightness ratios between task and surround should be kept low because the high footcandles necessary for many of the tasks increase the eye adaptation level and its sensitivity to contrast.  The engineer often has more control over the characteristics of the immediate surround in

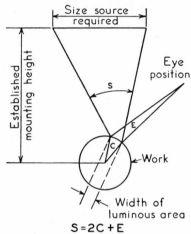

$$S = 2C + E$$

Where  S = Angle subtended by source on work
C = Angle subtended by luminous area
on work
E = Angle subtended by luminous area
at eye

Fig. 13-22.  Relationship between size of light source and size of reflected image in a convex surface.

factories than he has in schools and offices.  He can balance the surface reflection factors and brightness against the brightness of the task.

The balance between the brightness of the task and the brightness in the far surround is not so easy to accomplish.  Floors are usually dark.  Walls and ceilings, however, can be finished in light colors unless the atmosphere is dirty or corrosive.  Some plastic and prismatic direct luminaires are luminous and blend well with the background.  Some direct types of luminaires emit a small amount of light in the 90° to 180° zone.   This light aids in reducing contrast.

The majority of direct types of luminaires, however, are opaque, and the only light in the upper portion of the area arrives there by reflection from other areas.   For this reason it is difficult to avoid large differences in brightness between the work and the far surround.

There are no published brightness limits for industrial luminaires to serve as a guide, such as we have for schools and offices.   The shielding of lamps is fairly well established in several classes of equipment.   Standard dome reflectors have a cut-off of $17\frac{1}{2}°$ below the horizontal.   Deep bowl reflectors have a cut-off at 30° to 35°.   Many industrial fluorescent reflectors have a cut-off of approximately 13° ($11\frac{1}{2}°$ is the minimum acceptable).   It will be recalled that the direct glare zone is considered to be within the 45° to 90° angle.   Obviously then, many direct types of industrial luminaires are uncomfortably bright or emit large quantities of light in this zone.   The addition of louvers or baffles to the luminaires will decrease direct glare.   Mounting them as high as possible above the work plane is the other alternative.

## PROBLEMS

**1.** A machine shop is 40 by 70 ft with 14-ft ceiling.   Ceiling and side-wall reflectances are 30%.   Design a general lighting system of 20 ft-c, using standard cool (4,500°) white fluorescent lamps.   Suspend luminaires 1 ft below the ceiling.   Assume a $3\frac{1}{2}$-ft work plane.   Use luminaire No. 11, Table 9-5.

**2.** A wood-working shop is 50 ft square with 16-ft ceiling.   Wall and ceiling reflectances are 30% and 50% respectively.   Design a general lighting system of 20 ft-c, using luminaire No. 8, Table 9-5.   Suspend luminaires 15 ft above the floor.   Assume a $3\frac{1}{2}$-ft work plane.

**3.** An erecting shop is 80 by 200 ft with 50-ft ceiling.   Wall and ceiling reflectances are 30%.   Design a lighting system using a combination of mercury-vapor lamps (A-H1) and filament lamps to produce 40 ft-c in service on a plane 4 ft above the floor.   Suspend luminaires 3 ft below the ceiling.   Use luminaire No. 3, Table 9-5.

**4.** A foundry is 50 by 140 ft with 30-ft ceiling.   Wall and ceiling reflectances are 10%.   Work plane is the floor.   Suspend luminaires 2 ft below the ceiling. Select luminaire No. 4, Table 9-5. Design for 15 ft-c in service using

  a. Mercury-vapor lamps (A-H1).
  b. Filament lamps.

**5.** An assembly area is 160 by 600 ft with 60-ft ceiling. Wall and ceiling reflectances are 30%. Work plane is the floor. Suspend luminaires 50 ft above the floor. With a design level of 40 ft-c, develop four lighting systems as follows:

  1. Standard warm white 48-in. T-12 fluorescent lamps in luminaire No. 12, Table 9-5.
  2. 3-kw mercury lamp in luminaire No. 16, Table 9-5.
  3. Combination incandescent and A-H1 mercury lamp in luminaire No. 3, Table 9-5.
  4. Combination incandescent and A-H12 mercury in luminaire No. 3, Table 9-5. *Note:* Use any proportion of incandescent to mercury lumens between one-half and one.

## REFERENCES

*A. S. A.—Recommended Practice of Industrial Lighting.* Illuminating Engineering Society, 1942.

Committee Report, "Lighting for Canning," *Trans. Illum. Eng. Soc.*, Vol. 45, January 1950.

Darley, W. G., and Gaetjens, A. K., "What Price Eye Comfort," *Trans. Illum. Eng. Soc.*, Vol. 39, December 1944.

Fowler, E. W., "Lighting a Color Register Room," *Trans. Illum. Eng. Soc.*, Vol. 39, May 1944.

Ketch, J. M., Sturrock, W., and Staley, K., "Special Lighting Applications for Industrial Processes," *Trans. Illum. Eng. Soc.*, Vol. 28, no. 1, January 1933.

*Lighting Data Sheets*, Illuminating Engineering Society.

"Lighting for the Machining of Small Metal Parts," *Trans. Illum. Eng. Soc.*, Vol. 34, January 1939.

*Lighting Handbook*, 1st ed., New York: Illuminating Engineering Society, 1947.

"Lighting of Power Presses," *Trans. Illum. Eng. Soc.*, Vol. 34, February 1939.

"Report on Lighting in the Shoe Manufacturing Industry," *Trans. Illum. Eng. Soc.*, Vol. 32, March 1937.

"Report on Lighting in the Textile Industry, Grey Goods and Denim," *Trans. Illum. Eng. Soc.*, Vol. 32, March 1937.

"Researches on Industrial Lighting—Lighting for Silk and Rayon Throwing and Wide Goods Weaving," *Trans. Illum. Eng. Soc.*, Vol. 33, January 1938.

Sharp, H. M., "Light as an Ally of the Safety Engineer," *Trans. Illum. Eng. Soc.*, Vol. 34, June 1939.

Sharp, H. M., and Crouch, C. L., "The Influence of General Lighting on Machine Shop Tasks," *Trans. Illum. Eng. Soc.*, Vol. 34, March 1939.

"Studies in Lighting of Intricate Production, Assembly, and Inspection Processes," *Trans. Illum. Eng. Soc.*, Vol. 32, December 1937.

Wittekind, J. R., "Industrial Vision," *Trans. Illum. Eng. Soc.*, Vol. 38, February 1943.

# 14

## STORES

Lighting for stores or merchandising areas is often simply called commercial lighting. It is not subject to standardized or codified treatment because of the constantly changing patterns of merchandising. The illuminating engineer can only use the tools of lighting and his specialized knowledge to develop the lighting system that will best meet the needs of display and sales in a particular merchandising area.

The problems confronting the lighting designer are many. The merchandise displayed and sold varies in size from needles to automobiles, in color from black velvet to white satin with all the spectral tints and hues in between, in surface character from shiny hardware to deep-pile rugs. Vertical surfaces, oblique surfaces, rounded surfaces, and horizontal surfaces are used for the display and appraisal of merchandise.

The basic factors in design are no more difficult than those found in industry. But beyond this is the necessity for creating a comfortable and pleasant interior. There is often the compelling need for dramatic effects and theatrical artistry to create a buying mood. In these elements of design, the engineer without architectural training is usually ill at ease.

No single chapter in a single text can present store lighting adequately. It can be analyzed, however, and some of the components developed in sufficient detail to give the engineer a better working knowledge. From these beginnings he can develop reasonable skill and confidence.

### 14.1. Footcandles

The recommendations for footcandles in connection with merchandising activities are extremely elastic (Table 14-1). Materials which are displayed and sold vary greatly in color and reflectance. The amount of incident illumination must vary in order to maintain any semblance of effective brightness. This occurs not only between different types of stores, but within the same store on the same floor.

Brightness is a compelling factor in attracting attention. Inevitably, any area must be approximately equal in brightness to other

TABLE 14-1

Recommended Footcandles for Merchandising Areas

| Type of display | General | Supplementary— for emphasis |
|---|---|---|
| Show windows: | | |
| In well lighted districts | 300 | 500 |
| In moderately lighted districts | 100 | 200 |
| In relatively dark districts | 50 | 100 |
| Jewelry | 10–25 | 25–75 |
| Silverware | 10–25 | 25 |
| Leather goods | 10–25 | 25–50 |
| Drugs | 30 | 50–75 |
| Shoes | 25–50 | 50–75 |
| Clothing | 25–50 | 50–75 |
| Furs | 25–50 | 75 |
| China | 10–25 | 25–50 |
| Hardware and appliances | 25–50 | |
| Groceries | 25 | 25–75 |
| Flowers | 15–50 | 25–75 |
| Barber shops | 25–50 | |

areas if it is to attract attention. If it is higher in brightness, its attracting power is greater. Therefore, the amount of light specified for a show window, for example, will depend in part upon the amount of street and sign lighting and the brightness of adjacent windows. These factors are known only upon observation.

Competition between stores of the same class affects the level of lighting. A modern, well-lighted store will draw trade from its competitors until they in turn effect a change.

Therefore, the recommended footcandles (Table 14-1) serve only as a guide or indication of magnitude. Prevailing practice in each area of the country will determine the general design level. The size of the city is a factor also.

## 14.2. Brightness

The human eye functions the same in a store as it does in a school, office, or factory. The nature of the seeing task is, however, quite different. Shopping is essentially a search. The person moves about, and the eyes shift from one object to another. Differences in brightness aid this searching and change of focus. The brightness balance necessary for eye efficiency and comfort for "critical seeing tasks" is quite out of the question. It is obvious that the merchandise should attract the attention, not the lighting. Within 30° of the line of sight the light sources and their reflections should be unobtrusive. The brightness of light sources or luminaires within the direct viewing zone (45° to 90°) should generally not exceed 1,000 ft-L. Some types of merchandise and some types of businesses have a tradition of glitter and high brightness. Grocery stores, drug stores, jewelry stores, and hardware stores are examples. Other types favor low brightness and a "quiet" atmosphere, for example, fur shops, high-priced clothing stores, and furniture stores. Brightness is closely allied with the creation of a sales atmosphere and is therefore influenced by many factors not capable of precise definition.

The phenomenon of eye adaptation is of importance in store lighting. Most shopping is done during the daytime. The eye is adapted to the daylight. Upon entering a building your eyes immediately begin adapting to the lower brightness levels. This takes a few seconds. During this period the eye is quite inefficient. By means of merchandise layout and lighting, the shopper is encouraged to explore those portions of the store farthest from the street entrance. This takes time, during which adaptation can take place. Common experience is that a person sees more while on the way out of a store than upon entering it.

## 14.3. General Lighting

Uniform lighting of the entire interior by means of a general lighting system is *foundation* lighting. It serves to fill the space with light, to allow for safe passage of people, and in many stores

Fig. 14-1. Standard silvered-bowl lamp luminaires in circular domes produce an interesting effect and well diffused general lighting. Fluorescent lamps above large-scale louvers provide higher illumination at the sales counter. (*General Electric Co. photograph.*)

Fig. 14-2. Note the great variety of lighting forms in this store. Indirect lighting forms the general background of brightness. Lighted wall cases, floor cases, and wall niches provide interest, eye attraction, and additional sales appeal. The flush ceiling downlighting builds up the general horizontal illumination.

Fig. 14-3. The egg-crate ceiling with fluorescent lamps above gives an impression of space and dignity to this circulation and sales area. The temporary tinting of the center square of louvers shows the possibilities of variety for special occasions. (*Sylvania Electric Products, Inc. photograph.*)

Fig. 14-4. Note how conventional luminaires can conform to the shape of the room. The fluorescents along the wall cases have front shielding only. Thus light passes upward to brighten the walls, and downward to light the merchandise.

Fig. 14-5. Downlights provide high-level illumination for the floor cases in addition to the strip reflectors inside. The fluorescent lamps along the wall cases provide indirect and direct illumination. The continuous troffers accent the circulation area. Note the lighted, recessed mural for a decorative touch.

Fig. 14-6. General lighting is provided by attractive silvered bowl lamp luminaires. Ceiling downlights build up the illumination on the tops of the floor cases. Fluorescent lamps along the tops of the wall cases provide both direct and indirect lighting.

Fig. 14-7. The free-standing floor display utilizes a low-brightness diffusing glass background to silhouette the merchandise. An overhead panel provides some direct light to add highlights.

Fig. 14-8. In this store the continuous fluorescent luminaires over the wall cases and floor cases are concealed behind heavy valances which form an important element of the interior design. As in all merchandising areas, note that the floor cases have interior lighting even with high-level top lighting. (*Holophane Co. photograph.*)

Fig. 14-9. In this sales alcove the lighted display niches provide a considerable amount of general illumination. The indirect cove adds to the general effect of informality.

Fig. 14-10. This store illustrates the possibilities of using many forms of lighting treatment. The combination of diffused indirect and direct general lighting, and strong downlighting, produces a pleasant, comfortable effect with accent and sparkle on the displayed merchandise. The unsilvered portion of the reflector downlights is of clear glass to provide the necessary highlights on the jewelry. (*Courtesy of Levy Brothers, Buffalo, N. Y.*)

Fig. 14-11. The single-lamp fluorescent troffers have a moderate brightness, and by arrangement in an unsymmetrical pattern accentuate the shape of the room. Note the direct lighting on the planting in the background and the suspended trough for lighting the coats at the left. (*Sylvania Electric Products, Inc. photograph.*)

Fig. 14-12. Single rows of eight-foot T-12 fluorescent lamps are placed 2 feet apart above the egg-crate louvers and 32 inches apart. A high level of illumination is obtained without any undue brightness toward the eye. (*Sylvania Electric Products, Inc. photograph.*)

helps the sale, display, and appraisal of merchandise. Grocery, hardware, drug, shoe, and furniture stores depend almost entirely upon general lighting, with supplementary lighting here and there for special emphasis. Examples of store lighting are shown in Figs. 14-1 to 14-12.

General lighting is usually accomplished by means of luminaires suspended from the ceiling or recessed into it. Usually the design can be carried out by means of the lumen or flux-of-light method outlined in Chapter 10.

Cove lighting is often used in special areas or departments. Elements of design are outlined in Chapter 15.

Spotlighting and downlighting are extensively used. The light distribution is essentially concentrated within a narrow cone. Point-by-point calculations are generally used for the design. Sometimes such lighting is restricted to small areas such as display cards, mannequins, or counters. On the other hand a certain dramatic effect is achieved by lighting entire spaces in this manner. The elements of design are outlined in Chapter 15.

### 14.4. Supplementary Lighting

The general or foundation lighting may not always be sufficient to present some types of merchandise adequately. General lighting alone may also lack the variety and interest required by the owner. Additional or supplementary lighting is usually provided for wall cases, show cases, bins for vegetables, groceries, and hardware, free-standing displays, and wall niches.

Standardized designs are almost unknown. Much of the lighting is built into the display equipment by the manufacturer. The spotlighting of special areas and counters is often incorporated into the structure of the store and this requires coordination with the architectural features. An understanding of the relationship between beam characteristics, area to be lighted, length of throw, and direction of light is gained only through experience.

Many designs proceed on a "trial and error" basis until the designer is satisfied that the proper selection of equipment has been made.

**a. Display counters.** Exterior or "top" lighting of display counters is used when the merchandise must be equally highlighted within the case and on top of it. The top lighting is done by means of downlights usually located at or in the ceiling. The design methods are as outlined in Chapter 15.

Regardless of top lighting, the majority of floor display cases are lighted from within. They are miniature show windows and for attraction purposes must have a higher brightness than the surroundings. Usual practice is to provide two to five times as many footcandles in the case as are available from the general

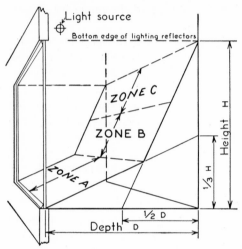

Fig. 14-13. Display zones in floor cases and show windows are chosen as design points for illumination.

lighting system. The practical range of footcandles is from 50 to 100 because space does not allow for more than one row of lamps.

Tubular filament lamps, both clear and side-silvered, are used where the warmer color of incandescent lamps is favored. The fluorescent lamp finds wider application because of its line characteristic and small diameter.

The show case is arbitrarily divided into three zones, representing display surfaces (Fig. 14-13). Obviously all of the surfaces will be lighted but one is selected as the most important. The lumens per foot of case required to deliver the footcandles are found by the following formula:

$$F_f = \frac{E}{K_u \times 0.8} \tag{14-1}$$

where $E$ = required footcandles,
 $K_u$ = constant from Table 14-2,
 0.8 = average depreciation factor.

The number of filament lamps, or the type of fluorescent lamp, is then found by matching the lamp output against the lumens per foot found from Eq. (14-1). The lamps are housed in a suitably finished reflector and placed snugly in the aisle corner of the case.

EXAMPLES:

1. A show case 20 in. deep, 27 in. high, and 54 in. long, inside measurement, is to be lighted to a level of 50 ft-c on plane $B$. Can a fluorescent lamp be used and, if so, what type?

### TABLE 14-2

**Utilization Factors ($K_u$) for Typical Showcase**

(20 Inches Deep and 10, 20, or 27 Inches High)*

| Zone | Fluorescent lamp in white diffusing reflector | Fluorescent lamp in concentrating reflector | Incandescent lamp, clear T-10 in semi-diffusing reflector | Incandescent lamp T-10 reflector showcase type | Height |
|------|------|------|------|------|------|
| A | 0.266 | 0.321 | 0.219 | 0.356 | |
| B | 0.122 | 0.198 | 0.137 | 0.359 | 10 |
| C | 0.051 | 0.093 | 0.095 | 0.128 | |
| A | 0.170 | 0.165 | 0.143 | 0.226 | |
| B | 0.137 | 0.192 | 0.119 | 0.333 | 20 |
| C | 0.081 | 0.139 | 0.122 | 0.184 | |
| A | 0.129 | 0.123 | 0.108 | 0.179 | |
| B | 0.112 | 0.145 | 0.093 | 0.238 | 27 |
| C | 0.094 | 0.150 | 0.121 | 0.207 | |

* From *Lighting Handbook*, Illuminating Engineering Society, New York, 1947.

If other considerations do not prevent, select the largest utilization factor, $K_u$, for the dominant zone. From Table 14-2 this is 0.145 representing a fluorescent lamp in a concentrating reflector. Then

$$F_f = \frac{50}{.145 \times 0.8} = 430 \text{ lm per ft of lamp}$$

From Table 3-6 in Chapter 3 we find that a 48-in. preheat cathode lamp in the soft white or 3,500° white color, or a 200-ma Slimline lamp in standard warm white color, produces enough light per foot to satisfy the requirements. If we do not find a lamp of sufficient output we must either be satisfied with less light in the showcase, or redesign for filament lamps.

**2.** In the same showcase let us design for the T-10 filament lamp in a semi-diffusing reflector.

From Table 14-2 the utilization factor is .093. Then

$$F_f = \frac{50}{.093 \times 0.8} = 670 \text{ lm per ft}$$

From a manufacturer's table of lamp data it will be found that the largest T-10 lamp is 40 watts and emits 430 lm per ft. The lamp is roughly 6 in. over-all in length. Therefore the desired illumination can be obtained by spacing these lamps approximately 9 in. between sockets.

**3.** Let us design for the T-10 reflector showcase lamp in this same case. One-half of this lamp is silver coated so as to form a reflector integral with the lamp. This produces an efficient and accurate light-control combination.

From Table 14-2 the utilization factor is 0.238. Then

$$F_f = \frac{50}{0.238 \times 0.8} = 263 \text{ lm per ft}$$

Manufacturer's data disclose that this lamp in the 25-watt size produces 230 lm and is approximately 6 in. long. If the sockets are located 10 in. apart the desired level of illumination will be obtained.

## 14.5. Show Windows

Show windows are an important merchandising area. They attract the attention of passers-by and permit the favorable inspection of goods displayed therein. High brightness is required, and often color, motion, shadow, and dramatic backgrounds are introduced as additional features. The general lighting is obtained by locating the lighting equipment along the upper edge of the window glass. When the window has no background separating it from the interior, the equipment should be concealed as far as possible and the lamps shielded from the view of anyone in the store. When the window is enclosed there is, of course, less necessity for concealment and shielding. In no event should the equipment be obvious or any glare apparent to the person looking into the window from the street. The merchandise displayed must be the sole point of eye attention. The dramatic effects possible in show window display are not standardized and are beyond the scope of this text. There are, however, thousands of business establishments whose window lighting requirements are satisfied by general, diffused lighting of a suitable amount. The design methods and the lighting equipment are standardized.

Filament lamps are extensively used. The light can be well controlled and great range of color is possible. Interchangeability of lamp sizes in a given luminaire introduces desirable flexibility to meet changing conditions. Compactness of equipment for large light output makes for easier installation and concealment. The lighting has a certain sharpness and sparkle which is attractive.

The fluorescent lamp is essentially a diffuse light source. The low output per foot sometimes makes impossible the attainment of the necessary footcandles. Equipment costs are high. Illustrations of show window lighting practice will be found in Figs. 14-14 to 14-17.

Both sources are sometimes used in the same window to achieve a great variety of effects. The design procedure, however, differs between filament and fluorescent sources.

Fig. 14-14. Flush ceiling reflectors of proper design will produce vertical illumination on high vertical displays. A light background increases the effectiveness of the lighting.

Fig. 14-15. Fluorescent lamps, shielded by deep louvers, provide uniform window illumination. Spotlights are usually added for accent.

Fig. 14-16. In open-back windows the display is usually on plane A. Flush reflectors are favored because of their neat appearance.

Fig. 14-17. A ceiling of diffusing material provides excellent over-all lighting and is of neat appearance. By carrying the same lighting over the entrance, unified treatment is achieved.

**TABLE 14-3**

**Illumination Factor (*F*) for Filament Lamps\***

| H/D ratio | Luminaire | Illumination factor | | |
| --- | --- | --- | --- | --- |
| | | Zone A | Zone B | Zone C |
| 4.0 | W | 95 | 60 | 260 |
| | S-c | 115 | 70 | 200 |
| | C | 200 | 105 | 135 |
| 3.5 | W | 130 | 75 | 260 |
| | S-c | 155 | 90 | 200 |
| | C | 260 | 110 | 130 |
| 3.0 | W | 170 | 95 | 260 |
| | S-c | 205 | 115 | 190 |
| | C | 310 | 120 | 130 |
| 2.5 | W | 215 | 140 | 260 |
| | S-c | 270 | 160 | 170 |
| | C | 380 | 120 | 130 |
| 2.0 | W | 280 | 190 | 260 |
| | S-c | 340 | 215 | 160 |
| | C | 465 | 140 | 130 |
| 1.5 | W | 355 | 260 | 260 |
| | S-c | 440 | 300 | 130 |
| | C | 575 | 165 | 110 |
| 1.0 | W | 490 | 345 | 215 |
| | S-c | 560 | 395 | 80 |
| | C | 685 | 215 | 80 |

W = wide spread light distribution; S-c = semi-concentrating light distribution; C = concentrating light distribution.
\* Derived from empirical data developed by Eby.

a. **Decide upon the design level of footcandles.** Figures given in Table 14-1 are a guide only. Conditions which prevail in the vicinity of the proposed window lighting will determine the necessary amount. These can be determined only by observation.

The filament lamp lumens necessary to obtain these footcandles are found by means of the following formula:

$$\text{lamp lumens per foot of window} = \frac{1630E}{K} \qquad (14\text{-}2)$$

where $K = \dfrac{F \times L \times S}{\text{depth of window, } D}$,

$F$ = illumination factor,

$L$ = length factor,

$S$ = shielding factor,

$E$ = design level of footcandles.

b. Decide which zone shall be the design point. This is determined by the type of merchandise and the display methods of the

TABLE 14-4

Illumination Factor ($F$) for Fluorescent Lamps*

| $H/D$ ratio | Luminaire | Illumination factor | | |
|---|---|---|---|---|
| | | Zone A | Zone B | Zone C |
| 4.0 | W | 50 | 25 | 80 |
| | S-c | 50 | 30 | 125 |
| | C | 70 | 45 | 115 |
| 3.5 | W | 60 | 30 | 80 |
| | S-c | 60 | 45 | 125 |
| | C | 90 | 55 | 120 |
| 3.0 | W | 75 | 45 | 85 |
| | S-c | 80 | 55 | 125 |
| | C | 120 | 70 | 110 |
| 2.5 | W | 90 | 60 | 90 |
| | S-c | 100 | 75 | 125 |
| | C | 160 | 80 | 100 |
| 2.0 | W | 110 | 80 | 100 |
| | S-c | 130 | 100 | 125 |
| | C | 210 | 105 | 80 |
| 1.5 | W | 150 | 120 | 90 |
| | S-c | 175 | 130 | 120 |
| | C | 280 | 120 | 70 |
| 1.0 | W | 210 | 155 | 55 |
| | S-c | 250 | 155 | 110 |
| | C | 375 | 110 | 40 |

W = wide spread light distribution; S-c = semi-concentrating light distribution; C = concentrating light distribution.

* Derived from empirical data developed by Eby.

merchant. Jewelry, for example, is generally displayed in Zone A (Fig. 14-13). Drugs, clothing, and hardware are grouped in Zone B. Regardless of the zone chosen there will always be light spilled into the other zones.

c. Selection of illumination factor (F). In choosing the illumination factor from Table 14-3 or Table 14-4, select the type of luminaire distribution which shows the largest factor for the desired zone. If the type of equipment is fixed by structural requirements or other factors beyond the control of the designer, the factor will be selected to agree with the distribution.

d. Selection of length factor (L). This factor takes into account the utilization of light from different light distributions in windows of different lengths. In a sense it is a modified coefficient of utilization. These factors are given in Tables 14-5 and 14-6.

### TABLE 14-5

#### Length Factor (L) for Filament Lamps*

| Equip-ment | Window length in feet | | | | | | | |
|---|---|---|---|---|---|---|---|---|
| | 3 | 4 | 5 | 6 | 8 | 10 | 12 | 15 |
| W | .70 | .80 | .85 | .87 | .92 | .97 | 1.05 | 1.05 |
| S-c | .77 | .83 | .87 | .92 | .97 | 1.00 | 1.05 | 1.05 |
| C | .90 | .92 | .97 | .97 | 1.00 | 1.00 | 1.00 | 1.00 |

* Derived from empirical data developed by Eby.

e. Selection of shielding factor (S). In most windows the lamps must have shielding in addition to the usual reflector. This shielding absorbs light and hence this factor is a modifying efficiency factor. Shielding factors are given in Tables 14-7 and 14-8.

f. Filament lamp lumens per luminaire. The various factors as found above are substituted in Eq. 14-2. The lamp lumens per luminaire are based upon equipment located on 12-in. centers and a depreciation factor of 75%. This is approximately a minimum spacing due to the physical size of the equipment. Spacings rarely exceed 24 in. because of the footcandle requirements.

The standard lamp nearest in lumen output to the value deter-

**TABLE 14-6**

**Length Factor ($L$) for Fluorescent Lamps***

| Footage of lamps | Nominal window length in feet | | | | | | | | |
|---|---|---|---|---|---|---|---|---|---|
| | 3 | 4 | 5 | 6 | 7 | 8 | 10 | 12 | 15 |
| 2 | .47 | | | | | | | | |
| 3 | .72 | .62 | | | | | | | |
| 4 | | .92 | .77 | | | | | | |
| 5 | | | .87 | .87 | | | | | |
| 6 | | | | .95 | .87 | .77 | | | |
| 7 | | | | | 1.02 | .95 | .82 | | |
| 8 | | | | | | 1.12 | .97 | | |
| 9 | | | | | | | .97 | | |
| 10 | | | | | | | 1.17 | 1.02 | |
| 11 | | | | | | | | 1.07 | |
| 12 | | | | | | | | 1.27 | 1.07 |
| 13 | | | | | | | | | 1.12 |
| 14 | | | | | | | | | 1.22 |
| 15 | | | | | | | | | 1.25 |

These values are based upon 3,500° lamps of approximately 475 lm per ft output. For any other lamp output, modify the above constants by the ratio of: lamp output per foot/475.

* Derived from empirical data developed by Eby.

mined above should be tentatively selected. It should always be larger than the calculated lamp because luminaires can rarely be placed closer than on 12-inch centers. Then the number of luminaires (N) will be equal to

$$N = \frac{\text{length of window} \times \text{calculated lamp lumens per foot}}{\text{selected lamp lumens}} \quad (14\text{-}3)$$

Space the reflectors uniformly along the window glass. If there are more than can be accommodated, place them in two rows, or choose a larger lamp and recalculate by the above formula. Do not use lamps larger than 500 watts except under unusual conditions.

EXAMPLE:

A show window is 15 ft long, 4 ft deep, and 6 ft high. 100 ft-c are desired on zone $B$. The reflectors will be recessed, with ring louvers for lamp shielding. How many and what size of filament lamps are necessary?

## TABLE 14-7

### Shielding Factor (S) for Filament Lamps*

| H/D ratio | Louvers† normal to window glass | | | Louvers† parallel with window glass | | | Eccentric ring louvers† | | |
|---|---|---|---|---|---|---|---|---|---|
| | Zone A | Zone B | Zone C | Zone A | Zone B | Zone C | Zone A | Zone B | Zone C |
| 4.0 | 0.77 | 0.72 | 0.72 | 0.85 | 0.74 | 0.46 | These louvers not usually used in windows of these proportions | | |
| 3.5 | 0.77 | 0.72 | 0.72 | 0.85 | 0.71 | 0.44 | | | |
| 3.0 | 0.75 | 0.72 | 0.68 | 0.85 | 0.66 | 0.38 | | | |
| 2.5 | 0.75 | 0.70 | 0.64 | 0.83 | 0.62 | 0.33 | | | |
| 2.0 | 0.73 | 0.70 | 0.62 | 0.83 | 0.57 | 0.27 | 0.69 | 0.62 | 0.35 |
| 1.5 | 0.71 | 0.68 | 0.58 | 0.81 | 0.52 | 0.22 | 0.69 | 0.54 | 0.30 |
| 1.0 | 0.69 | 0.68 | 0.54 | 0.79 | 0.47 | 0.19 | 0.69 | 0.45 | 0.25 |

\* From data by Eby.
† Semi-mat aluminum.

The $H/D$ ratio is 1.5. From Table 14-3 the greatest illumination factor, $F$, is 300 with semi-concentrating reflectors. The length factor (Table 14-5) is 1.05 and the shielding factor, $S$ (Table 14-7), is 0.54. Then

$$K = \frac{300 \times 1.05 \times 0.54}{4} = 42.5$$

Lamp lumens per foot of window $= \dfrac{1630 \times E}{K} = 3830$

From a lamp manufacturer's data sheet the nearest standard lamp size is found to be the 200-watt lamp, producing 3,700 lm. Then

$$N = \frac{15 \times 3830}{3700} = 15.5$$

This number of reflectors will place the luminaires closer together than 12 in. on centers. Because of reflector size, a 12-in. spacing is usually the minimum. In this case, limiting the number of reflectors to 15 will not reduce the expected footcandles more than 4%. If the reduction in footcandles would amount to more than 10%, then select a larger lamp and reduce the number of reflectors to be installed.

**g. Fluorescent lamp system.** When designing for the use of fluorescent lamps

$$E = \frac{F \times L \times S}{\text{depth of window, } (D)} \qquad (14\text{-}4)$$

where $E$ = footcandles obtainable from two rows of fluorescent lamps.

The factors $F$, $L$, and $S$, are selected from Tables 14-4, 14-6, and 14-8. If the value of $E$ as found above does not equal the required design level, the necessary number of rows of lamps can be found by a simple ratio.

TABLE 14-8

**Shielding Factor ($S$) for Fluorescent Lamps***

| $H/D$ ratio | Shielding factors | | |
|---|---|---|---|
| | Eggcrate louvers† shielding lamps to 45° crosswise and 25° lengthwise | | |
| | Zone A | Zone B | Zone C |
| 4.0 | 0.90 | 0.83 | 0.88 |
| 3.5 | 0.90 | 0.83 | 0.88 |
| 3.0 | 0.90 | 0.85 | 0.88 |
| 2.5 | 0.90 | 0.85 | 0.88 |
| 2.0 | 0.90 | 0.85 | 0.86 |
| 1.5 | 0.92 | 0.87 | 0.84 |
| 1.0 | 0.92 | 0.91 | 0.79 |

\* From data by Eby.
† Mat white.

The number of lamps end-to-end needed to fill a row can be determined easily by reference to the manufacturer's data. If the window is 13 ft long, three 4-ft lamps can be accommodated. If it is exactly 12 ft or 11 ft 6 in. long, only two 4-ft lamps and one 3-ft lamp can be used.

EXAMPLES:

**1.** A show window is 10 ft long, 3 ft deep, and 6 ft high. 100 ft-c are desired on zone $B$. How many rows of 3,500° white fluorescent lamps of 475 lm per ft output will be required? The lamps will be louvered.

The $H/D$ ratio is 2.0. From Table 14-4 the illumination factor, $F$, is 105 for concentrating reflectors, the highest value in the table.

Only two 4-ft lamps can be used in one row. From Table 14-6 the length factor, $L$, is 0.97. The shielding factor, $S$ (Table 14-8), is 0.85. Then

$$E = \frac{105 \times 0.97 \times 0.85}{3} = 29.$$

Since 100 ft-c are required, 6 rows of lamps, each row containing two 48-in., 40-watt white lamps, will be necessary.

**2.** Assume that you are asked to design for the use of 300-ma standard warm white Slimline lamps in this same window.

By reference to Table 3-6, Chapter 3, the 8-ft lamp emits 518 lm per ft. The illumination factor, $F$, is 105. The length factor, $L$, is now $\frac{518}{475} \times 0.97$ = 1.06. The shielding factor, $S$, is 0.85. Then

$$E = \frac{105 \times 1.06 \times 0.85}{3} = 31.4 \text{ ft-c}$$

Since this is the footcandles produced by 2 rows of lamps, and 100 ft-c are required, 6 rows of lamps will be necessary.

## PROBLEMS

**1.** A delicatessen is 18 by 40 ft with 12-ft ceiling. Ceiling reflectance is 75%; walls 30%. Design a general lighting system to provide 25 ft-c in service, using luminaire No. 32, Table 9-7, as a prototype. Work plane is 3 ft above the floor.

**2.** a. A grocery store is 38 by 80 ft with 13-ft ceiling. Ceiling reflectance is 75%; side walls 30%. Design a general lighting system of 40 ft-c level, utilizing the bare 3,500°, 93 in., 120-ma iron-cathode fluorescent lamp, mounted on the ceiling. Use luminaire No. 22, Table 9-7, as a prototype.

b. A vegetable display counter in this store is 30 in. wide and 12 ft long. Design a downlighting system, luminaires flush in the ceiling, to provide 100 ft-c on this display.

**3.** A jewelry store is 22 by 58 ft with 12-ft ceiling. Ceiling reflectance is 75%; side walls 30%. Design a general lighting system of 25 ft-c using luminaire No. 37, Table 9-7, as a prototype.

**4.** Design an incandescent lighting system for a show window 6 ft deep, 16 ft long, and 8 ft from platform to ceiling. Provide 300 ft-c on zone *B*. Specify the number and size of lamps, spacing, and reflector distribution. Use louvers parallel to glass.

**5.** A window devoted to display of women's wearing apparel is 5 ft deep, 13 ft long, and 7 ft from platform to ceiling. The owner desires to use Warmtone, 300-ma Slimline fluorescent lamps producing approximately 530 lm per ft. How many and what length lamps will be necessary to produce 150 ft-c on zone *B*?

**6.** A shoe fitting area is 8 ft wide and 30 ft long. Light this floor space by means of reflector or projector lamps located in the ceiling. Ceiling is 13 ft above the floor. Design level of footcandles is to be 40.

**7.** A typical showcase is 27 in. high. A level of illumination of 80 ft-c is required on plane *B*. Design three lighting systems using fluorescent lamps, T-10 clear lamps in reflectors, and T-10 side-silvered reflector showcase lamps, respectively.

**8.** A drug store window in a suburban area is 3 ft deep, 7 ft high from floor to ceiling, and 12 ft long. Design an incandescent lighting system to produce 100 ft-c on plane *B*.

**9.** A specialty department in a store is oval in shape. Long dimension is 50 ft, width is 28 ft, ceiling height 14 ft. Ceiling has 75% reflectance; walls 30% reflectance. Design a cove to produce 15 ft-c for general lighting. Use fluorescent lamps.

Design also a downlighting system using reflector lamps located in the ceiling to produce 35 ft-c on the floor.

## REFERENCES

Eby, W. J., "Design Data for Show Window Lighting," Nela Park Engineering Department, General Electric Company, Cleveland, Ohio.

"Ideas," suggestions for modernizing business interiors, Armstrong Cork Company, Lancaster, Pennsylvania.

"Lighting Practices for Stores," *Trans. Illum. Eng. Soc.*, Vol. 43, no. 6, June 1948.

"Modern Stores, 1946," National Retail Furniture Association, Chicago.

"Post-War Lighting Perspectives," Lamp Department, General Electric Company, Cleveland, Ohio.

"The Right Way to Light Your Merchandise," Sylvania Electric Products, Inc., New York.

"Selling with Light," Grand Rapids Store Equipment Company, Grand Rapids, Michigan.

# 15

# LIGHTING DESIGN—
# SPECIALIZED TECHNIQUES

There are a number of important specialized lighting design techniques that are used in a variety of buildings and spaces. The principles of floodlighting design, for example, are used for the lighting of building fronts, gasoline filling stations, parking lots, railway classification yards, loading platforms, sports areas, and the like. Cove lighting is used in homes, churches, auditoriums, and offices. Downlighting is used in stores, churches, auditoriums, and homes.

The form in which these methods are applied will differ, but the basic design considerations remain the same. They will therefore be treated in detail in this chapter.

## 15.1. Floodlighting

Floodlighting is considered to be that form of lighting in which the light is projected over relatively large areas from a considerable distance. The floodlighting of buildings and monuments is more of an art than a science. Much of the effect hinges upon direction of light, shadows, and intensity of light. Once these have been decided upon, the achievement depends upon calculation. Many of the applications, however, are strictly utilitarian and lend themselves to straightforward calculation right from the start.

Floodlight projectors are commonly classified by beam spread (Table 15-1). A beam spread of 30° means a total of 30°, that is, 15° on each side of nadir. The beam limit is that point at which the beam candlepower falls to 10% of maximum. The spill light outside of this limit is not of much use except when the floodlight is close to the area to be lighted. The efficiency of a floodlight is the ratio of beam lumens to lamp lumens, *not* the ratio of total output in lumens to lamp lumens.

TABLE 15-1

**Floodlight Beam Characteristics**

| Class | Beam spread | Usual distance from lighted surface |
|---|---|---|
| Narrow | 15° and less | 100 ft or more |
| Medium | 16° to 29° | 50 ft to 100 ft |
| Broad | 30° or more | less than 50 ft |

Floodlights are usually substantially constructed of copper or aluminum. Sometimes they are equipped with internal reflectors of mirrored glass or metal. The units are generally totally enclosed for protection against weather, dirt, and insects. The reflector and projector types of lamps are popular for the lighting of filling stations, small parking lots, protective lighting, garden areas, and so forth. They are small, light in weight, inconspicuous, easily installed, and inexpensive. Illustrations of floodlights and flood-lighting applications are found in Figs. 15-1 to 15-5.

Floodlight projectors may be equipped with two types of incandescent lamps; the general service lamp, or the floodlight lamp. The floodlight lamp has a concentrated filament shape and hence is best suited for use in narrow-beam projectors. It is less efficient, shorter lived, and more costly than the general service lamp.

Enclosed floodlights may be equipped with coverglasses (lenses) of three types. The clear glass lens does not alter the beam spread and hence is used as a protective element without affecting the beam characteristics.

The diffusing or stippled lens enlarges the beam spread and reduces the central beam candlepower. The lighted pattern is quite uniform and free from filament images. For this reason the stippled lens is often used on medium and wide-spread beam units where the projectors are generally a moderate distance away from the area to be lighted.

The spread lens utilizes prism action to produce a rectangular beam pattern.   The narrow dimension of the pattern conforms to the normal beam.   The long dimension generally enlarges the beam spread to anywhere between 60° and 90°.   As may be expected, there is no central beam candlepower, hence the light will not be projected any great distance.

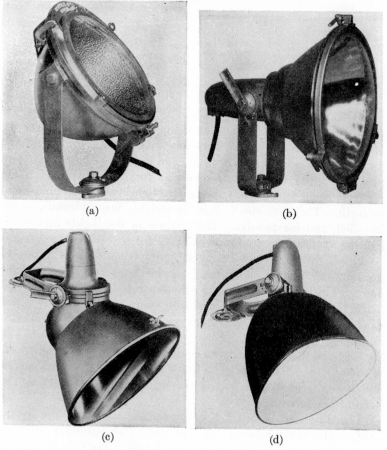

(a)

(b)

(c)

(d)

Fig. 15-1.   Representative types of floodlight projectors.   (*General Electric Co. photograph.*)

Fig. 15-2. Lighting designs for baseball depend upon the degree of professionalism of the players. Layouts are well standardized and will be found in the I.E.S. *Lighting Handbook* and various publications of manufacturers.

Fig. 15-3. Fields devoted to the playing of football are lighted from each of the long sides, with projectors mounted 40 to 50 feet above the ground.

Fig. 15-4. When floodlights are mounted close to a soaring wall the fading of the illumination toward the top emphasizes the impression of height.

Fig. 15-5. The architectural details of monumental buildings can be emphasized by skillful use of shadows and a certain unevenness of illumination.

Beam pattern dimensions can be determined from the data in Table 8-4. Assume that a floodlight whose normal beam spread is 15° is equipped with a spread lens. The rectangular beam which results will be 15° in width and, let us say, 50° in length. For any distance of throw the dimensions of the lighted pattern can be determined by referring to the 15° beam and 50° beam characteristics in Table 8-4.

a. Design Procedure. The locations for projectors are often quite obvious. Sometimes, however, the designer must make a decision hinged upon the interrelation of beam spread, beam lumens, and physical dimensions of a building or area. There are no exact rules which apply; experience in design and familiarity with floodlight characteristics will develop the necessary skill. The data in Table 15-1 will be useful as an indication of the relationship between beam spread and "throw."

The footcandles suggested for a number of floodlight uses will be found in Table 15-2. After selecting a beam spread and a footcandle value, two steps remain:

1. Determine the number of floodlights which will produce the desired footcandles.

2. Check to insure that this number of floodlights will cover adequately the area to be lighted.

**TABLE 15-2**

**Suggested Footcandles for Floodlight Application**

| Type of application | Footcandles |
|---|---|
| Automobile parking areas | 1–2 |
| Shipping platforms | 5 |
| Storage yards | 1 |
| Railway classification yards | 0.1–1.5 |
| Construction | 5 |
| Service stations: | |
|   Buildings—*see below* | |
|   Yards and driveways | 5 |
|   Pump areas | 20 |
| Protective lighting | 0.1–0.2 |
| Buildings:* | |
|   Light colored—Terra cotta, marble, limestone | 5–20 |
|   Medium colored—Sandstone, gray brick, tan brick | 10–25 |
|   Dark colored—Common red brick, brownstone, dark grey brick | 12–30 |

* The amount of light will depend upon the degree of competing illumination. Buildings in parks and residential areas, for example, need less light for conspicuous appearance than buildings in business districts.

To determine the number of projectors or the necessary beam lumens (if the number of projectors is fixed) use the following formula:

$$N = \frac{E \times A}{0.7 \times F_b} \tag{15-1}$$

where $E$ = maintained average footcandles,
    $A$ = area (square feet) to be lighted,
    $F_b$ = initial beam lumens,
    $0.7$ = average depreciation factor.

The beam lumens should be found from manufacturers' data, or assumed for initial design purposes from Table 15-3.

The number of projectors determined from Eq. (15-1) may not be sufficient to light the area with reasonable uniformity. The

## TABLE 15-3

### Average Beam Lumens for Typical Floodlights*

| Beam spread | Floodlights with floodlight lamps | | Floodlights with general service lamps | | | Projector- and reflector-type lamps | |
|---|---|---|---|---|---|---|---|
| | | | | Initial beam lumens | | | |
| | Lamp size in watts | Initial beam lumens | Lamp size in watts | Reflector diam. 12 to 16 in. | Reflector diam. 18 to 24 in. | Lamp | Initial beam lumens |
| Narrow | 250 | 1,300 | 300 | 1,400 | | | |
| | | | 500 | 3,800 | | | |
| | | | 750 | .. | 3,500 | | |
| | 500 | 4,300 | 1,000 | .. | 7,800 | | |
| | | | 1,500 | .. | 10,500 | | |
| Medium | 250 | 1,150 | 300 | 1,700 | .. | 75-w R30 reflector spot | 220 |
| | | | 500 | 3,000 | .. | 150-w PAR 38 spot | 1,150 |
| | | | 750 | 4,900 | 6,000 | 150-w R40 reflector spot | 600 |
| | 500 | 2,800 | 1,000 | 8,000 | 8,500 | 200-w PAR46 spot | 1,600 |
| | | | 1,500 | 13,600 | 12,500 | 300-w PAR56 spot | 2,400 |
| | | | | | | 300-w R40 reflector spot | 1,350 |
| Broad | 250 | 1,200 | 300 | 1,900 | | | |
| | | | 500 | 3,400 | .. | 75-w R30 reflector flood | 300 |
| | | | 750 | 5,200 | 6,200 | 150-w R40 reflector flood | 800 |
| | 500 | 2,900 | 1,000 | 7,400 | 8,900 | 150-w PAR38 flood | 1,400 |
| | | | 1,500 | .. | 13,000 | 300-w R40 reflector flood | 1,600 |

\* In the absence of specific values, typical or "rule of thumb" values are as follows:

    Narrow beam projectors—40% of lamp lumens;
    Medium beam projectors—45% of lamp lumens;
    Wide beam projectors—40%–60% of lamp lumens.

## TABLE 15-4

### Dimensions and Areas of Illuminated Spots Produced by Various Types and Arrangements of Floodlights*

| D† | Z† | 10° BEAM | | | 15° BEAM | | | 20° BEAM | | | 25° BEAM | | |
|---|---|---|---|---|---|---|---|---|---|---|---|---|---|
| | | Area† | Length† | Width† | Area | Length | Width | Area | Length | Width | Area | Length | Width |
| 15 | 0 | 5 | 3 | 3 | 10 | 4 | 4 | 18 | 5 | 5 | 30 | 7 | 7 |
| | 10 | 8 | 4 | 3 | 20 | 6 | 5 | 33 | 8 | 7 | 50 | 10 | 8 |
| | 20 | 21 | 7 | 4 | 50 | 11 | 7 | 93 | 16 | 9 | 160 | 20 | 12 |
| | 30 | 52 | 14 | 6 | 130 | 21 | 9 | 250 | 30 | 13 | 460 | 41 | 17 |
| | 40 | 113 | 22 | 8 | 290 | 37 | 12 | 620 | 55 | 17 | 1,300 | 83 | 23 |
| 25 | 0 | 11 | 4 | 4 | 25 | 7 | 7 | 44 | 9 | 9 | 70 | 11 | 11 |
| | 20 | 23 | 7 | 5 | 50 | 11 | 8 | 100 | 15 | 12 | 150 | 19 | 14 |
| | 40 | 71 | 16 | 8 | 170 | 25 | 13 | 330 | 34 | 17 | 540 | 45 | 22 |
| | 60 | 195 | 31 | 11 | 490 | 49 | 18 | 1,030 | 73 | 25 | 1,960 | 105 | 34 |
| | 80 | 450 | 54 | 15 | 1,200 | 90 | 24 | 2,920 | 145 | 36 | 7,270 | 261 | 53 |
| 50 | 0 | 38 | 9 | 9 | 90 | 13 | 13 | 155 | 18 | 18 | 210 | 20 | 20 |
| | 20 | 47 | 11 | 9 | 110 | 15 | 14 | 195 | 21 | 19 | 320 | 26 | 24 |
| | 40 | 81 | 14 | 11 | 190 | 22 | 17 | 330 | 30 | 23 | 550 | 38 | 29 |
| | 60 | 150 | 22 | 14 | 340 | 33 | 20 | 630 | 45 | 28 | 1,070 | 58 | 36 |
| | 80 | 260 | 32 | 17 | 600 | 49 | 25 | 1,160 | 68 | 35 | 2,060 | 90 | 45 |
| 75 | 0 | 67 | 13 | 13 | 170 | 20 | 20 | 310 | 26 | 26 | 480 | 33 | 33 |
| | 40 | 110 | 17 | 14 | 250 | 25 | 22 | 440 | 34 | 30 | 710 | 43 | 38 |
| | 80 | 220 | 28 | 18 | 540 | 43 | 29 | 1,010 | 59 | 39 | 1,630 | 75 | 50 |
| | 120 | 530 | 48 | 25 | 1,210 | 74 | 38 | 2,320 | 102 | 52 | 3,930 | 135 | 67 |
| | 160 | 1,040 | 76 | 32 | 2,500 | 119 | 49 | 5,050 | 171 | 67 | 9,060 | 238 | 88 |
| 100 | 0 | 120 | 17 | 17 | 310 | 26 | 26 | 490 | 35 | 35 | 770 | 44 | 44 |
| | 40 | 150 | 20 | 19 | 390 | 31 | 28 | 610 | 41 | 38 | 980 | 52 | 48 |
| | 80 | 250 | 29 | 22 | 580 | 44 | 34 | 1,050 | 59 | 46 | 1,700 | 75 | 58 |
| | 120 | 470 | 43 | 28 | 890 | 66 | 41 | 2,000 | 90 | 56 | 3,290 | 116 | 72 |
| | 160 | 830 | 63 | 33 | 1,950 | 98 | 51 | 3,700 | 136 | 69 | 6,340 | 180 | 89 |
| | 200 | 1,300 | 80 | 42 | — | — | — | 6,650 | 201 | 84 | — | | |
| 150 | 0 | 270 | 26 | 26 | 610 | 39 | 39 | 1,100 | 53 | 53 | 1,740 | 67 | 67 |
| | 40 | 300 | 28 | 27 | 680 | 42 | 41 | 1,230 | 57 | 55 | 1,940 | 71 | 69 |
| | 80 | 400 | 34 | 30 | 900 | 51 | 45 | 1,630 | 69 | 60 | 2,580 | 87 | 76 |
| | 120 | 570 | 43 | 34 | 1,310 | 65 | 51 | 2,380 | 89 | 68 | 3,820 | 113 | 87 |
| | 160 | 860 | 57 | 39 | 1,970 | 86 | 58 | 3,610 | 117 | 79 | 5,920 | 151 | 100 |
| | 200 | 1,280 | 74 | 44 | — | — | — | 5,550 | 156 | 91 | — | | |
| 200 | 0 | 480 | 35 | 35 | 1,090 | 53 | 53 | 1,940 | 71 | 71 | 3,090 | 89 | 89 |
| | 40 | 510 | 37 | 36 | 1,160 | 55 | 54 | 2,080 | 73 | 72 | 3,280 | 92 | 91 |
| | 80 | 600 | 41 | 38 | 1,360 | 61 | 57 | 2,470 | 82 | 77 | 3,910 | 104 | 96 |
| | 120 | 770 | 48 | 41 | 1,730 | 72 | 61 | 3,160 | 97 | 83 | 5,030 | 123 | 104 |
| | 160 | 1,030 | 58 | 45 | 2,330 | 87 | 68 | 4,240 | 118 | 91 | 6,800 | 150 | 115 |
| | 200 | 1,370 | 71 | 50 | — | — | — | 5,800 | 146 | 102 | — | | |
| 300 | 0 | 1,080 | 52 | 52 | 2,460 | 79 | 79 | 4,400 | 106 | 106 | 6,940 | 133 | 133 |
| | 40 | 1,110 | 53 | 53 | 2,520 | 80 | 80 | 4,520 | 108 | 107 | 7,140 | 136 | 134 |
| | 80 | 1,200 | 56 | 54 | 2,720 | 85 | 82 | 4,890 | 114 | 110 | 7,740 | 143 | 138 |
| | 120 | 1,350 | 61 | 57 | 3,070 | 92 | 85 | 5,530 | 123 | 114 | 8,790 | 156 | 144 |
| | 160 | 1,580 | 68 | 60 | 3,590 | 102 | 90 | 6,480 | 137 | 120 | 10,300 | 173 | 152 |
| 500 | 0 | 3,010 | 87 | 87 | 6,810 | 132 | 132 | 12,200 | 176 | 176 | 19,300 | 222 | 222 |
| | 40 | 3,030 | 88 | 88 | 6,870 | 133 | 132 | 12,300 | 177 | 177 | 19,500 | 223 | 222 |
| | 80 | 3,120 | 90 | 89 | 7,070 | 135 | 133 | 12,700 | 181 | 179 | 20,100 | 228 | 225 |
| | 120 | 3,270 | 93 | 90 | 7,410 | 139 | 135 | 13,300 | 187 | 181 | 21,100 | 235 | 228 |
| | 160 | 3,490 | 97 | 92 | 7,900 | 145 | 138 | 14,200 | 195 | 185 | 22,500 | 246 | 233 |

### TABLE 15-4. Continued

| D | Z | 30° BEAM Area | Length | Width | 35° BEAM Area | Length | Width |
|---|---|---|---|---|---|---|---|
| 15 | 0 | 45 | 8 | 8 | 60 | 9 | 9 |
|  | 10 | 80 | 12 | 10 | 110 | 14 | 12 |
|  | 20 | 240 | 26 | 14 | 360 | 32 | 17 |
|  | 30 | 790 | 56 | 21 | 1,430 | 79 | 27 |
|  | 40 | 2,900 | 133 | 33 | 8,690 | 622 | 50 |
|  | — | — | — | — | — | — | — |
| 25 | 0 | 100 | 13 | 13 | 140 | 16 | 16 |
|  | 10 | 140 | 16 | 15 | 170 | 19 | 17 |
|  | 20 | 220 | 23 | 18 | 310 | 28 | 20 |
|  | 30 | 430 | 36 | 21 | 660 | 45 | 27 |
|  | 40 | 920 | 59 | 28 | 1,430 | 75 | 34 |
|  | 50 | 1,930 | 94 | 37 | 3,270 | 131 | 45 |
|  | 60 | 3,950 | 155 | 46 | 8,590 | 249 | 63 |
| 50 | 0 | 350 | 27 | 27 | 510 | 32 | 32 |
|  | 20 | 450 | 33 | 29 | 650 | 37 | 34 |
|  | 40 | 800 | 46 | 35 | 1,160 | 55 | 41 |
|  | 60 | 1,590 | 73 | 44 | 2,440 | 90 | 53 |
|  | 80 | 3,200 | 117 | 56 | 5,300 | 151 | 69 |
|  | — | — | — | — | — | — | — |
| 75 | 0 | 700 | 40 | 40 | 970 | 47 | 47 |
|  | 20 | 790 | 43 | 42 | 1,070 | 51 | 49 |
|  | 40 | 1,060 | 53 | 46 | 1,460 | 63 | 54 |
|  | 60 | 1,590 | 69 | 53 | 2,280 | 83 | 61 |
|  | 80 | 2,480 | 93 | 61 | 3,620 | 114 | 73 |
|  | 100 | 4,000 | 128 | 72 | 5,780 | 160 | 84 |
|  | 120 | 6,400 | 175 | 84 | 10,100 | 226 | 103 |
| 100 | 0 | 1,130 | 54 | 54 | 1,560 | 63 | 63 |
|  | 40 | 1,430 | 63 | 58 | 1,980 | 74 | 68 |
|  | 80 | 2,550 | 92 | 70 | 3,560 | 110 | 82 |
|  | 120 | 5,050 | 146 | 89 | 7,510 | 180 | 106 |
|  | 160 | 10,300 | 234 | 112 | — | — | — |
| 125 | 0 | 1,760 | 67 | 67 | 2,440 | 79 | 79 |
|  | 40 | 2,130 | 73 | 71 | 2,870 | 88 | 83 |
|  | 80 | 3,090 | 97 | 80 | 4,350 | 116 | 96 |
|  | 120 | 5,200 | 138 | 96 | 7,430 | 167 | 113 |
|  | 160 | 9,140 | 200 | 116 | — | — | — |
| 150 | 0 | 2,540 | 80 | 80 | 3,510 | 95 | 95 |
|  | 40 | 2,880 | 86 | 85 | 3,900 | 102 | 97 |
|  | 80 | 3,820 | 105 | 92 | 5,300 | 125 | 108 |
|  | 120 | 5,700 | 135 | 107 | 8,000 | 166 | 123 |
|  | 160 | 10,300 | 234 | 112 | — | — | — |
|  | — | — | — | — | — | — | — |
| 200 | 0 | 4,500 | 107 | 107 | 6,250 | 126 | 126 |
|  | 40 | 4,800 | 111 | 109 | 6,660 | 132 | 129 |
|  | 80 | 5,700 | 125 | 116 | 7,950 | 149 | 136 |
|  | 120 | 7,500 | 150 | 127 | 10,300 | 178 | 148 |
|  | 160 | 10,200 | 184 | 141 | — | — | — |
|  | — | — | — | — | — | — | — |

| D | Z | 40° BEAM Area | Length | Width | 50° BEAM Area | Length | Width |
|---|---|---|---|---|---|---|---|
| 15 | 0 | 80 | 11 | 11 | 130 | 14 | 14 |
|  | 5 | 110 | 13 | 12 | 175 | 17 | 16 |
|  | 10 | 150 | 17 | 14 | 260 | 22 | 18 |
|  | 15 | 310 | 25 | 19 | 530 | 33 | 25 |
|  | 20 | 630 | 43 | 23 | 1,250 | 63 | 30 |
|  | 25 | 1,150 | 65 | 27 | — | — | — |
| 25 | 0 | 185 | 18 | 18 | 305 | 23 | 23 |
|  | 10 | 240 | 22 | 20 | 400 | 28 | 26 |
|  | 20 | 450 | 33 | 24 | 800 | 44 | 32 |
|  | 30 | 970 | 55 | 32 | 2,050 | 83 | 44 |
|  | 40 | 2,300 | 98 | 42 | 6,950 | 187 | 66 |
|  | 50 | 6,450 | 194 | 60 | — | — | — |
| 35 | 0 | 320 | 26 | 26 | 520 | 33 | 33 |
|  | 10 | 380 | 28 | 27 | 580 | 37 | 32 |
|  | 20 | 510 | 35 | 32 | 890 | 47 | 39 |
|  | 30 | 850 | 49 | 35 | 1,550 | 67 | 47 |
|  | 40 | 1,490 | 71 | 43 | 3,000 | 105 | 59 |
|  | 50 | 2,700 | 106 | 52 | — | — | — |
| 45 | 0 | 470 | 33 | 33 | 780 | 42 | 42 |
|  | 10 | 520 | 35 | 34 | 820 | 44 | 42 |
|  | 20 | 650 | 40 | 37 | 1,070 | 52 | 47 |
|  | 30 | 890 | 49 | 42 | 1,550 | 67 | 53 |
|  | 40 | 1,320 | 66 | 46 | 2,460 | 91 | 62 |
|  | 50 | 2,100 | 87 | 55 | — | — | — |
| 55 | 0 | 640 | 40 | 40 | 1,030 | 51 | 51 |
|  | 20 | 790 | 46 | 44 | 1,300 | 59 | 56 |
|  | 40 | 1,320 | 66 | 51 | 2,330 | 88 | 68 |
|  | 60 | 2,650 | 104 | 65 | 5,250 | 152 | 88 |
|  | 80 | 5,600 | 172 | 83 | — | — | — |
| 70 | 0 | 1,020 | 51 | 51 | 1,680 | 65 | 65 |
|  | 20 | 1,180 | 55 | 54 | 1,940 | 72 | 69 |
|  | 40 | 1,680 | 71 | 60 | 2,860 | 93 | 78 |
|  | 60 | 2,700 | 98 | 70 | 5,000 | 135 | 94 |
|  | 80 | 4,700 | 142 | 84 | — | — | — |
| 85 | 0 | 1,500 | 62 | 62 | 2,460 | 79 | 79 |
|  | 20 | 1,680 | 67 | 64 | 2,750 | 85 | 82 |
|  | 40 | 2,130 | 78 | 69 | 3,600 | 102 | 90 |
|  | 60 | 3,080 | 100 | 78 | 5,400 | 133 | 103 |
|  | 80 | 4,750 | 132 | 92 | — | — | — |
|  | 100 | 7,500 | 181 | 106 | — | — | — |
| 100 | 0 | 2,100 | 73 | 73 | 3,400 | 93 | 93 |
|  | 20 | 2,280 | 78 | 74 | 3,700 | 98 | 96 |
|  | 40 | 2,700 | 86 | 79 | 4,500 | 112 | 102 |
|  | 60 | 3,500 | 104 | 87 | 7,800 | 138 | 113 |
|  | 80 | 5,000 | 130 | 98 | — | — | — |
|  | 100 | 7,300 | 168 | 110 | — | — | — |

\* Allowance made for necessary beam overlap.
† Dimensions may be in feet and square feet or in other units if more convenient.

\* Reproduced by permission of the Illuminating Engineering Society, from *I.E.S. Lighting Handbook*, 1947.

chosen beam spread may be too small or the beam lumens too great. A spotty lighting effect on a building is a sure indication of poor design. Dark areas in a parking space or work area may be hazardous. Therefore a check calculation is performed by the following formula:

$$N_c = \frac{A_t}{A_f} \tag{15-2}$$

where $N_c$ = number of projectors necessary for uniform coverage,
$A_t$ = total area to be lighted,
$A_f$ = area lighted effectively by one floodlight.

$A_f$ is determined from Table 15-4. Figure 15-6 explains the symbols found in this table. The figure for effective area allows

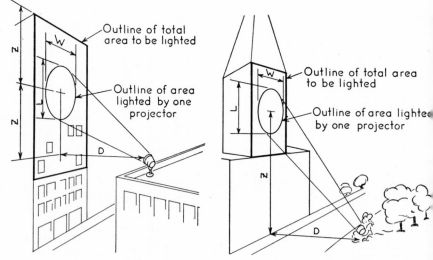

Fig. 15-6. These illustrate the "lumen method" of floodlighting design. The average area lighted by one floodlight is assumed to be that obtained by directing the beam to the center of the lighted surface.

for the beam overlap which experience has shown will provide the necessary uniformity.

If $N_c$ is less than $N$ the design is satisfactory. It might be wise, however, to re-examine the beam characteristic to see if, perhaps, more beam lumens for the same spread could be obtained. This would reduce the number of floodlights.

If $N_c$ is greater than $N$, more floodlights must be added, or a floodlight selected with a greater beam spread.

The high beam candlepower of a floodlight always presents a glare problem.  It is very difficult to see anything if floodlights are directed toward an observer.  The floodlights should, if possible, be mounted high enough to allow the beam axis to strike the ground at an angle of 45°.  The lighting is also improved if the floodlights are located in several places about or around the area, instead of in one central bank.

It is helpful to prepare a plan of the area to be lighted, to some convenient scale.  On this plan, sketch to scale the beam pattern of the floodlights.  This visualization of the lighting will be of aid in selecting floodlight locations or checking the effectiveness of the only possible locations.

The floodlighting of buildings introduces artistic considerations beyond the scope of this text.  The mathematics of design are the same as for ground areas.  The location and beam characteristics of floodlights, however, will depend upon such factors as accentuation of architectural details, use of color, and structural limitations on floodlight placement.

EXAMPLE:

It is desired to light a parking space immediately adjacent to one wall of a factory building.  The lot is 100 ft wide and 200 ft long.

A good location for the lights would be on the parapet of the building, 30 ft above the ground.  Electric service is readily available, and the lights could be maintained safely from the flat roof.

From Table 15-1 a broad beam characteristic is indicated.  The foot-candle requirement is low (2 ft-c from Table 15-2) so perhaps a 500-watt general service lamp in a small floodlight will be satisfactory.  The beam lumens (Table 15-3) are 3,400.

The number of floodlights necessary to provide the 2 ft-c will be

$$N = \frac{2 \times 20,000}{0.7 \times 3,400} = 16.8 \text{ (or 17)}$$

The check coverage will now be made.  Let us see what a 40° beam spread will do.  The distance $D$ is 30 ft, and $Z$ (Fig. 15-1) is 50 ft.  By interpolation in Table 15-4, $A_f = 4,575$ sq ft.  Then

$$N_c = \frac{20,000}{4,575} = 4.4$$

The number of floodlights for illumination is so greatly in excess of the number required for coverage that our choice of beam lumens was too low. Let us now recalculate, using a floodlight with a 1,000-watt general service lamp.

With typical beam lumens of 7,400, the number of floodlights to produce the 2 ft-c will be 7.7 (8). If this number of floodlights is installed the entire area can be covered about twice. This will insure a good lighting result.

A 1,500-watt floodlight might appear a more reasonable choice. This is a very large unit and its weight and cost might rule against it. However, a cost analysis could be made to determine the facts.

For this example we will settle on the eight 1,000-watt floodlights. The question then is whether to place them in two banks of four each, or in a single bank. The lighting will be better if two banks are used, but the wiring may be cheaper if one bank is used. However, the lighting requirements are not too strict, so if the owner does not object to a large mass of floodlights in one spot, locate them midway of the lot, on the building parapet.

## 15.2. Cove Lighting

Cove lighting is basically a form of indirect lighting in which the lighting equipment is made part of the structure or the ornamentation. If the lighting is to serve visual tasks, then close attention must be paid to efficiency of luminaires, maintenance, and high reflectances of surrounding surfaces. If the major purpose is esthetic, then these factors are of lesser importance.

There are, however, certain features which must be carefully attended to in order to avoid uncouth results. These are (1) the sight lines and (2) avoidance of unseemly shadows or variations in light pattern.

The sight line is easily determined (Fig. 15-7). Each light source is studied from the viewpoint of the occupants of the space. The maximum eye position is noted and a line from there to the shielding medium is drawn. No portion of the light source or reflector may project above this line. When fluorescent lamps are used, as shown, the shadow cast by the channel should be concealed below the sight line. The cove section should be laid out to scale to determine the relationships. If the lamps are recessed in the wall, the upper edge of the recess should be below the sight line.

There will be situations in which complete concealment of the lighting equipment is impossible from all viewing positions.   For example, those in the choir loft of a church may see the inside of a cove.   The number of people so disturbed is so small in relation to the congregation that if the view from the auditorium is serene, then the design will be judged competent.

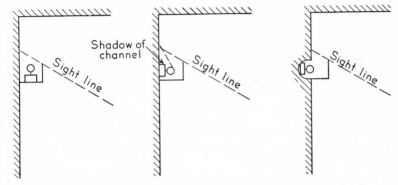

Fig. 15-7.   All lamp, reflector, and equipment shadows should fall below the sight line in order to be concealed.

Bright spots and shadows on ceiling and upper walls are caused by:

1. Socket shadows.
2. Spacing between lamps.
3. Improper light distribution patterns.

These defects may appear regardless of whether the light source is concentrated or continuous.

Socket shadow is inevitable with single rows of tubular lamps unless the socket and channel are recessed or the ends of the lamp are overlapped.   As a rule, double rows of lamps are used and the socket positions offset (Fig. 15-8).

Incandescent lamps must be closely spaced in a cove to achieve an illusion of uniformity.   If the lamps are placed in reflectors, the light distribution must conform to the space.   When the light is to be projected to some distance, then a relatively narrow beam and close spacing of lamps is necessary.   For narrow rooms and short projection distances, a wide distribution of light and greater distance between lamps is indicated.

a. Placement.   Coves may be placed in many "natural" appearing locations. Some of these locations are: the capitals of columns, window ledges, window heads, door heads, structural divisions of wall spaces, edges of domes, juncture of walls and arched ceiling, and as applied ornament on flat wall surfaces.

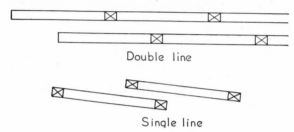

Double line

Single line

Fig. 15-8. Socket shadows should be eliminated if possible. An overlap of sockets from a single row of lamps can be obtained by placing the lamps on a slight diagonal.

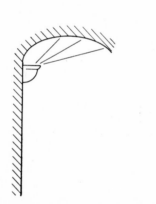

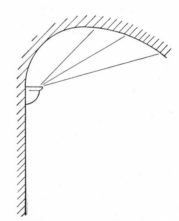

Fig. 15-9. Flat or shallow arched ceilings are difficult to light to any degree of uniformity. Use concentrating types of reflectors and locate the cove as far below the ceiling as possible.

Fig. 15-10. A well rounded arch allows more freedom of light control. If the ceiling has projecting elements, well diffused light from a number of lamps will eliminate disturbing shadows.

With an arched ceiling the natural location of a cove is at or below the juncture of sidewall and ceiling. If the arch is flat, concentrating equipment is desirable, with the light directed across the ceiling (Fig. 15-9). If the arch is well rounded, the light may be more diffuse and thus spill to the surface nearer the cove (Fig. 15-10). When the ceiling has projecting ornamentation such as groins and plaster figures, the light must be well distributed to avoid unseemly shadows.

When the cove is placed on a wall, it should satisfy the laws of balance and proportion in size and placement. A good general rule is that to light a flat ceiling, the cove should be located at a distance down from the ceiling equal to 1/10 the room width. This arrangement will give the designer an opportunity to distribute light across the ceiling in an acceptable manner. There is nothing objectionable about non-uniformity across the ceiling if the ratio of brightness adjacent to the cove to that of distant portions is no greater than 10 to 1 with gradual gradation from one to the other.

**b. Cove construction.** The projecting cove is the most common type used. Filament lamp systems should have lamps placed on

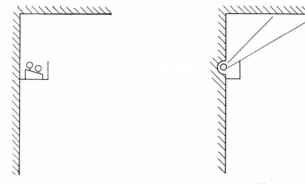

Fig. 15-11. When lamps are offset there is less interference of useful light and hence improved appearance of the ceiling and greater efficiency.

Fig. 15-12. The recessed cove allows the designer greater freedom and improves the lighting effect.

6- to 12-in. centers and rarely should exceed 100 watts in lamp size. If the cove is vertical, as is often the case behind a column in a church sanctuary, spacings of 12 to 15 in. are satisfactory with lamps up to 150 watts in size. Reflectors are usually unnecessary in these vertical coves because the projection distance is short.

When more than one row of line sources are used, the lamps should be offset to reduce absorption and increase the throw across the ceiling (Fig. 15-11). If the sockets are staggered as suggested in Fig. 15-8, the light distribution will be even.

A refinement of the projecting cove is obtained by forming the bottom of the cove of diffusing glass or louvers. The wall is thus luminous above and below the cove, producing a most pleasing effect.

The recessed cove (Fig. 15-12) is lower in efficiency and more costly to construct but has several excellent features. Socket shadows are eliminated, as is the uneven splash of light on the wall above. Filament lamps may be spaced 12 to 18 in. apart and may be of correspondingly larger size.

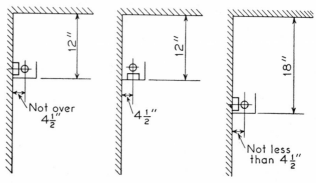

Fig. 15-13.    Tubular lamp arrangements for good wall lighting.

The lumiline lamp offers a good answer to cove lighting of low footcandles. The lamps have disk end-connectors and produce acceptable "continuous" lines of light. An advantage lies in the simple wiring channel required. The lamps are obtainable in clear and frosted tubing and an assortment of ceramic colors.

When a single row of fluorescent lamps is used without reflectors the arrangements shown in Fig. 15-13 produce the best brightness ratios on the wall behind the cove. Either a curved or flat wall and ceiling section may be used with equally good results.

With a single row of fluorescent lamps in a projecting cove, the dark scallops due to socket location can be reduced but not eliminated, by placing the lamps rather far from the wall as shown in Fig. 15-14.

When a reflector is placed back of the lamps as shown in Fig. 15-15a the brightness distribution across the ceiling is very even. However, if the wall is curved, the reflector casts an unpleasant

shadow (Fig. 15-15b). The only solution in such a case is to recess the reflector. No reflector should be less than 5 in. across the
opening; this increases the cost and size of the cove. Experience
shows that reflectors should be used behind fluorescent lamps only
in large rooms, or in rooms with low reflectances of walls and ceilings.

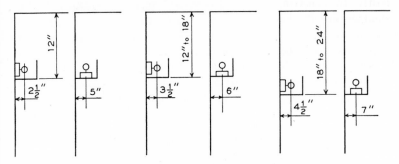

Fig. 15-14. A wide cove allows the lamp to be placed farther from
the wall, thereby improving the lighting results.

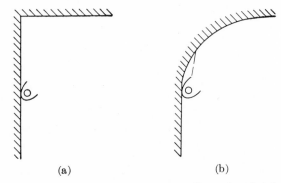

(a) (b)

Fig. 15-15. Reflectors are not generally used with tubular
lamps because of cost. When they are used, installation must
be carefully arranged.

**c. Ceiling and wall brightness.** The brightness pattern on the
ceiling above the cove is less of a problem than wall brightness.
Ceiling brightness is almost entirely a function of lamp lumens and
the distance of the cove from the ceiling. A cove with a single
row of lamps should be no closer than 1 ft from the ceiling. A two-
lamp cove should be 18 in. from the ceiling. The amount and
distribution of horizontal footcandles in the room is quite inde-

pendent of this distance, provided the cove is at least 1 ft below the ceiling.

When more than one row of lamps are used, the matter of concealment becomes more difficult. One arrangement is shown in Fig. 15-11. Obviously the lamps can also be placed in a horizontal plane or a vertical plane. Horizontal placement multiplies the brightness of the back wall in proportion to the number of rows of lamps. That is, two rows of lamps produce double the brightness of one row of lamps. The ceiling brightness, on the other hand, increases, not in direct ratio, but approximately as shown in Table 15-5. If the lamps are placed one over the other, vertically, the ceiling brightness increases in direct ratio. The wall brightness increases as shown in Table 15-6 because there is some "blocking effect" by the top row.

### TABLE 15-5

**Effect of Multiple Rows of Line Sources in a Horizontal Plane upon Ceiling Brightness above Cove**

|  | Ceiling brightness |
| --- | --- |
| 1 row of lamps | 1.00 |
| 2 rows of lamps | 1.60 |
| 3 rows of lamps | 2.25 |

### TABLE 15-6

**Effect of Multiple Rows of Line Sources in a Vertical Plane upon Wall Brightness above Cove**

|  | Wall brightness |
| --- | --- |
| 1 row of lamps | 1.00 |
| 2 rows of lamps | 1.60 |
| 3 rows of lamps | 2.25 |

In general, vertical placement is best for lighting, but in order to accommodate the lamps and arrange for concealment, the cove must be high and may be out of proportion to room size.

The arrangement shown in Fig. 15-11 is a good compromise because the increase in brightness of both side-wall and ceiling is about as shown in Tables 15-5 and 15-6.

The ceiling brightness is less of a factor in comfort than wall brightness. Experience shows that if the wall brightness resulting from a certain design is satisfactory, the ceiling brightness will also be satisfactory. If fluorescent lamps are used without reflectors, in coves dimensioned as in Figs. 15-13 and 15-14, acceptable wall brightness will be obtained as follows:

| Lumens per foot of cove | Distance from ceiling |
|---|---|
| Under 300 | 8 in. |
| 500–600 | 12 in. |
| 600–1000 | 18 in. |
| 1000–1500 | 24 in. |

The efficiency of multiple lamp coves is less than that of single lamp coves as shown in Table 15-7.

### TABLE 15-7

**Effect of Multiple Rows of Line Sources on Cove Efficiency**

| | Cove efficiency, % |
|---|---|
| 1 row of lamps | 100 |
| 2 rows of lamps | 93 |
| 3 rows of lamps | 85 |

**d. Reflector materials.** When it is necessary to project the light to some distance, filament lamps and individual reflectors of polished surface (mirrored glass or aluminum) are required. For shorter throws, and line sources, diffuse reflecting materials such as mat aluminum, porcelain enamel, or white plaster are used. Many coves have no provisions for reflectors. They depend upon white paint only for secondary reflection. Troughs made of continuous specular surfaces are not recommended for filament lamps because of the multiplicity of reflections and the likelihood of shadows and bright streaks.

It must be emphasized that the use of reflectors in fluorescent lamp coves may improve the distribution of light, but they may only increase the over-all efficiency by as little as 5%. The most important feature of a fluorescent cove is to have all interior surfaces of high reflection factor. The surfaces should be dull finished, not specular.

Fig. 15-16. In this type of cove, uneven ceiling illumination is to be expected, but does not detract from the effect. The socket shadows could have been eliminated by careful design.

Fig. 15-17. This installation features a large cove, a moderate width of area to be lighted, and good distance from cove to ceiling. Even illumination of the surface is desirable from the esthetic viewpoint because the cove emphasizes the purpose of the passageway.

**e. Room finishes.** The effect of ceiling and wall reflectances upon brightness ratios and efficiency of light utilization will be the same as for any lighting system.   One factor is important and that is the use of mat or eggshell finishes for reflecting room surfaces. Any shiny or specular ceiling or upper wall may image the light source and produce a most displeasing effect.   Even a dull finished surface may act like a mirror when the light falls obliquely upon it. Examples of cove lighting are illustrated in Figs. 15-16 and 15-17.

**TABLE 15-8**

**Typical Cove Efficiencies**

Projecting cove:
  No reflector:
    Filament lamps................................... 40%
    Single row of line sources........................ 65%
    Double row of line sources........................ 60%
    Triple row of line sources........................ 55%
  Reflector:
    Filament lamps................................... 55%
    Line sources—add 5% to above values
Recessed cove:
  No reflector:
    Filament lamps................................... 25%
    Single row of line sources........................ 40%
  Reflector:
    Filament lamps................................... 45%
    Single row of line sources........................ 42%

**f. Lighting calculations.**   When the cove is used to provide general illumination the calculations are the same as for any indirect system.

The room index is determined and a coefficient of utilization for an indirect luminaire is selected from any standard table.   This coefficient is corrected by the ratio of efficiencies (Table 15-8). Then either the footcandles are calculated for a given size of light source or a light source is determined from a desired level of footcandles.   Experimental work has also produced coefficients of utilization for certain cove designs.   They are listed in Tables 15-9 and 15-10.

**TABLE 15-9**

**Coefficients of Utilization for Projecting Fluorescent Lamp Coves***

(Single lamp only)

| Room index | 75% ceiling | | | | | | 50% ceiling | | | | | |
|---|---|---|---|---|---|---|---|---|---|---|---|---|
| | 50% sidewall | | | 30% sidewall | | | 50% sidewall | | | 30% sidewall | | |
| | H-12 | H-18 | H-24 | H-12 | H-18 | H-24 | H-12 | H-18 | H-24 | H-12 | H-18 | H-24 |
| J 0.6 | .10 | .11 | .11 | .08 | .08 | .08 | .07 | .07 | .07 | .05 | .05 | .05 |
| I 0.8 | .14 | .15 | .15 | .11 | .11 | .12 | .09 | .09 | .09 | .07 | .07 | .07 |
| H 1.0 | 17 | 18 | 18 | 14 | 14 | 15 | 10 | 11 | 11 | .09 | .09 | .09 |
| G 1.25 | 21 | 21 | 22 | 17 | 18 | 18 | 13 | 14 | 14 | 11 | 11 | 12 |
| F 1.50 | 23 | 23 | 25 | 20 | 21 | 22 | 15 | 15 | 16 | 13 | 13 | 14 |
| E 2.00 | 27 | 28 | 29 | 24 | 25 | 26 | 17 | 17 | 19 | 15 | 16 | 17 |
| D 2.50 | 31 | 32 | 33 | 28 | 29 | 31 | 20 | 21 | 21 | 19 | 19 | 20 |
| C 3.0 | 33 | 34 | 35 | 30 | 31 | 33 | 21 | 22 | 23 | 20 | 20 | 21 |
| B 4.0 | 34 | 35 | 37 | 32 | 33 | 35 | 22 | 23 | 24 | 21 | 21 | 23 |
| A 5.0 | 37 | 39 | 40 | 36 | 37 | 38 | 24 | 25 | 26 | 23 | 24 | 25 |

* Data compiled from studies of Brown and Jones, *Illuminating Engineering*, April 1949.

**TABLE 15-10**

**Coefficients of Utilization for Filament Lamp Coves***

(Based upon cove efficiency of 55%)

| Room index | 75% ceiling | | 50% ceiling | |
|---|---|---|---|---|
| | 50% s.w. | 30% s.w. | 50% s.w. | 30% s.w. |
| J 0.6 | .11 | .09 | .07 | .06 |
| I 0.8 | .14 | .11 | .09 | .08 |
| H 1.0 | 16 | 13 | 10 | .09 |
| G 1.25 | 18 | 16 | 13 | 10 |
| F 1.50 | 20 | 17 | 14 | 12 |
| E 2.0 | 23 | 20 | 15 | 13 |
| D 2.5 | 25 | 22 | 16 | 15 |
| C 3.0 | 27 | 24 | 18 | 16 |
| B 4.0 | 29 | 27 | 19 | 18 |
| A 5.0 | 31 | 29 | 21 | 19 |

* Data compiled from *Bulletin LD-6A*, General Electric Company, Nela Park.

EXAMPLES:

1. A room 12 ft by 18 ft with 10-ft ceiling is to be lighted by a continuous projecting cove utilizing two rows of 25-mm warm-white, 120-ma cold-cathode lamps. Ceilings are light, walls medium. No reflectors will be used, simply white paint within the cove. Find the average horizontal ft-c.

$$\text{room index} = \frac{3LW}{2H_c(L+W)} = 1.55$$

This index is between the letter indexes of $F$ and $E$ in any standard table. Enter any table of coefficients of utilization such as Table 9-5, Chapter 9, and select a totally indirect luminaire with two fluorescent lamps. Depending upon your choice of luminaire, the coefficient will be about 27%. This will be for a luminaire of approximately 80% efficiency. From Table 15-8 we find that our cove can be expected to be 60% efficient. Therefore we ratio the coefficient of 27% by

$$\tfrac{60}{80} \times 27 = 20\%$$

There will be 60 ft of cove and 120 ft of lamps. Allowing for socket displacement of 5% of lamp length gives us an effective light-producing footage of 114 ft. The lamps produce 270 lm per ft. Therefore the generated flux is

$$270 \times 114 = 30,800 \text{ lm}$$

A safe depreciation factor for any cove is 50%. The footcandles in service will be

$$\text{ft-c} = \frac{30,800 \times 0.20 \times 0.5}{216 \text{ sq ft}} = 14 \text{ plus}$$

There then remains the problem of fitting the lamps into the cove, staggering the sockets, and so forth, before a final specification is possible.

2. Assume a lobby 35 ft wide and 80 ft long with 15-ft ceiling. The ceiling is 50% reflectance; sidewalls 30% reflectance. The cove can be as low as 24 in. from the ceiling. Fifteen footcandles will be sufficient for this space. Let us assume the use of 300-ma Slimline lamps and make calculations to determine how many will be necessary.

$$\text{room index} = \frac{3LW}{2H_c(L+W)} = 2.43$$

Let us use Table 15-9 to determine the coefficient of utilization. It is 0.19. The generated lumens will be

$$\text{G.L.} = \frac{(35 \times 80) \times 15}{0.19 \times .5} = 441,000$$

There will be 230 ft of cove, but as we must allow at least 5% for socket displacement, we have 218 ft available for light production. Dividing 441,000 by 218 results in 2,020 lm per ft of cove. The 300-ma Slimline lamp produces about 550 lm per ft. Four rows will be required producing 2,200 lm per ft. Standard channel is available.

Correction must be made for loss of at least 15% due to multiple lamp channel (Table 15-7). Therefore 1,870 lm will be available, producing 13 ft-c. The cove can be laid out to scale to determine essential dimensions. The minimum size might well be greater than esthetic considerations will tolerate.

Suppose we check to see what results could be obtained with filament lamps. From Table 15-10 the coefficient of utilization is 0.15. The generated lumens are

$$\frac{(35 \times 80)15}{0.15 \times .50} = 560,000$$

We must produce these lumens in 230 ft of cove. Therefore, $560,000/230 = 2,435$ lm per running foot of cove. This can be done with 150-watt lamps on 1-ft centers. The illumination produced will be

$$\frac{2,600}{2,435} \times 15 = 16 \text{ ft-c}$$

A scale section of the cove will determine whether it can be built within the desired size limits. If it proves to be too large or too costly, some reduction in lighting below the 15 ft-c may be necessary.

These two examples indicate that the production of more than 15 ft-c of general illumination from a cove is apt to prove a difficult task or a costly one.

## 15.3. Downlighting

Downlighting is a colloquial expression for concentrated direct lighting. The introduction of reflector and projector lamps in many sizes and distributions of candlepower has served to increase the use of this form of lighting. The small size of the lamps and the simplicity of maintenance are favorable factors for their use. The general practice is to design the luminaires so that practically all of the light is emitted in the 0° to 45° zone. The luminaires are located flush in the ceiling or attached to the ceiling. For supplementary lighting, the luminaires are often attached to a wall or suspended some distance from the ceiling on slender rods.

Downlighting has two disadvantages which can be minimized by careful design; one is shadow and the other is bright reflected images. Shadows can be reduced in number and intensity by overlapping the light from a number of downlights. Bright reflected images can sometimes be directed away from normal view by proper placement of the luminaire and direction of its light beam.

Downlighting is extensively used for the supplementary lighting of counters and isolated displays. The calculations are performed by the point-by-point method. It is also effective for lighting auditoriums, lobbies, and entire sales floors or departments. For such large areas the flux-of-light method of calculation can be used for the design. Tables 15-11 to 15-14 present pertinent data. Many of the illustrations in Chapter 14 show the uses to which downlighting is put.

**a. Downlighting for general areas.** The intent of general lighting is to provide a reasonably uniform level of illumination over the work surface. The ratio of spacing of luminaires to mounting height above the work plane determines the degree of uniformity. This ratio in turn depends upon the beam spread of the luminaire. In Table 15-11 will be found the recommended spacings for the usual light distribution patterns. On a scaled ceiling plan the

**TABLE 15-11**

**Spacings of Downlights as a Function of Mounting Height**

| Height (in feet) above work plane | 30° Beam spot lamp distribution, in feet | 60° Beam flood lamp distribution, in feet |
|:---:|:---:|:---:|
| 5 | 2.5 | 5.5 |
| 6 | 3 | 6 |
| 7 | 4 | 7 |
| 8 | 4.5 | 8 |
| 9 | 5 | 9 |
| 10 | 5.5 | 10 |
| 11 | 6 | 11 |
| 12 | 6.5 | 12 |
| 13 | 7 | 13 |
| 15 | 8 | 15 |
| 17 | 9 | 17 |

### TABLE 15-12

### Coefficients of Utilization for Reflector-Lamp Downlights

(Normal reflectances of sidewalls and ceilings have little effect upon utilization)

| Room index | Reflector spot | | | Reflector flood | Projector spot | | | Projector flood | | |
|---|---|---|---|---|---|---|---|---|---|---|
| | *flush | 30°s | 45°s | flush | flush | 30°s | 45°s | flush | 30°s | 45°s |
| J 0.6 | .64 | .52 | .45 | .52 | .69 | .61 | .53 | .66 | .56 | .49 |
| I 0.8 | .71 | .57 | .48 | .60 | .77 | .66 | .57 | .73 | .60 | .53 |
| H 1.0 | .75 | .59 | .50 | .64 | .81 | .68 | .59 | .78 | .63 | .55 |
| G 1.25 | .78 | .61 | .52 | .67 | .84 | .70 | .61 | .81 | .66 | .57 |
| F 1.50 | .80 | .63 | .53 | .70 | .87 | .72 | .63 | .84 | .68 | .58 |
| E 2.0 | .84 | .65 | .55 | .75 | .91 | .75 | .65 | .89 | .70 | .60 |
| D 2.5 | .88 | .67 | .57 | .79 | .95 | .77 | .67 | .93 | .73 | .62 |
| C 3.0 | .90 | .68 | .58 | .82 | .97 | .79 | .68 | .96 | .74 | .64 |
| B 4.0 | .93 | .70 | .59 | .85 | 1.0 | .80 | .69 | .99 | .76 | .65 |
| A 5.0 | .94 | .71 | .60 | .87 | 1.0 | .81 | .70 | 1.0 | .77 | .66 |

* In a flush mounted luminaire there is no shielding other than that provided by the reflector coating on the lamp.

### TABLE 15-13

### Coefficients of Utilization for Lamp and Reflector Combinations
### Based upon Efficiency of 50%

(The reflectances of sidewalls and ceilings have no significant effect upon the coefficient of utilization)

| Room index | Coefficient of utilization |
|---|---|
| J 0.6 | .27 |
| I 0.8 | .33 |
| H 1.0 | .35 |
| G 1.25 | .37 |
| F 1.50 | .39 |
| E 2.0 | .42 |
| D 2.5 | .43 |
| C 3.0 | .43 |
| B 4.0 | .45 |
| A 5.0 | .45 |

outlets are located in accordance with this table. The total number so located is then a fixed quantity in our design calculations. If the plan proves unworkable, closer spacings may be taken. Greater spacings lead to shadows and nonuniformity.

### TABLE 15-14

**Depreciation Factors for Downlights**

150-watt reflector or R type............................ 85%
150-watt projector or PAR type...................... 75%
300-watt reflector type.............................. 90%
Reflector and lamp combination...................... 65%

For louvers subtract 10 points from the above.
For lens or glass cover subtract 15 points from the above.

### TABLE 15-15

**Estimated Initial Beam Lumen Output and Maximum Beam Candle-power of Reflector and Projector Lamps**

| Lamp* | Beam lumens | Maximum cp | Beam spread |
|---|---|---|---|
| 75-watt R30 spot | 220 | 2,000 | 30° |
| 75-watt R30 flood | 300 | 475 | 60° |
| 150-watt R40 spot | 600 | 7,000 | 30° |
| 150-watt R40 flood | 800 | 1,400 | 60° |
| 150-watt PAR38 spot | 1,150 | 12,000 | 30° |
| 150-watt PAR38 flood | 1,400 | 3,500 | 60° |
| 200-watt PAR46 spot | 1,600 | 50,000 | 16° × 23° |
| 300-watt R40 spot | 1,350 | 16,000 | 30° |
| 300-watt R40 flood | 1,600 | 2,800 | 60° |
| 300-watt PAR56 spot | | 100,000 | 12° × 19° |
| 500-watt R52 | total lumens 8,000 | | 60° |
| 750-watt R52 | total lumens 12,500 | | 60° |

* These are the most commonly used lamps, although there are a number of other sizes. For complete information, consult recent catalogs of the various lamp manufacturers.

If the size of a lamp in the luminaire is fixed, we calculate the footcandles to be delivered by the total number of luminaires. If the lamp size is not fixed by the luminaire design, we can calculate the size by establishing a desired footcandle level. The room index is found by the usual formula, and the coefficient of utilization is determined from Tables 15-12 or 15-13.

### TABLE 15-16

#### Estimated Initial Average Candlepower of Projector and Reflector Lamp Types

| Degrees | 75-watt R30 spot, cp | 75-watt R30 flood, cp | 150-watt PAR38 projector spot, cp | 150-watt PAR38 projector flood, cp |
|---|---|---|---|---|
| 0  | 2,000 | 475 | 12,000 | 3,500 |
| 5  | 1,920 | 475 | 9,000 | 3,400 |
| 10 | 1,575 | 470 | 5,000 | 3,100 |
| 15 | 1,220 | 465 | 2,400 | 2,400 |
| 20 |       | 450 | 1,600 | 1,600 |
| 30 |       | 405 | 300 | 400 |
| 40 |       |     |     | 250 |
| 50 |       |     |     | 150 |

| Degrees | 150-watt R40 spot, cp | 150-watt R40 flood, cp | 300-watt R40 spot, cp | 300-watt R40 flood, cp |
|---|---|---|---|---|
| 0  | 7,000 | 1,400 | 16,000 | 2,800 |
| 5  | 6,000 |       | 12,300 | 2,700 |
| 10 | 3,000 | 1,250 | 7,000 | 2,600 |
| 15 | 1,800 |       | 3,500 | 2,500 |
| 20 | 700   | 950   | 1,900 | 2,200 |
| 30 | 300   | 600   | 700   | 1,300 |
| 40 |       | 350   |       | 800 |
| 50 |       | 150   |       | 400 |

The depreciation factor for projector and reflector lamps is more favorable than the depreciation factor for a luminaire consisting of lamp, reflector, and shield. The recommended factors are given in Table 15-14.

EXAMPLES:

1. Let us assume an auditorium 30 by 50 ft with 20-ft ceiling. Work plane is 2 ft above the floor. A 300-watt reflector spot lamp is to be used

in a flush-mounted luminaire with louvers.   The louvers cut off all light above 45°.   How many footcandles can be expected in service?   The room index is

$$RI = \frac{LW}{H_s(L + W)} = 1.04$$

From Table 15-12 we find that the coefficient of utilization is 0.50. The spacing of luminaires from Table 15-11 should be 9 ft.   By drawing a reflected ceiling plan and spotting the luminaires on it, we find that 24 downlights are needed for uniform illumination.   The generated lumens for a 300-watt R40 spot lamp are 1,350 (Table 15-15).   From Table 15-14 the depreciation factor is 0.8.   The total generated lumens for the area are then 24 × 1,350 = 32,400.   The footcandles are

$$\text{ft-c} = \frac{32,400 \times .5 \times .8}{1,500} = 8.65$$

2. Let us assume a high-ceilinged church nave in which we wish to secure approximately 10 ft-c at pew level.   Dimensions are 40 ft by 100 feet with 45-ft ceiling.   Assume pew reading level to be 3 ft above the floor. The room index is 0.68.   For this high mounting we know that projector-type spot lamps would be necessary because of the need for a high intensity concentrated beam.   Because of the mounting height, louvers giving a 30° cutoff would be suitable.

The coefficient of utilization (Table 15-12) is 0.63.   The depreciation factor is 0.80.   The generated lumens are then

$$\text{G.L.} = \frac{10 \times 4,000}{0.63 \times 0.80} = 79,500$$

The initial lumen output of the 150-watt projector spot lamp is 1140 (Table 15-15).   The generated lumens divided by the output of one lamp will give the total number of lamps required.   In this case it will be 70.   A ceiling plan drawn to scale will show that 70 spots can be placed on 7- by 8-ft centers.   This is satisfactory.

Instead of reflector lamps, suppose we used a lamp and reflector combination.   From Table 15-13 we find the coefficient of utilization is 0.29. The depreciation factor is 0.65.   Then the generated lumens are

$$\text{G.L.} = \frac{10 \times 4,000}{0.29 \times 0.65} = 212,500$$

From Table 15-14 we note that concentrating beam equipment should be spaced a distance of about one-half the mounting height.   By locating the luminaires on a plan of the ceiling, we find that two rows of 5 each will satisfy the spacing-mounting height requirement.   Thus there will be required 212,500/10 or 21,250 generated lumens per outlet. A 1,000-watt standard lamp will meet the requirements. Such a lamp and reflector combination will have a diameter of almost $1\frac{1}{2}$ ft. If there is no decorative restriction against ceiling openings of that size, this plan would probably be acceptable. If 500-watt lamps were used, a smaller reflector could be installed. The illumination would be better because double the number of reflectors will allow a more uniform coverage and less shadows.

For downlighting installations, providing substantially uniform illumination, the average or lumen method just described is a satisfactory design approach. Of course the point-by-point method is more exact, but it is also more tedious.

**b. Downlighting for display counters.** When lighting glass display counters with downlights located at the ceiling, each point on the counter should receive light from at least two lamps in order to reduce shadows. The lamps should also be located above the customer edge of the counter so that a reflected image does not obscure a view of the merchandise within the case.

EXAMPLE:

It is desired to light a jewelry counter to a level of approximately 100 ft-c in service, using reflector type lamps. The luminaire will be recessed into the ceiling. Distance from the counter top to the ceiling is 6 ft. The lamp should be well shielded from normal viewing, that is, to within 45° of nadir. To reduce shadows every point along the counter top should receive light from at least two lamps.

Values of beam candlepower for various reflector lamp types are given in Table 15-16. These are initial values. Therefore the footcandles calculated from them will be initial also. The depreciation factor to be applied to these initial values will depend upon the type and size of reflector lamp, as indicated in Table 15-14.

It is obvious that reasonably uniform beam candlepower over a 15° to 20° cone will produce a more uniform illumination with moderate spacing of lamps. Also, the end-on candlepower should not be too great. An inspection of Table 15-16 will show that the maximum candlepower of the 150-watt projector spot lamp will provide around 330 ft-c on the counter top. This is too high. The 150-watt PAR38 floodlamp will produce about 97 ft-c directly underneath it on the counter. The desired overlapping may increase this to the required level. The candlepower distribution is reasonably uniform, so select this lamp for the first trial. Draw to any convenient scale an elevation of lamp and counter as in Fig. 15-18. Calculate the footcandles at various points along the counter, representing a number of angular candlepower values. Use the formula

$$E = \frac{I}{H^2} \cos^3 \theta$$

It will be noted that beyond 30° from nadir the footcandles are small enough to disregard. Note the footcandles on the elevation and label them. It is now apparent that if lamps are so located that the 30° candlepower

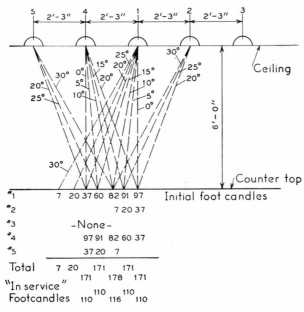

Fig. 15-18. Plot the illumination from one downlamp and then tentatively locate one to each side of it, at various spacings, to secure a reasonably uniform distribution of light.

values just overlap, we will not reach the required level of footcandles. A closer spacing is necessary. As a trial, select one corresponding to the 20° candlepower overlap. Indicate on the plan the footcandles contributed by each lamp within range. Total these contributions for the various points and apply the correct depreciation factor. In this instance the lamp alone has a depreciation factor of 75%, plus an additional 10 points for the louver shield. Applying the depreciation factor of 65% to the tabulated initial values, we find that the expected service values are close to the design point. If the luminaires are spaced $2\frac{1}{4}$ ft apart along the counter the design will be satisfactory.

The only other lamp that might be considered, would be the 300-watt R40 flood lamp. Inspection alone, however, indicates that inasmuch as the lamp wattage is doubled, the candlepower values should be doubled if operating costs are to be comparable. This is not the case.

Another design technique would be to plot isofootcandle curves to a convenient scale and shift them around on a plan of the counter top to the same scale until the necessary lamp spacing was disclosed.

If the display counter is not glass, the lighting technique is varied only in that reflections from the counter top are of no account. The lamps do not need to be so carefully positioned with respect to the counter. Sometimes in shoe departments, downlights are located in the ceiling to light the floor strongly in front of the fitting chairs. The design method is the same as for solid counters; the floor fitting area is simply treated as a counter top.

## PROBLEMS

**1.** A bulletin board is 15 by 50 ft. It is mounted on a roof 20 ft from the parapet. Design a floodlighting system to provide 15 ft-c. Locate the luminaires on the roof, 18 ft from the board.

**2.** A parking lot is 200 ft square. Floodlights can be mounted at the four corners and midway along the boundary. Design a floodlighting system, to provide 2 ft-c, giving full details.

**3.** A private parking lot is in the shape of a T. One pole is located at the crossing. Using this as the only floodlight location, design a lighting system to provide 1 ft-c. Each arm of the T is 80 ft long and 50 ft wide.

**4.** A parking lot adjacent to a three-story building is 60 by 180 ft. Design a floodlighting system to provide 1 ft-c, using projector lamps located on the building parapet 28 ft above ground.

**5.** A gasoline filling station is located on a triangular plot 100 ft long on each side. Design a floodlighting system to light the ground area and the station. Station is a white building 16 by 40 ft, located at one side of the plot. Floodlight poles can be placed at each corner of the lot. Provide 10 ft-c on the station and 5 ft-c on the ground area.

**6.** A bank building is 60 ft high by 150 ft long, of gray limestone. It is desired to floodlight the building from a building 25 ft high across the street, a distance of 120 ft. Prepare the lighting specifications to provide 20 ft-c.

**7.** For protective purposes it is desired to light a narrow strip of land 10 by 500 ft between a factory building and a fence to a level of 0.2 ft-c.

Mount lights on the building parapet, 50 ft above the ground.   Specify the number, type, wattage, location, and direction of floodlights.

**8.** A glass floorcase containing diamonds is located on one side of a store.   The case is 12 ft long, 40 in. high and 24 in. wide.   The front edge of the counter is 5 ft from the sidewall.   Design a downlighting system to provide approximately 125 ft-c of illumination on the case-top.   (a) Use louvered reflector lamps recessed in the ceiling 12 feet above the floor.   (b) Use a lamp and reflector combination recessed in the ceiling.

**9.** An auditorium 50 ft wide and 150 ft long has an arched ceiling rising from 20 ft at the walls to 30 ft in the center.   Ceiling has 75% reflectance; walls 50% reflectance.   Design a cove lighting system, using a projecting cove, to provide approximately 12 ft-c in service.   Run the coves on the long walls only.

(a) If fluorescent lamps are used, specify the number and type of lamps, arrangement within the cove, cove size and placement on the wall, and total wattage.

(b) If incandescent lamps are used, specify the size of lamp, distribution pattern of reflector, lamp spacing, and total wattage.

**10.** A private office is 18 by 24 ft with 11-ft ceiling.   Ceiling has 75% reflectance; walls 30%.   Design a continuous cove, using iron cathode fluorescent lamps, to provide about 10 ft-c in service.   Open up the bottom of the cove to allow light to spill down the sidewalls.   Specify the treatment of the cove bottom to prevent any direct view of the lamps from normal positions of room occupancy.

**11.** A small lecture room is 36 by 60 ft with 12-ft ceiling.   Ceiling has 75% reflectance; sidewalls 30%.   For soft, over-all lighting, design a cove to provide approximately 5 ft-c.   Use fluorescent lamps and place the coves on the long walls only.

To provide more light for note taking, design a downlighting system to supply an additional 15 ft-c.   Use deep-shielded reflector lamps, located flush in the ceiling.

**12.** A church nave is 38 ft wide and 86 ft long.   The ceiling slopes from the ridge 46 ft above the floor to 40 ft at the walls.   Using reflector lamps, design a downlighting system to provide 6 ft-c at the floor.   By means of a scaled floor plan and section, trace out the beam patterns to insure that every portion of the floor receives light from at least four downlights.   The walls and ceiling can be assumed to have a reflectance of 30%.

**13.** Cove lighting is desired in a dining room 12 by 15 ft with a 9-ft ceiling.   Walls have 50% reflectance; ceiling 75%.   The cove can be no more than 1 ft below the ceiling, and not over 5 in. wide, inside dimension.

What light sources could be used to produce approximately 6 ft-c in service? Show by sketch how they would be placed in the cove.

**14.** Short cove sections can be placed above 6 windows and doors in a living room 13 by 21 ft with $8\frac{1}{2}$ ft ceiling. Ceiling has 75% reflectance; sidewalls 30% reflectance. Maximum length of cove is $3\frac{1}{2}$ ft. What would the average footcandles be if one 30-watt, soft-white fluorescent lamp were placed in each cove?

## REFERENCES

Brown, L. C., and Jones, J. R., "Engineering Aspects of Cove Lighting Design," *Trans. Illum. Eng. Soc.*, Vol. 44, No. 4, April 1949.

Brown, L. C., and Presbrey, Priscilla, "Application Data for Downlighting Equipment," *Trans. Illum. Eng. Soc.*, Vol. 43, No. 1, January 1948.

Dearborn, R. L., "Floodlighting Design by Graphical Method," *Trans. Illum. Eng. Soc.*, Vol. 30, No. 8, September 1945.

General Electric Company, *Bulletin LD-6*, Nela Park, Cleveland, Ohio.

Hallman, Eric B., "Floodlighting Design Procedure as Applied to Modern Setback Construction," *Trans. Illum. Eng. Soc.*, Vol. 29, No. 4, April 1934.

*Lighting Handbook.* New York: Illuminating Engineering Society, 1947, Chapter 8.

# 16

# LIGHTING COST ANALYSIS

---

The designer of a lighting system often has a wide choice of light sources and luminaires with which to achieve the desired results. His final decision then depends upon the relative costs of several comparable designs. A reliable, comprehensive method of analysis will allow the designer to develop the facts upon which a decision can be made.

The total cost of a lighting system depends upon two fundamental factors:

1. Owning cost: depreciation, interest, taxes, and insurance upon total capital invested.

2. Operating cost: repairs, replacements, cleaning, and electric power.

The relative weight of these two factors will depend entirely upon the specific situation; not merely the type of lighting system, but where it is used. Quite often the engineer will wish to make theoretical studies based upon assumptions. These are very useful but the derived conclusions should be used with caution. For any given situation the lighting systems should be designed for the specific areas under discussion and the analysis should be based upon those designs.

## 16.1. Cost Analysis Procedure

A systematic form of analysis is given in Table 16-1. This general approach may be used in many ways:

1. To analyze lighting systems,
2. To compare the lumen-hour costs of light sources,
3. To compare the lumen-hour costs of luminaires.

**TABLE 16-1**

**Analysis Form for Calculating Lighting Costs**

I. Ownership costs
    1. I.C.I. type of lighting system
    2. Luminaire—description—manufacturer's name, number, amp
    3. Total number of luminaires
    4. Individual luminaire cost
    5. Installation cost per luminaire
    6. Total luminaire cost
    7. Branch circuit wiring cost
    8. Total investment—sum of items 6 and 7
    9. Annual ownership cost of luminaires
    10. Annual ownership cost of branch wiring
    11. Total annual ownership costs
II. Operation costs
    12. Lamp watts per luminaire
    13. Auxiliary watts per luminaire
    14. Total watts per luminaire
    15. Total wattage of system—item 14 $\times$ item 3
    16. Total number of lamps
    17. Individual lamp cost
    18. Total lamp cost
    19. Rated lamp life in hours
    20. Weighted yearly hours use of complete system
    21. Yearly lamp cost—$\dfrac{\text{item } 20}{\text{item } 19} \times$ item 18
    22. Lamp replacement labor cost—$\dfrac{\text{item } 20}{\text{item } 19} \times$ (item 16 $\times$ \$.50)
    23. Kwhr per year—item 15 $\times$ item 20
    24. Electric rate per kwhr
    25. Annual electrical energy cost
    26. Annual maintenance cost
III. Summary
    27. Total annual charges—sum of items 11, 21, 22, 25, and 26
    28. Average footcandles in service
    29. Cost per footcandle year

**Item 1. I.C.I. type of lighting system.** When developing the costs of several lighting plans, systems of equal lighting quality should be compared. In terms of visual performance it is inaccurate to compare an indirect lighting system with a direct lighting system. Therefore, indicate in this item the I.C.I. classification of luminaires, as this classification is one index of the general quality of the lighting system (Chapter 6).

Item 2. Luminaire. The manufacturer's name and catalog number and the trade-marked name of the luminaire will identify the study adequately.

Item 3. Total number of luminaires. This total is for a particular space for which the room index and coefficient of utilization can be determined. Thus, the study would be for a particular area such as a classroom, an office, or a machine shop, instead of an entire school, office building, or industrial plant.

Item 4. Individual luminaire cost. This is the net cost to the consumer. If not obtainable, use published list prices.

Item 5. Installation cost per luminaire. The man-hours necessary to install a luminaire vary widely, depending upon the structural details of the luminaire and the total number to be installed. Fluorescent luminaires, because of their size and number of component parts, require more man-hours to unpack, assemble, and erect on the job than filament luminaires. Obviously a large-scale installation will result in lower unit charges than a small installation.

Item 6. Total luminaire cost. (Item 4 plus item 5) × item 3.

Item 7. Branch circuit wiring cost. The design of feeders and the over-all capacity of the electric service is rarely influenced by the light source. However, the branch circuit layout may be affected. For example, a classroom lighted with six 500-watt filament luminaires will require two branch circuits of 20-ampere capacity each. There will be three outlets per circuit. If the classroom is lighted with two or three continuous rows of fluorescent luminaires, two branch circuits of 20-amp capacity will still be required. However, the continuous rows of luminaires can be supplied from one outlet for each row.

Item 9. Annual ownership cost of luminaires. Over-all ownership costs are made up of three items:

1. Interest on the money spent for the lighting system.

2. Depreciation—a yearly sum set aside to replace the equipment when worn out or made obsolete by technological advances.

3. Taxes and insurance on the addition to capital represented by the lighting system.

The interest charge will depend upon the user. School boards and governmental bodies, for example, secure money at lower rates than commercial or industrial organizations.

Depreciation practices are highly variable. In general, the "straight line" depreciation policy is favored. The investment is divided by the number of years of estimated use and the quotient taken as the yearly depreciation. Luminaires rarely "wear out" but are discarded because of obsolescence or changes in the interior space. In general, an amortized life of 3 to 10 years is selected. The accounting practice of the client will determine the exact figure.

The percentage necessary for taxes and insurance likewise varies. Governmental bodies, churches, and charitable institutions, for example, pay no taxes on physical property. Inquiry will disclose the accounting practice for the particular type of space being analyzed.

**Item 10. Annual ownership cost—branch wiring.** The branch wiring may not rate the same annual charges in per cent as the luminaires, because of a difference in useful life. Charges for interest, taxes, and insurance will be the same as for luminaires. The depreciation rate is usually less. This would be particularly true in schools, churches, factories, houses, and the like, where the physical space is relatively stable. In these areas changes in lighting could be made with little or no change in existing branch circuit wiring. At this point in the technology of light sources, it can be expected that many areas lighted by filament lamps will be relighted in the future by more efficient sources. The branch wiring can be expected to have a long, useful life.

**Item 11. Total ownership cost.** Item 9 plus item 10.

**Items 12 to 18 (inclusive). Operation costs.** These items are largely self-explanatory. Lamp costs should be net to the consumer when possible to ascertain. Otherwise use published list prices or "over the counter prices."

**Item 19. Rated lamp life.** The life of tungsten-cathode fluorescent lamps, sodium-vapor lamps, and mercury-vapor lamps depends upon the burning hours per start. A careful estimate of the way the lamps will be used must be made before consulting the manufacturer's data on lamp life. The life of iron cathode lamps and incandescent lamps is not affected by the number of starts.

Item 20. Average yearly hours of use. Many lighting systems are operated in total for a few hours per day but with portions operated full time. Individual lamps would, therefore, have different replacement cycles, but the average burning hours of all lamps in the system is the figure of interest. For example, the inside row of luminaires in a classroom will generally be lighted many more hours than the row nearest the window, but the weighted burning time of all the room luminaires is the figure of interest.

Item 21. Yearly lamp cost. This should include the labor cost of replacement as well as the cost of the lamp itself.

Item 22. Lamp replacement labor cost. Self-explanatory.

Item 23. Kwhr per year. Self-explanatory.

Item 24. Electric rate. This is the rate that applies to the lighting load. In the case of a block rate schedule, any increase in electrical use may be on a lower step of the rate. If the average rate earned is to be applied, then the effect of increment kwhr on the average rate should be ascertained.

With demand and energy types of rate schedules the effect of the lighting load on both demand and energy should be studied. In most instances, however, average charge per kwhr, including both demand and energy, is applied to the lighting load.

Item 25. Annual electrical energy cost. Self-explanatory.

Item 26. Annual maintenance cost. This is a difficult figure to ascertain because reliable records are not usually available. Man-hours for replacement of worn or defective lamp parts should be included. The circuit and equipment for preheat fluorescent lamps is the most complicated, involving the starter, double-pin lamp socket and ballast. Fluorescent luminaires possess large areas to be cleaned and tend to collect dust and dirt at a faster rate than filament or mercury-vapor luminaires.

Obviously the quality of the maintenance affects the cost. Cleaning four times a year costs more than cleaning once a year; replacing burned out lamps at stated intervals is less costly than spot replacement.

As an indication of magnitude, however, the following tabulation is of interest:

*Fluorescent Lighting*

Starter replacement:

Ordinary starter...................... 50% per year
Manual reset starters................. 20% per year
Sockets............................... 5% per year
Ballasts.............................. 1% per year
Cleaning.............................. $1.00 per luminaire

*Filament and Mercury-vapor Lighting*

Cleaning.............................. $ .50 per luminaire
Repairs............................... $ .10 per lamp

Average labor cost of replacing all types of lamps is $.50 per lamp.

The economics of maintenance is an important subject and one that warrants far more attention than it is possible to give here.

**Item 27.  Total annual charges.**  Self-explanatory.

**Item 28.  Average footcandles in service.**  Self-explanatory.

**Item 29.  Cost per footcandle year.**  It is not always possible to design comparative systems having the same estimated service footcandles.  The total annual charges should therefore be brought to a common base by placing them on a footcandle-year basis.

When systems possessing equal lighting quality are compared, it is safe to assume that the one yielding the lowest footcandle-year cost will be the most desirable.

The use of this cost analysis is not confined to complete lighting systems.  Different light sources in the same system may be compared; such as the 8-ft, 75-watt T-12 Slimline versus two 40-watt, 48-in. T-12 preheat fluorescent lamps.  Luminaires also may be compared; for example, an aluminum reflector versus a glass reflector having comparable candlepower distribution.

EXAMPLE:

A classroom is to be lighted to a level of 25 ft-c.  Indirect lighting is chosen for the purpose, and a comparison between the cost of fluorescent and incandescent sources is desired.  The school board wishes to amortize the luminaire investment in ten years.  The wiring will be amortized in twenty years.  Money is borrowed at 2%.  No taxes are paid; insurance is 2%.  Annual ownership cost is, therefore, 14% for the luminaires, and 9% for the wiring.  Experience has shown that for this school the classroom lights are in use for an average of 600 hr a year.

Based upon standard design methods, a room 22 ft by 30 ft, lighted to 25 ft-c in service, requires six 750-watt silver bowl filament lamp luminaires and 21 two-lamp fluorescent luminaires utilizing 40-watt, 48-in. lamps (preheat cathode, standard white color).

The analysis follows:

*Comparative Lighting Costs for a Classroom*

I. Ownership

| | | Filament indirect | Fluorescent |
|---|---|---|---|
| 1. | I.C.I. type of lighting system....... | Silvered bowl | Indirect |
| 2. | Luminaire........................ | 750-watt | 40-watt, 48-in. lamp |
| 3. | Total number of luminaires......... | 6 | 21 |
| 4. | Individual luminaire cost........... | $29.00 | $29.00 |
| 5. | Installation cost per luminaire....... | $1.50 | $1.50 |
| 6. | Total luminaire cost............... | $183.00 | $640.50 |
| 7. | Branch circuit wiring.............. | $120.00 | $75.00 |
| 8. | Total investment (sum of items 6 and 7)......................... | $303.00 | $715.50 |
| 9. | Annual ownership cost of luminaires. | $25.65 | $89.60 |
| 10. | Annual ownership cost of branch wiring.......................... | $10.80 | $6.75 |
| 11. | Total annual ownership costs....... | $36.45 | $96.35 |

II. Operation

| | | | |
|---|---|---|---|
| 12. | Lamp watts per luminaire.......... | 750 | 80 |
| 13. | Auxiliary watts per luminaire....... | 0 | 17 |
| 14. | Total watts per luminaire........... | 750 | 97 |
| 15. | Total wattage of system (item 14 × item 3)........................ | 4,500 | 2,037 |
| 16. | Total number of lamps............. | 6 | 42 |
| 17. | Individual lamp cost............... | $4.75 list | $1.00 list |
| 18. | Total lamp cost................... | $28.50 | $42.00 |
| 19. | Rated lamp life in hours........... | 1,000 | 7,500 |
| 20. | Average yearly hours use of complete system........................ | 600 | 600 |
| 21. | Yearly lamp cost: $\frac{\text{item } 20}{\text{item } 19} \times$ item 18. | $17.10 | $3.36 |
| 22. | Lamp replacement labor cost: $\frac{\text{item } 20}{\text{item } 19} \times$ (item 16 × $.50)....... | $1.80 | $1.68 |
| 23. | Kwhr per year (item 15 × item 20).. | 2,700 | 1,200 |
| 24. | Electrical rate per kwhr............ | 2.5 cents | 2.5 cents |
| 25. | Annual electrical energy cost........ | $67.50 | $30.50 |
| 26. | Annual maintenance cost........... | $3.60 | $26.00 |

III. Summary

| | | | |
|---|---|---|---|
| 27. | Total annual charges: items 11, 21, 22, 25, and 26.................. | $126.45 | $157.89 |
| 28. | Average footcandles in service....... | 25.7 | 23.8 |
| 29. | Cost per footcandle year........... | $4.92 | $6.62 |

## 16.2. Effect upon Air-conditioning Costs

When a space is air-cooled, all sources of heat must be taken into account by the designing engineer. Electric lamps of any type produce heat. Because of higher efficiency of light production, fluorescent and mercury lamps produce more light for a given wattage than filament lamps. Conversely, for a given level of footcandles less wattage is required if fluorescent or mercury lamps are used. This means less heat for extraction by the air-cooling system. To offset the lesser demand upon the air-conditioning system, there will be the higher capital costs of fluorescent and mercury lighting systems.

### TABLE 16-2

#### Analysis of Air-cooling Capacity Assignable to Lighting

1. Kw of lighting load requiring additional cooling capacity
2. Btu per hour = kw × 3414
3. Tonnage of air-cooling system $= \dfrac{\text{Btu per hour}}{12,000}$
4. Installed cost of air-cooling system
5. Hours use of air-cooling
6. Annual power cost—average air-cooling system input approximately 1,200 watts per ton; power cost = air-cooling tons × hours use of compressor × energy rate
7. Hours use of water
8. Water cost—dependent upon water temperature, average 2.5 gallons per minute per ton; water cost = 150 × air-cooling tons × hours use of water × water rate
9. Refrigerant cost—one charge per year average at $3.00 per capacity ton
10. Labor and maintenance—average $30.00 per ton per year
11. Taxes, insurance, interest and depreciation (total per cent × item 4)
12. Total yearly charges (sum of items 6, 8, 9, 10, and 11)
13. New funds required: (a) Lighting (item 8, Table 16-1); (b) Air-cooling, item 4
14. Annual ownership cost: (a) Lighting (item 11, Table 16-1); (b) Air-cooling, item 11
15. Annual operating costs: (a) Lighting items 21, 22, 25 and 26 (Table 16-1); (b) Air-cooling items 6, 8, 9, and 10
16. Total yearly charges: (a) Lighting (item 27, Table 16-1); (b) Air-cooling, item 12
17. Combined total yearly charges
18. Combined total per footcandle year

Therefore a systematic analysis of costs will be necessary before valid conclusions can be reached. A form for such an analysis is given in Table 16-2. Explanations of the various items will be given in order.

**Item 1. Kw lighting load.** If a complete new air-cooling system is to be installed, the total lighting load in kw is considered. If an air-cooling system is already installed with reserve capacity, the full lighting load is considered in calculating operating costs, but the amount of reserve capacity is deducted to arrive at the amount of additional air-cooling tonnage required.

Item 2. Btu per hour. The thermal equivalent of a kilowatt hour is 3,414 Btu.

Item 3. Tonnage of air-cooling system. Air-cooling equipment is rated in tons. One ton is defined as the capacity to absorb 12,000 Btu per hour.

Item 4. Cost of air-cooling system. The installed cost of air-cooling equipment depends upon the size of the unit, the type of building in which it is installed, and the geographical location. Inquiry will disclose the price situation in any locality. As an indication of magnitude, the following averages will be helpful.

| Size of unit | Average cost per ton |
|---|---|
| 1–10 tons | $1,000.00 |
| 10–50 tons | 800.00 |
| 50–200 tons | 750.00 |
| Over 200 tons | 700.00 |

Item 5. Hours use of air-cooling. This will depend upon geography, and kind of space conditioned.

Item 6. Annual power cost. The electrical energy rate is found by the same procedure as was outlined for lighting.

Item 7. Hours use of water. The hours use of water may not coincide with hours use of the cooling compressor. Under certain conditions, water alone may be used during certain periods to remove heat from the interior.

Item 8. Water cost. If cooling towers or evaporating condensors are used, the amount of water required is about 4% of that consumed by the "once-through" use of water. The cooling towers, of course, add to the investment and increase the use of auxiliary power.

When the water is taken from city mains, the established rate is known. When water is taken from privately owned sources, the cost will depend upon the particular situation.

Item 9. Refrigerant cost. This will depend upon the type of refrigerant used. For computation purposes, estimate $3.00 per ton per year.

Item 10. Labor and maintenance. This varies between types of systems and areas of the country; it should be determined locally. For computation purposes, however, estimate $30.00 per ton per year.

Item 11. Taxes, insurance, interest, and depreciation. The same conditions apply here as for lighting systems. In general, however, the rate of depreciation is set at 10%. Interest, taxes, and insurance will vary.

Item 12. Total yearly charges. Self-explanatory.

Item 13. New money required. The total cash outlay necessary to acquire a lighting system or an air-cooling system often determines the choice. A design which promises the lowest over-all costs over a period of years may not always be acceptable. The economics of the use of capital are beyond the scope of this text. The engineer must, however, be aware that the figures disclosed in item 16 may not be the determining factors in the ultimate choice.

Item 14. Annual ownership cost. Self-explanatory.

Item 15. Annual operating cost. Self-explanatory.

Item 16. Total yearly charges. Self-explanatory.

Effect of lighting upon heating system. Over a large portion of the world there are many months of the year when air-heating is necessary. The heat which is given off by lighting can therefore be utilized to reduce the amount of fuel necessary for the furnace.

The value of the fuel thus saved is computed from the following formula:

$$V = \frac{3414 \times C_u}{H \times E_f} \qquad (16\text{-}1)$$

where $V$ = value of fuel equivalent of one kwhr,

$\quad C_u$ = cost of unit of fuel (pounds, cubic feet, or gallons),

$\quad H$ = Btu per unit of fuel,

$\quad E_f$ = furnace efficiency.

To determine the amount of fuel which will be the equivalent of one kwhr,

$$W = \frac{3414}{H \times E_f}$$

where $W$ will be in pounds, cubic feet or, gallons per hour.

Typical furnace efficiencies are given in Table 16-3. The Btu content of various fuels is given in Table 16-4.

## TABLE 16-3

### Typical Furnace Efficiencies

| | |
|---|---|
| Hand-fired coal furnace | 45% |
| Stoker-fired coal furnace | 60% |
| Oil-fired furnace | 70% |
| Gas-fired furnace | 75% |

## TABLE 16-4

### Btu Content of Various Fuels

| | |
|---|---|
| Coal | 12,000 Btu per lb |
| Manufactured gas | 500 Btu per cu ft |
| Natural gas | 900 Btu per cu ft |
| Fuel oil | 141,000 Btu per gal |

EXAMPLE:

An office is heated by an oil-fired boiler. Fuel oil is purchased for 14 cents a gallon. The lighting system totals 20 kw. The fuel equivalent of this lighting system will be

$$W = \frac{3413}{141,000 \times 70\%}$$
$$= 0.03455 \text{ gallons of fuel oil per hr per kw of lighting}$$

or

$$20 \times 0.03455 = 0.691 \text{ gals. per hr}$$

If the lighting system is in use 8 hr per day, the daily reduction in fuel oil consumption amounts to 5.5 gal., with a value of 76 cents.

Arrangements are sometimes made to remove the heat from especially designed luminaires and exhaust it to the outside air. During the winter this air can be returned to the space.

Enclosed show windows usually accumulate considerable amounts of heat from the high intensity lighting system and solar radiation. Mechanical ventilation may be used to remove this heat, which during the cold months can be introduced into the store interior. The effect upon the main heating plant can be calculated by the methods described.

# PROBLEMS

**1.** The main floor of a department store is 40 by 150 ft with 15-ft ceiling. Walls have 30% reflectance; ceiling 75% reflectance. The owner wishes to know the comparative cost of lighting with louvered troffers flush with the ceiling and lighting with suspended louvered direct-indirect luminaires. A level of 40 ft-c is desired at counter tops, 36 in. above the floor.

For the study select luminaires whose photometric data and costs are known. Use the 4-ft T-12, 425-ma white Slimline fluorescent lamp. Assume 2,000 hours yearly use of the lighting system and an electric energy rate of 2 cents per kwhr. Assume that the ownership cost of luminaires is 18% and of wiring 13% per year.

**2.** What are the comparative costs per million lumen-hours, of an 8-ft T-12, 425-ma white Slimline lamp and an 8-ft, 25-mm, 120-ma white iron-cathode lamp? Obtain the local purchase price of the two lamps and assume energy cost of 3 cents. Would the price of electrical energy have any effect upon the relative costs of light production?

**3.** A general office is 40 by 70 ft with 12-ft ceiling. Ceilings have 75% reflectance; walls 30%. A level of 30 ft-c is desired. Two lighting systems are proposed. One consists of silvered-bowl filament luminaires and the other of luminous indirect fluorescent luminaires utilizing 8-ft, T-12, standard, warm-white fluorescent lamps. Ownership cost of luminaires is 18% and of wiring 13% per year.

a. Compare the cost per footcandle year of the two systems.

b. What will be the yearly cost of that portion of the air-cooling system necessary to offset the heat gain from each system? Assume cooling system is in use the same hours as the lighting system, hours use of water to equal hours use of air-cooling.

c. What will be the combined cost per footcandle year of the lighting and air-cooling? Assume the use of city water at 15 cents per 1,000 gal. and an electric energy rate of 2 cents per kwhr. The lighting system will operate 2,000 hours per year. Select luminaires and lamps for which data is available locally.

**4.** For the office described in Problem 3, calculate the value of the fuel equivalents of the full lighting system on a daily basis, assuming the use of

a. Stoker-fired coal boiler.
b. Gas-fired boiler.
c. Oil-fired boiler.

Obtain the local prices of the three fuels.   Assume that the office is in use 250 days per year.

## REFERENCES

"Lighting and Air-conditioning Design Factors," *Trans. Illum. Eng. Soc.*, Vol. 36, No. 8, page 853, September 1941.

*Lighting Handbook.*   New York: Illuminating Engineering Society, 1947.

Sharp, H. M., "Lighting and Air-conditioning," *Lighting and Lamps*, January, February, April, June, August, October, 1946.

————, "Radiant Temperatures from Lighting Systems," *Trans. Illum. Eng. Soc.*, Vol. 35, No. 9, page 809, November 1940.

# INDEX

## A

Absorption factor, 58
Accommodation of human eye, 189
Acuity, visual, 190
Adaptation of human eye, 190
Air conditioning, effect of light on, 323
Aluminum:
    Alzak finish, 65
    reflection factor, 65
American Home Lighting Institute, 7
Angle of cutoff, 90
Angstrom, 4
Angular errors:
    cosine law, 104, 165
    light meters, 104
Arcs:
    cathode discharge, 41
    gaseous discharge, 32
Argon, use in fluorescent lamp, 37, 44
Auxiliaries:
    basic requirements, 48
    iron-cathode fluorescent, 48
    mercury lamp, 50
    neon, 48
    noise, 53
    power factor, 49
    preheat cathode lamp, 51
    Slimline lamp, 50
    sodium-vapor lamp, 50

## B

Ball bearing inspection, lighting for, 248
Bar photometer, 96, 97
Barrier layer cell:
    construction of, 103
    correction factors for, 108
    errors of, 104, 106
    light meters, 106, **107**

Barrier layer cell (*cont.*):
    response curves of, 105
Bases:
    fluorescent lamp, 38
    incandescent lamp, 27, 28
Beam dimensions, floodlights, 290
Beam lumens:
    floodlights, 289
    projector-reflector lamps, 309
Beam spread:
    floodlights, 282
    projector-reflector lamps, 309
Bi-pin lamp base, 38
Bi-post lamp base, 28
Brightness:
    contrast, 190, 198, 201, 213
    definition, 3
    effect upon vision, 198
    fluorescent lamp, 37, 40
    light sources, 37, 40
    luminaires, 88, 210, 254, 259
    measurement of, 113
    of walls and ceilings (cove lighting), 299
    points of measurement on luminaires, 126
    ratios for factory lighting, 253
    ratios for good vision, 197
    ratios for office lighting, 215
    ratios for school lighting, 216
    values for store lighting, 259
Bulb:
    definition of, 25
    designation, 27, 28

## C

Candles per square inch:
    conversion to, 18, 19
    unit of brightness, 12, 14, **15**

Candlepower:
    definition of, 4
    discussion of, 13, 14
    horizontal, 4
    measurement of, 13, 126
    spherical, 4
Candlepower distribution curves:
    asymmetrical distribution, 123
    calculation of flux from, 127
    curve of vertical distribution, 125
    how determined, 96, 126
    presentation of data, 124
    simplified, 132
    symmetrical distribution, 125
    table of zonal constants, 129
    typical curves, 96, 125, 126, 133,
        134, 135, 136, 137, 138, 139
Cathodes, 38
Ceiling reflectance, effect upon coeffi-
    cient of utilization, 153
Cells (see Barrier layer cell)
Certification programs, 7
Certified Lamp Manufacturers
    (CLM), 7
Circular reflector, 70
Circular surface sources, 178
Coefficient of utilization:
    cove lighting, 304
    definition, 141
    direct flux ratios, 150
    downlighting, 308
    effect of ceiling reflectance, 153
    effect of light distribution from
        luminaires, 146
    effect of room shape, 141
    tables of, 155
    zonal constants for determination
        of, 148, 149
Cold cathode lamp (see Iron-cathode
    lamp)
Concave lens, 75
Contrast:
    brightness, 198, 213
    sensitivity, 190, 201
Convex lens, 75
Cosine distribution, 15
Cosine law, 15, 104, 165
Cost of lighting:
    effect of air conditioning, 323
    effect on heating, 326
    table of analysis, 318

Counter lighting, 312
Cove lighting, 294
    ceiling brightness, 299
    coefficient of utilization, 304
    construction, 297
    efficiency, 301, 303
    placement, 295
    reflector materials, 301
    sight lines, 294
    socket shadow, 296
    wall brightness, 299
Current density of fluorescent lamp:
    effect upon efficiency, 39
    effect upon light, 39
Current inrush, tungsten filament
    lamp, 26
Cylindrical light source, flux from,
    19

D

Depreciation:
    ceilings and walls, 180
    coves, 305
    downlights, 309
    factor, definition of, 180
    lamps, 31, 36, 39, 182, 309
    luminaires, 182
Diameter of fluorescent lamp, effect
    upon efficiency, 39, 41
Diffuse reflection, 59
Diffuse transmission, 60
Diffusion, perfect, 15
Dimming of lamps:
    fluorescent, 39, 41
    mercury, 35
Direct current operation of fluorescent
    lamps, 44, 52
Direct-indirect lighting, 87
Direct lighting, 86
    ICI classification, 83
Display cases, 267
Distribution curves (see Candlepower
    distribution curves)
Double surface, flux from, 19
Downlighting, 306
    beam characteristics, 309, 310
    coefficient of utilization, 308
    depreciation, 309
    spacing, mounting heights, 307, 312

## E

EEI, 6
Economics (see Cost of lighting)
Efficacy, light sources, 4
Efficiency:
  coves, 301, 303
  definition, 4
  of light sources, 29, 30
  of luminaires, 84, 92
Electric lamp, classes of, 24
Electron emission:
  iron-cathode, 38
  tungsten-cathode, 40
Ellipse; ellipsoidal, 71
Energy:
  radiant dissipation from fluorescent
    lamp, 44
  radiant dissipation from incan-
    descent lamp, 31
Eye, human:
  field of vision, 194
  optic nerve, 192
  response to radiation, 193
  retina, 191
  structure, 190
  visibility curve, 194

## F

Factory lighting:
  brightness ratios, 253
  design:
    for mercury lamps, 233
    general lighting, 231
    supplementary lighting, 244
  footcandles for, 232
  luminaires, 236
  spacing of luminaires, 231
Fatigue, of barrier layer cells, 110
Filaments:
  characteristics, 26
  material, 224
  types, 25
Fleur-o-lier association, 7
Flicker, of gaseous discharge lamp, 44
Floodlighting, 282
  beam dimensions, 290
  beam lumens, 131, 289
  beam spread, 282
  design data, 287
  footcandles, 288

Floodlighting (cont.):
  luminaires, 283
Fluorescent lamps (see Lamps)
Fresnel lens, 75

## G

Gaseous discharge lamps:
  common characteristics, 32
  fluorescent, 36
  mercury, 34
  neon, 32
  sodium, 33
  theory, 32, 38
General diffuse lighting, 86
  ICI classification, 83
Glare:
  definition, 203
  direct, 197, 203
  reflected, 203
  zones on luminaires, 88
Glass, 65
  heat absorbing, 66
  light control characteristics, 66
Globe, 4
Glow-switch starter, 56

## H

Heat from lighting systems, 323
Homogeneous emission, 25
Horizontal candlepower, 4
Horizontal component flux, 147
Hot cathode (see Preheat cathode)

## I

Illuminating Engineering Society:
  description of, 8
  standard method of measuring
    footcandles, 115
Illumination (see Light and Lighting
    design)
Illumination factor (show windows):
  filament lamp, 274
  fluorescent lamp, 275
Illuminometer (see Macbeth)
Incandescent lamps:
  bases, 27, 28
  bulbs, 25, 27, 28
  characteristics, 29
  coatings, 28

Incandescent lamps (*cont.*):
  current inrush, 26
  effect of voltage variation, 29, 30
  filaments, 25, 26
  lumens from, 31
  special radiation, 25
Indirect lighting, 87
  ICI classification, 83
Instant-start cathode, 38
Inverse square law, derivation of, 10
Iron-cathode lamp:
  brightness, 37
  depreciation of, 39
  dimming of, 39
  electron emission, 38
  lumens, 37
Isocandle curves, 131
Isofootcandle curves, 169

K

Krypton, use in gaseous discharge lamps, 37, 44

L

Lambert's cosine law of illumination, 104, 165
Lambert's law of emission, 5
Lamp, 4
Lamp manufacturers, 5
Lamps:
  efficiency, 4
  fluorescent, 36
  gaseous discharge, 32
  incandescent, 24
  iron-cathode fluorescent, 38
  maintenance costs, 322
  mercury, 34
  neon, 32
  projector, 28
  silvered bowl, 28
  sodium, 33
  tungsten-cathode fluorescent, 40
  white bowl, 29
Length factors (show windows), 276, 277
Length of fluorescent lamps, effect upon efficiency, 39, 40
Lens:
  concave, 75
  convex, 75

Lens (*cont.*):
  fresnel, 75
  human eye, 190
  prismatic, 75
Light:
  calculation of flux from:
    candlepower distribution curve, 127
    cylinder (toroid), 19
    point, 10
    surfaces, 16
  cost of, 318
  definition of, 1
  distribution curve, 128
  polarized, 76
Lighting design:
  lumen method (flux of light), 180
  point-by-point, 165
  to facilitate vision, 200
Light sensitive cells (*see* Barrier layer cells)
Light spectrum:
  mercury, 34
  sodium, 33
Linear sources, illumination from, 170
Localized lighting (*see* Supplementary lighting)
Luckiesh-Taylor brightness meter, 101
Lumen:
  definition of, 2
  derivation of, 9
Lumen constants, 129
Lumen distribution diagram:
  floodlight, 131
  show window reflector, 130
Lumen method of design, 180
Lumens:
  incandescent lamp, 31
  iron-cathode lamp, 37
  mercury lamp, 36
  sodium lamp, 34
  tungsten cathode fluorescent lamp, 40
Lumens, determination of:
  from cylinder, 10
  from double surface, 19
  from infinite plane, 20
  from point source, 9
  from single surface, 16
Luminaires:
  arrangement in rooms, 183
  brightness limits, 88, 210, 259

Luminaires (*cont.*):
  component parts, 81, 85
  definition of, 4
  design of, 68
  effect of lamp size on candlepower, 137
  efficiency, 84, 92
  floodlights, 283
  for factory lighting, 236
  for office lighting, 209
  for school lighting, 209
  for store lighting, 259, 267
  ICI classification, 83
  maintenance costs, 322
  manufacturers, certified lamp manufacturers, 6, 7
Luminous efficiency, 4
Luminous flux, 1
Luminous intensity, 3

M

Macbeth illuminometer, 99
Magnetic starter, 54
Maintenance cost, lamps and luminaires, 322
Mean horizontal candlepower, 4
Mean spherical candlepower, 4
Mercury lamps:
  characteristics, 36
  component parts, 34
  effect of voltage variation on operation of, 35
Metal scribing, lighting for, 247
Meters:
  brightness, 99, 101
  footcandle, 106, 107
Mixed reflection, 59
Mixed transmission, 61
Mounting heights:
  downlights, 307
  for factory luminaires, 231
  generalized data, 184

N

NEMA, 6
Neon, 32
No-blink starters, 56

O

Office lighting:
  brightness limits for luminaires, 210

Office lighting (*cont.*):
  brightness ratios for, 215
  footcandles, 208
  lighting systems, 210
  luminaires, 209
Optic nerve, 192

P

Painted surfaces, light control characteristics, 68
Papers and inks, reflectances, 213
Parabolic reflector, 71
Paracyl reflector (parabolic-circular), 73
Parafovea, 192
Phosphor, 37
Photometers, 97, 98
Photopic curve, 194
Photronic cells (*see* Barrier layer cells)
Plaster surfaces, light control characteristics, 68
Plastics, 66
  light control characteristics, 67
  types of, 67
Plate glass inspection, lighting for, 250
Point-by-point method:
  basis of, 10
  use in lighting design, 165
Point light source:
  calculation of flux from, 10
  effect upon reflector design, 74
Polar distribution curves (*see* Candlepower distribution curves)
Polarized light, 76
Porcelain enamelled steel, 64
Power factor:
  correction of, 49
  gaseous-discharge lamps, 35
  incandescent lamps, 32
Preheat cathode, 38
Prism:
  classical, 75
  lens, 75
  lens plates, 75
Projector lamps (reflector lamps):
  beam spread, 309
  candlepower, 309, 310
  depreciation of, 309

Projector lamps (reflector lamps)
    (*cont.*):
  lumens, 309
Punch press lighting, 244
Purkinje effect, 194

### R

Radiant energy:
  fluorescent lamp, 44
  incandescent lamp, 31
Radio interference, from gaseous-
    discharge lamp, 44
Rectangular sources, illumination
    from, 173
Reflectance (*see* Reflection factor)
Reflected glare, 203
  calculation of size of glare source,
    205, 252, 253
Reflection:
  classes of, 58
  definition of, 3
  determination of, for room surfaces,
    151
  diffuse, 59
  effect of color, 63
  effect of incident angle, 62
  measurement of, 111
  mixed, 59
  regular or specular, 59
  scattered, 60
  spread, 59
Reflection factor:
  glass, 66
  metals, 65
  papers and inks, 213
  plaster, 67
  plaster and paint, 68
Reflector, 4
Reflectors:
  circular, 70
  ellipsoidal, 71
  parabolic, 71
  parabolic-circular (paracyl), 73
Refraction, 74
Regular (direct) transmission, 60
Response curves:
  barrier layer cells, 105
  human eye, 194
Retina, 191
RLM Standards Institute, 7

Room index:
  formulas, 143, 146
  tables, 144, 145

### S

Scattered reflection, 60
Scattered transmission, 61
School lighting:
  Brightness limits for luminaires,
    210, 213
  brightness ratios for, 216
  footcandles, 208
  lighting systems, 210
  luminaires, 209
Scotopic vision, 193
Selective reflection, 63
Selective transmission, 63
Semi-direct lighting, 86
  ICI classification, 83
Semi-indirect lighting, 87
  ICI classification, 83
Show windows:
  illumination factors, 274, 275
  length factors, 276, 277
  lumen distribution diagram, 130
  shielding factors, 278, 279
Sight lines, cove lighting, 294
Silvered bowl lamp, 28
Simplified flux calculation from can-
    dlepower distribution curve,
    132
Sodium lamp, 33
  lumens from, 34
Spacing of luminaires, 183
  spacing-mounting height tables, 184,
    231, 307
Specular reflection (regular reflection),
    59
Spherical reduction factor, 21
Spread reflection, 59
Spread transmission, 61
Stainless steel, 65
Starters:
  glow-switch, 56
  magnetic, 54
  no-blink, 56
  thermal, 55
Store lighting:
  brightness values, 259
  display counters, 267
  footcandles, 258

Store lighting (*cont.*):
  luminaires, 259, 267
  show windows, 270
  supplementary, 267
Stroboscopic effect, correction for, 53
Supplementary lighting:
  for factories, 244
  for stores, 267
Surface sources:
  calculation of flux from, 16, 19, 20
  circular, 178
  design tables, 173, 175, 179
  rectangular, 173

## T

Taylor reflectometer, 112
Temperature, ambient:
  of fluorescent lamp, 42
  of mercury lamp, 35
  of neon lamp, 33
  of sodium lamp, 33
Testing laboratories, 8
Thermal starter, 55
Time, visual, 199
Toroid (cylinder), flux from, 19
Trade associations, 6
Transmission:
  classes, 60
  diffuse, 60
  factor, definition of, 3
  measurement of, 111
  mixed, 61
  regular or direct, 60
  scattered, 61
  spread, 61
Trigonometric functions for point-
      by-point calculations, 168
Tungsten-cathode fluorescent lamp:
  electron emission, 40
  lumens from, 40

## U

Ulbricht sphere, 97
Utilization coefficients (*see* Coeffi-
      cients of utilization)

## V

Vapor pressure:
  effect on efficiency of light produc-
      tion, 43
  influence of temperature, 42
Viscor filters, 104, 105
Visibility:
  loss of, due to glare, 197
  standard curve for human eye, 194
Vision:
  external factors, 198
  standard visibility curves, 194
Visual size:
  definition of, 190
  effect upon vision, 198
  of common objects, 196
Voltage:
  effect on life of incandescent lamp,
      29, 30
  effect on mercury lamp, 35
  operating, of fluorescent lamp, 38,
      40, 41

## W

Wax engraving, lighting for, 197
White bowl lamp, 29
Work plane, 143, 146

## Z

Zonal constants:
  for calculating coefficients of utiliza-
      tion, 148, 149
  for calculating lumens, 129

HETERICK MEMORIAL LIBRARY
621.32 S53                              onuu
Sharp, Howard M./Introduction to lightin

3 5111 00056 5717